To: Sue,
It is wonderful to have great neighbors, good friends, + walking partners. Thank you so much!
Doris DeeDee Walker
6/08

All I Have Left To Do Is Live!

Doris D. Walker

authorHOUSE®

Doris Dee Walker
Contact: 770-490-0518
Thank You!

AuthorHouse™
1663 Liberty Drive, Suite 200
Bloomington, IN 47403
www.authorhouse.com
Phone: 1-800-839-8640

First published by AuthorHouse 10/26/2007

ISBN: 978-1-4343-3513-5 (e)
ISBN: 978-1-4343-3512-8 (sc)

Library of Congress Control Number: 2007906421

Printed in the United States of America
Bloomington, Indiana

This book is printed on acid-free paper.

Dedication

This book is dedicated to my father, Rev. J. H. Walker, who became critically ill on July 26, 2006, and is currently hospitalized. I love you so much, Daddy. I, (we) pray for a full and complete recovery for you each and every day. I love you and appreciate you for everything. Thank you for your input in seeing that this book be written.

I also dedicate this book to my dear friend Celcelia Sapp Johnson, who passed away on May 16, 2006. I want to thank you again for the vital role you played in my life. I do not believe neither you nor me realized it at the time. I know you are sitting high and looking down smiling at me.

Acknowledgments

I thank you God for the parents that I was so fortunate to be blessed with Rev J.H. and Lillie C. Walker. I feel blessed to have been born into their lives, and into such a great family. I thank my family for their support. I especially thank my sister Veola who has lived through many of my life's experiences. I thank you for your unconditional love and faith in me. Family, I thank all of you for listening to me over the phone while expressing my interest in writing a book. I want to thank my friends and relatives. You all had faith in me. I did not expect to receive the positive feedback, and anticipation you expressed about reading my work of art. I thank you Porter for your patience, support, and faith. I cannot name each of you individually, because there are too many of you, but you know who you are. I thank you Genia for always encouraging me. I also thank you for understanding. I wish each of you much love. May God richly bless each of you.

The Purpose of This Book

It is my sole purpose to help someone who is trying to discover the meaning of life, and its purpose. If it seems difficult for you to find happiness and peace of mind, I hope this book will be a source of inspiration and help to you. On the other hand, if you are already experiencing joy, peace, and happiness, hopefully this book will encourage you to reach out to others. Depression is real. It can be debilitating. I describe it like building an automobile. You put in the engine, the ignition, the brakes, the tires, and everything that is required, but for some reason it will not go; something is missing. It has a steering wheel but you do not know how to steer it in the direction you desire to go. That is what depression did for me. It affected every aspect of my life. It even convinced me that my family and love ones cared very little for me. If you feel helpless, tired, or just feel like giving up; hopefully this book will help you to get it together by getting help. There are treatments that can help you to live a happier life. I pray God will send someone to show you the way. With the help of God, all things are possible.

About the Book

It is a spiritual, humorous, informative, educational, inspiring, sad, and joyful book. It is a book that you will not want to stop reading. It is one of the greatest memoirs ever written in mere words, by a first-time writer with no prior writing experiences. Based on a true story, the names have been changed to protect the privacy of the innocent.

About the Author

Doris "Dee Dee". Walker is a first-time writer. She was inspired to write by God. Born in Ozark, Alabama, she attended undergraduate school in Alabama. She is the fourth child of five children. She loves God, family, and friends more than anything else in the world.

All I Have Left to Do Is Live

All I ever wanted out of life was to be happy. This was the prayer that I learned to pray. It was the dream that I dreamed, but happiness seemed to pass me by. It was my desire to discover the true meaning of life and overcome the misery of life. I longed for joy, for happiness, and for peace of mind. I longed and hoped and prayed for happier days, but most of my heavily burdened days seemed to have outweighed my good days, and when people asked what it takes to make me happy, I didn't know. I hadn't the slightest clue. But thank God, I can finally say: I have had some good days and *All I Have Left To Do Is Live*.

All I Have Left to Do Is Live is a book about my personal experiences, and struggles throughout life. Every day was a struggle. I struggled, I struggled, and I struggled. I struggled to wake up most mornings, and then I struggled to fall asleep at night. Every aspect of my life seemed to be a struggle. I struggled to live. I struggled to stay alive, and then I struggled to keep alive. The little voice inside my head haunted me. I longed for understanding. But the little voice was determined to keep me down. Where was the joy? Where was the happiness? And where was the peace of mind?

How?

I didn't know how I was going to overcome the troubles, the obstacles, the fears, and the barriers that kept me from living the peaceful and joyous life, which God had promised. What was wrong with me? What was stopping me from accomplishing anything worthwhile in life? I was on the verge of giving up. "I can't stop now," I told myself. "I have to keep trying. I have been trying for too long." I could not lie down and will myself to die, for a very small part of me wanted to live. I cried. I cried oceans of tears, and my oceans had almost drained. "What can I do, and whom can I run to," I thought, when all I have left to do is live?

I will lift up my eyes to the hills - where does my help come from? My help comes from the Lord, the Maker of heaven and earth. He will not let your foot slip - he who watches over you will not slumber; indeed, he who watches over Israel will neither slumber nor sleep. The Lord watches over you - the Lord is your shade at your right hand; the sun will not harm you by day, nor the moon by night. The Lord will keep you from all harm - he will watch over your life; the Lord will watch over your coming and going both now and forevermore.

Psalm 121:1–8

The Lost Jobs

I was trying to live, but I couldn't even keep a job. I exhausted myself trying. I almost gave up hope. But I wanted to live the beautiful, peaceful, enjoyable, and successful life, which God had promised. But without a decent job, without a steady income, and the constant loss of jobs, I didn't see how I was going to make it. I gave up. Then life each day became just another day--days when I felt like dying would be better than living, crying was better than laughing, and being miserable, sad, and unhappy was the only way of life. It seemed simple, when all I wanted was to be happy and live, but happiness for me was high in the sky, way above the clouds, untouchable, unreachable, only thinkable. It must have been an illusion. How am I supposed to live? I have been asking for the past twenty-five years of my life. It is not hard to feel like giving up when your source of income is taken away from you, and your savings is rapidly depleting, and you cannot replenish it fast enough to keep the creditors off your back. I had managed to keep the creditors off my back, and I had managed to maintain a fairly decent credit score, at least I thought I had, until the company I was working for informed me that my credit was not good enough to work for them. I could buy a house, furnish a house, and buy a car; but I could not work for their company. "Unbelievable," I thought to myself. "Lord, what is this world coming to? Don't they know that if they will not hire me to work, I'll never make money to pay off my debts? Lord, don't they even care? Lord, what am I going to do now? I really thought this one was for me. I've worked so hard. I've enjoyed the job, I've enjoyed the people, and I even enjoyed working with the boss. Everything seemed so perfect. How many more times must I be told for some reason or another that this job is not for me?"

The Insurance Company

Before taking the job at the insurance company, I had worked a few temporary assignments. I had been let go and told that I was not a fit. But I kept trying. I was like a kid learning to walk: You know how the baby falls down, attempts to cry, and a little voice speaks, saying, "Uh oh, uh oh, don't do it. Get up, brush off your knees, and try it again." I was determined to keep right on moving.

I was feeling fresh and alive when I went to interview for the job. My confidence was about as high as it had ever been. I was able to sell myself and get the pay that I felt was comfortable for me. Life was carefree. I was young, single, and I didn't have a lot of responsibilities. I was excited about my new career. I was feeling very confident that things would work out. I had had my share of experiences in the world of work, and it was a great feeling knowing that I had found this job, the job just for me.

Before I accepted the offer, I prayed. I asked God to first let me get the job, and he did. Then I asked God to allow me to stay on the job for at least three years; this would have been a record for me, and he did that too. I was so happy after the first year passed and I survived. I was even happier after the second year passed and I was still hanging in there. My self-esteem and confidence were really boosting. I had never felt so good in all my life. But I struggled. I had to learn and relearn the job, but somehow I managed to keep up the good work. I was feeling great. The feeling was so rewarding and refreshing; I could hardly believe I was this enthusiastic about work. God had answered my prayer, and I felt like I was sitting on top of the world. Time was moving along and I was approaching my third year anniversary. It was as if I had just begun to live. "Life was not so bad after all," I thought to myself. I was mentally ready to take on the challenge of finally finding a real job, and being able to focus and concentrate. Yes, this was a big deal, being able to focus and concentrate, thank you, God. I was working, meeting, and getting to know new people.

It was an interesting experience getting to know my coworkers, who would later become some of my closest and dearest friends. It was a new and different experience for me. Being from a small town must have had a major affect on me when it came to getting to know people. Then on the other hand, it might have just been plain old fear.

It was not an easy thing for me to get to know people, which was so ironic because I liked people. I liked conversations, and I liked laughing, and I liked getting to know others; but I was oh, so afraid to let people inside of my world. I had my friends from home, and I thought they were the only friends I would need in this lifetime. I thought they were the only friends I would need in the whole wide world. There were no friends like my friends back home. They all knew me and accepted me for who I was. I knew them and accepted them for who they were. I didn't feel that anyone else in the world had the time, or would take the time to get to know me and vice versa. We grew up together and knew each other oh so well. We laughed, we cried, we sympathized and empathized with each other's joy and pain. Looking back, except for my being a constant worrier and a secret loner, life was great. It was not unusual for me to be a part of the crowd and yet feel so alone. I loved my friends, but we had all grown up now and gone our separate ways, and meeting new folk was a challenge. I never realized that getting to know and understand people would be such a challenge. It was an awakening. I learned things about myself that I didn't know—things that were not so pleasant to hear, but things I felt like I needed to hear. They say the truth hurts; yes, the truth can hurt sometimes, but the good thing about the truth is that the truth shall also set you free. It frees the mind, but I still found it interesting how people had their way of expressing their truths to you, about you.

Hearing about Me

It was interesting hearing others express themselves to me about me. I was told different things by different people. I was told that I was a complicated person until you really got to know me. I was told that I was unique, impetuous, humorous, arrogant, crazy, and full of life. I was even told that I was a phony and just plain fun to be around. To sum it up, I was just an intricate person. Some of the descriptions were flattering, and others not so flattering. I had to learn that everyone has the right to his or her opinion, even if you know for certain they are wrong about you.

I didn't know how to respond to the different adjectives that described me; so most times I would smile until I got home, then I would worry and try to figure out why I was so difficult to people. Why did they have to find a certain way to describe me? Why did they have to define me period? Was I really as complicated as they thought? It seemed simple to me, because all I wanted was to be happy and to make others happy. This was the me, that I knew. The only problem I knew I had was *sadness*. Most times I felt sad inside, and most times I didn't know why. I knew I wanted to be loved. If someone for any reason did not like me, it made me sadder.

I made everyone happy at some point in time, and at other times I made everyone mad. I was told that I was a very unique person. But before it all ended, I think everyone loved me. I loved people and it was important to me that they loved me back. I felt a strong need to be liked by everyone, and I didn't know why. I suppose it was my nature. It bothered me if someone did not like me. It was heartbreaking, but also an awakening. It would be years later that I came to realize that everyone would not like you, no matter who you are or how successful you may become. It was a hard lesson for me to learn, but I learned.

I was doing a great job at the insurance company, and was into my third year on the job. Everything seemed promising. "How could a perfect day end this way?" I wondered. I was so excited about my new friends and how things were working so well for me. I could not believe three years had come. I had finally succeeded in doing what I had set out to do. Three years just as I had prayed for, achieving my goals, what more could I ask for?

I loved the job, coworkers, and my supervisors. For the first time, I was not feeling intimidated by them. For once I could actually talk to my supervisors and managers without feeling afraid, threatened, or intimidated. For the first time, they didn't seem to notice my feelings of fear, or my low self-esteem, and lack of confidence. For the first time I was not afraid; I felt very comfortable. My fears had not surfaced, and neither had my fears become seemingly more than I could bear. This made it easier for me. It was easier to work and do the good job that I had set out to do, and this was a dream come true. There were times when I experienced fear, but not like the fear that I would later come to face.

A New Opportunity

Things were going well, and new opportunities were arising. There was no doubt that this would be the job I would have for many years. There was growth and opportunity. I was moving on up, climbing the ladder, and happy as I could be. I felt good. But the moment of happiness came to an end much too soon.

I had proven myself by being the worker that I set out to be. I had done such a good job that I was offered a new opportunity. My supervisor informed me of a position that was about to become available in a new department. She asked if it might be something that would interest me. "Me?" I thought to myself, smiling underneath my skin. I was flattered. I could not believe my supervisor was considering me for the new position. There hadn't been many times in my life that I got the chance to be offered such an opportunity. There hadn't been many times when I felt like I had even been noticed, at least not in a positive way. I felt great and truly blessed. Maybe I was doing a good job just like they said I was. Someone had finally recognized my ability. I was so happy. But as happy as I was about being considered for the position, I knew I couldn't make a hasty decision. I always needed time. I needed time to think things over. However, this time seemed different. Just the thought of being considered for the new position made me want to answer right away, "Yes, I'll take it! Life is good after all," I thought to myself. It really didn't take a lot to make me happy, so why was happiness so hard to find?

I knew this opportunity could be a chance of a lifetime, and I thought taking the job would be a great leap into the deep. I wasn't sure if the job was something that I would enjoy doing, and I wasn't confident that I would even do a good job. More than anything, I was excited that I had been considered. I gave the job some thought, and insisted on finding out as much as possible about it. After learning what the position entailed, I later informed my supervisor that I was interested.

Considering the New Opportunity

I wasn't sure if I had the courage to take that chance, even though I had slightly committed myself to the job in a subtle kind of way. My fears and my self-doubt were slowly sneaking up on me, but in my heart I was willing to take the chance. "This is something that I must do to prove to myself and others that I am good," I thought. "This is something that I must do to show them that I am strong, and intelligent too. I am a quick study, even if I do catch on slower than most. Yes, I can do this; I can accept the new job and do a good job." All of these things were fiercely running through my mind. Before I knew it, I was ready to take on the challenge.

A few days later, I was approached again. This time the manager approached me. She wanted to know if I had gotten back with my supervisor regarding the new position in the newly developed department. Before I could respond, she assured me that if I decided to take the new position, it would not only be a transfer but I would be highly compensated come review time, which was slowly approaching. This sounded really good. The thought of being compensated and possibly getting a promotion sounded great. I was so happy and alive, and time was going by so fast. I am a witness that time flies when you are having fun. This time on the job, I was having fun, and time was certainly flying.

Time was moving so fast that I had not realized three years and two days had passed. It was time for me to celebrate. The Lord had allowed me to stay on this job for three years, just like I had asked. But I had no idea that after my third year, the Lord would allow my assignment at the insurance company to end so abruptly. I was confident that I would be on the job for a very long time. I worked hard, the boss liked me, and I was getting along well with my coworkers. Everything was working out perfectly. They were beginning to understand me, and I was beginning to understand them. The different names they used to describe me no longer mattered. I had adjusted, and we had become one big, happy family. Most of us got along well with each other. We shared each other's joy and pain. We socialized on and off the job. We were definitely like one big, happy family. Being at work with such a nice group of people didn't seem much like work. I didn't dread going to the job or doing the job. However, I had to make some changes. I had to learn that all people were not the same, and you could not laugh and joke with strangers in the same manner you could with longtime friends. I was narrow-minded in thinking that all folk were alike. It was obvious that I had had only a few friends in my lifetime, and they were all very close friends. By working at the insurance company, I was getting to know more people. I was feeling loved and I was loving it. But I had no idea that my time on the job was about to come to a complete end. It must have been my fate.

I took my scheduled break, and it was about time to return to work. I was rushing to my desk after a few abbreviated stops to say hello to some of my coworkers, whom I had not had the opportunity to visit with. We laughed and talked for a few minutes before getting back to work, trying to catch up on the office gossip. Overall, it was a good day; I could feel the joy, the excitement, and love all in the air. I enjoyed the small talk and the good spirit that everyone seemed to have. However, I had to cut it short. I tried to hurry because I didn't want to be late since I was a potential candidate for the new position. I was sure I was being observed, and I wanted to make a good impression. But something happened. Daddy would say, "The devil got in the way."

As I was walking back to my desk, Jan called me over to her desk. I rushed over quickly and quietly to see what she wanted. I didn't want to ignore her or anyone else; in my head the spotlight was on me for once in my life, and I didn't want to do anything to jeopardize that. Besides, I wanted everyone to like me, and I didn't want to give anyone any reason to not like me.

Jan was a well-liked person in the office also. From all that I knew, she was an excellent worker as well. She didn't have an outgoing personality, but everyone thought she was cool and composed. She was short and stout. She didn't smile a lot unless you made her laugh. At times she seemed okay to be around and other times I wasn't sure. She was unlike me; I was outgoing and not very reserved. I was a lightweight. I smiled a lot, and most people thought without a doubt that I was friendly and approachable. I didn't initially show my fears and insecurities. It wasn't until I was faced with challenges that fear and doubt would reveal their ugly faces.

I didn't want to seem rude, so I walked over to her desk to see what she wanted. I was hoping that whatever it was would only take a few minutes. Besides, I couldn't imagine what was so important that she thought I should stop by her desk. You could count the times that I stopped by to holler at her. As nice as she was and as great as everyone seemed to think she was, I often got negative vibes around her. I decided to stop by her desk just to see what she wanted. It's interesting how having your moment of fame makes everyone want to gravitate to you. She had questions. She had many questions. She wanted to know if I was going to accept the new position that I had been offered. She wanted to know why I was approached by the supervisor and manager regarding the position. I tried to act like it wasn't a big deal. It's no big deal, I thought to myself. But on the other hand it was a big deal to me. It was a very big deal to me. Even though from my understanding, I was not the only person who had been offered the position, but maybe one of the few who was willing to make a move and take the chance.

There is always some fear of leaving behind what you already know so well to take that leap into learning something new. Since I had not made up my mind, I stood there and didn't know exactly how to answer the question. As I stood at her desk contemplating if I would accept or decline the offer, she began to stare at me very hard. "What is she looking at?" I asked myself. I was beginning to feel unnerved. She looked at me from head to toe. "Why is she looking at me this way?" I wondered. I looked down at my feet to see if something was wrong. I looked over my clothes to see if I was missing a button or something, and that is when the (it) hit the fan.

Before I could gather my thoughts to answer her questions, she was coming up with more questions than my mind could compute. She had so many questions for me; I couldn't think fast enough. She wanted to know why my feet were so small and why my legs were so skinny. At that moment I felt like I was in grade school all over again. She was beginning to give me the impression that she wasn't the nice person that she was perceived to be. I felt interrogated. All of a sudden the nice person that I thought I knew and the entire office knew was not being very nice. Children in my fourth-grade classroom didn't act this way. I was confused and very upset. I was about to become pissed off! Before I realized it, I struck back. I couldn't resist asking her the same questions, except she was not skinny, and that is when she reached up to grab me and started punching me in the face. I reached for her hands and accidentally scratched her, and for a quick second I remembered that this was my third year and second day on the job, and what had I gotten myself into? Needlessly to say, I was fired on the spot and so was she.

The Beginning of the Ending

"Was this the beginning or the ending for me in the world of work?" I asked myself. Where do I go from here? Oh my God, I had just begun to live. I had just begun to breathe, and it happened. Twenty-five years have passed, and I am still looking for a job. I am still being told that this job is not for me; and I am still being told that I am not a match. Lord, what am I going to do?

After I lost the job at the insurance company, I wasn't sure if I would ever get over it. I cried day after day and lay awake most nights. I questioned how something so promising could turn out to be so devastating. I wondered what I had done wrong to cause such a thing to happen to me. I didn't want to be alone at any time. Why did this have to happen to me? I couldn't figure it out. I wanted to get away. I wanted to escape the thoughts, the disappointment, the hurt, and the shame. I wanted to escape from it all. How could something so promising end up so devastating? I escaped as much as possible by hanging out with friends. During the day, I would hang out with my beau. My beau was not my beau at the time. He was a friend of mine. He was the guy friend that you saw every once in a while. He was the guy friend that you called when your car wouldn't start. He was the guy friend who called when he needed money to get out of trouble. He was the guy friend you called when you needed help disassembling your waterbed. We got along well like that. He, Naomi, and I were friends from high school who occasionally hung out together.

During the evening I hung out with Jeanette. She was my former boss from the insurance company and had become one of my best friends. I could hardly wait until five o'clock. I knew Jeanette would be getting off work. I knew that I would spend the rest of my day with her, at least what was left of the day. I needed someone around to keep my mind off the agony of losing my job.

Most days I was able to talk my beau into hanging out with us. He would come with me to Jeanette's house in the evening. We would cook burgers, fry French fries, drink wine, and listen to music. We had so much fun. I had almost forgotten about the terrible experience. Every evening was like a Friday night, except when the thought of loosing my job reentered my mind. I was not happy. The thoughts of waking up each morning with no job to go to, sadden me deeply. I often felt like crying. God must have sent my support group because that is exactly what they were for me.

My beau didn't always like to come over to Jeanette's house with me; nor did he like the fact I visited him everyday. I didn't mean to be selfish, but I needed company. I had heard about an idle mind, and I didn't want to go there! I would hang around him and the guys the entire day. If they played cards, I played cards with them. One time they went to the shaky booty joint, and I went there, too. It was not a place I would have chosen, but at the time it was better than being alone. I could not believe my eyes. The women at the shaky booty joint were butt naked. I never knew this, and they were black women, too. I had no idea that anyone had the nerves to really do this, walk around in front of people without any clothes on. I thought they only teased the guys, but they were for real. I barely walked around naked in front of my husband, and here they were leaving nothing for the imagination. My being there didn't seem strange to anyone but me, it seemed. I was asked by a few of the girls if I was Nikki, Kee Kee, or some dancer that they thought they knew. I wasn't about to get upset and try to defend myself; surely, if I was hanging out there, I had to have been a dancer. No one but my beau (P. J.) and I knew why I was stuck in the middle of all of these guys and these dancers. I'm sure he had given the fellows some explanation for my always being around. I'm sure it made him and them very unhappy seeing me every time they turned around. Since I had proven my friendship to him on many occasions, he had to deal with me, if just to show his loyalty to our friendship. The one thing I liked most about him was the respect he had for me. Out of my presence he had a foul mouth. I had heard him cuss up a storm many times without him knowing I was anywhere around. I appreciated the fact that he didn't do that around me. No one could quite understand why two people so opposite could get along so well. He drank like a whale, and me, I drank occasionally. He smoked cigarettes religiously, and I didn't smoke at all. I couldn't stand the smell of a cigarette, and because of that, he never smoked in my presence. He didn't mind cussing a person out if they got in his way, but he held his tongue in my presence. I was like a queen to him. Actually, he treated me better than many of the guys I had dated. And on top of it all, he was not flirtatious with me; he had the utmost respect. Sometimes I wondered why he didn't flirt a little. I wanted him to know I was a woman, even if I was a friend. Every woman wants to be flirted with every once in a while. Oftentimes I would make flirtatious comments to him so that he would know that it was okay to come on to me just a little. He was a quick study, too. In so many ways I think we complemented each other. I had faith in him. I didn't believe there was anything he couldn't do. If it was broken, he could fix it! If he could not fix it, he certainly knew how it was supposed to be done and who would be most likely to fix it for you. I don't think he ever realized this great gift about himself until I came along. It was in high school when he first noticed me. I knew him well before he knew me. He played basketball, he was a close friend to my first cousin, and for some reason I just knew him. His respect did not stop there; the one thing that has held us together for so many years is his faith in me. The man had more faith in me than I had in myself. Somehow he had always managed to make me feel like there was nothing, absolutely nothing that I could not do. When I told him I was thinking about writing a book, he told me it would be a million-dollar book. When I told him I was fed up with many jobs, he said it was okay, don't worry about it, you will find another one. When I told him I felt like I could no longer go on, he told me to just hold on; everything was going to be all right. When I told him it felt like it was just he and I against the world, he said that was all we needed. He knew I believed in God and so did he. But he did not confess to be a Christian. He thought it meant being perfect. But he always encouraged me to pray. He believed that prayer worked. "Pray, baby, pray," he would say, "And pray for me too. I believe, but I don't pray like *y'all* Christians do." He would say.

It wasn't until years later that P.J. told me how he resented my company. He told me how he dread seeing so much of me at that time. He later expressed that he had some habits that he needed to support, but with me always in the way he couldn't do all the things he wanted to do. I consider myself a blessing to him. Because today he is habit free, and today he is my beau.

The Computer Company

It took about six weeks to find another job. Those six weeks seemed like the longest six weeks of my life. I went to work for a contracting company. I was excited about finding another job. Once I started working again, the job lapse did not seem that long. However, the job didn't last very long either. I enjoyed the brief period of time that I worked for the company in many ways.

I was excited to be working for the company, except the company didn't seem to have enough work to keep me busy. Already I felt like a target, but I did all I could to keep busy. Some days I would finish all of my work and start all over again. It had become a daily task for me, trying hard to look busy, and trying even harder to keep busy. That was a major task.

My job was supposedly an important job, but little emphasis was placed on it. I tried to make it interesting, and I tried to make it seem important. I was blessed, no doubt, to have a new job, but I desired more responsibilities. At the end of the day, I wanted to feel like I had contributed something. Instead, I felt like I had worked all day long and accomplished very little. Even with all of the stress of trying to keep busy, I still wanted to become permanent. I desired a job, with real benefits, and real nice people.

I don't recall my job title. I am not sure if I was really given one, but the most important thing is that I had a job and I was grateful to be working again. I knew it was supposed to be an elite position, but I expected more. Having an elite position with very little work to go along with it was not a good position to be in. For some people it may have been a great job, going to work every day, having little to do, and getting paid. But this was quite boring for me. The job was important, and important responsibilities came along with it, but it didn't seem important to anyone accept me.

I had been blessed to get the job, and I was going to do the best I could. I was going to try very hard to make it work. The job required lots of phone work and very little paperwork. It did not require a lot of brainstorming either. My duties were to contact the district managers, making sure that they had followed up with their people, to remind them the importance of getting their paperwork into the home office. The branch manager had explained to me how important this assignment was. " It's an important job Kenzie, because we just bought the company." He would say. The job sounded really good, but the results I got were not so good. I would call the district managers several times a day. Once I completed the list of names, I would start all over again. I called the managers so often that they made comments about talking more to me than to their own wives—very funny. At first I felt their humor and I laughed a few times, but after a while it was no longer funny. I had a quota to reach that I never met, because none of the district managers followed up with me. It was not a good thing. My important and elite job didn't seem important after all. I tried many things to make it interesting. Whenever I called the managers, I would try to make my voice sound heavy and strong. I wanted to make sure the managers knew that I meant business. Sometimes a few of the mangers proclaimed to take me serious and promised that they would get back with me; of course, it never happened. Many times I would sit at my desk, clicking the keys on my keyboard pretending to be interested. This had begun to frustrate me, but I still wanted the job.

Meeting A New Friend

There were several of us from the agency. But Marian became a close friend. It was funny how I was meeting people, and trying to get to know them. I was warming up more and more. I wasn't feeling as uncomfortable as I once had. Actually, at times I felt comfortable and relaxed. "Amazing," I thought. There were times, when I didn't feel afraid at all. Because most of the people I came in contact with seemed very nice. "It just might be possible to make friends with others." I thought to myself, especially after meeting Marian. She was very nice and friendly. She became a close friend, and fifteen years later, she is still a close friend.

Marian was a bubbly person. She had an impeccable personality. She always seemed to be in good spirits. I admired her. Apart from her great personality, I think it was her positive image I loved most. Unlike me, it did not seem to matter to her if people liked her. She seemed confident in just being Marian, and this seemed to draw people to her. Everyone seemed to like her. She was always encouraging and uplifting my spirit. Somehow she understood me. I was not the unique person to her that I had been described as by many others in the workplace. I was just crazy Kenzie, as she would call me. She knew I was all about laughs and fun. I knew when I met Marian I had met a friend for life. She was the only person I knew who smiled more than me.

By the boss giving her all the work to do didn't have any affect on our friendship. The only thing that affected our friendship was our religious beliefs. She was a Jehovah's Witness, and I was a Methodist. Marian didn't believe in Christmas, Thanksgiving, and birthday celebrations. I believed in them all. I could hardly wait for someone's birthday. I knew we would have cake in the office, and I looked forward to that. I loved birthday cake. She loved it too, but only if it was not called a birthday cake. I argued with her every day about how blessed she was to live to see another year, and that it was okay to celebrate. She argued with me every day that Jesus was not a baby, that he was a grown man, and we are still celebrating his birth. Other than the religious differences, we got along well.

The good thing about her was that she did not have to worry about the job. She didn't seem to worry much about anything. She probably did not worry much about becoming permanent either. Marian always had enough work to keep her busy. It seemed the boss liked her. He entrusted her to learn how to do many other jobs. From time to time I would see him handing her paperwork. I didn't know exactly what it was he was always handing her, but I knew that whatever it was, it kept her busy on the job. I would often kid her about being the boss's pet. This never offended her; she would laugh and call me crazy. Crazy had become her nickname for me. It did not bother me that she called me crazy; everyone back home called me that too, because I was always making them laugh. I wanted to be happy, and I wanted everyone around me to be happy too. Making people laugh came so natural for me. One time some friends tried to talk Mama into letting me do standup comedy because I enjoyed talking and laughing so much. Of course, this was not something Mama would have agreed to. Mama wanted all of us to go to school and become a professional. It did not matter to her what profession we chose, but she wanted all of us to go to school and make the best of whatever we chose to do.

Looking Forward to
<u>Becoming Permanent</u>

Time was moving right along, and before I knew it three months had passed. I was excited, because prior to going to the company, we were told by the agency that the job could become permanent, after ninety days. We all looked forward to that day. We had begun talking amongst ourselves about becoming full-time. We questioned if they were really going to hire us, and guessed about how much we thought they would pay. We had become very anxious. We were acting like kids waiting for Christmas, impatiently waiting for Santa to bring us jobs with joy. We talked about how exciting it would be to become full-time employees. I laughed and expressed how nice it would be getting a permanent job. Even though I was excited about the thought, I could not escape my fears: fears of self-doubt and fears of being judged. My mind drifted to how well things had gone for me back at the insurance company. I had met new people and made new friends, something that I didn't think could be, and here I was starting all over again. I had proven to be the worker I always desired to be, and now I had to do this all over again. I had to prove to Varney, the supervisor, and to myself that I was a good worker. I was excited, but I faced much fear.

The boosting self-esteem that I had had at the insurance company was no longer there, and I worried. I worried about whether I would be able to keep the job if I was hired. I worried if everyone would like me, once I became permanent. Despite my beautiful smile and warm, outgoing personality, I worried. I worried that I might be a disappointment to the trainer who had placed me in what was supposed to have been the elite position. I was also afraid that I might be a disappointment to Mr. Varney. I did not want to have to continue to prove myself. I didn't want to deal with the little voice inside of my head, with all the negative thinking; no, I did not want to deal with it. I wanted to be like Mama and Daddy when they were working. Even with Mama facing many challenges on her job, she never feared the boss or the job. She never doubted herself about her work, as far as I knew. She had faith in herself and faith in her God. She always did a good job. She accepted their decisions, took it all in stride, and moved on with her life. I was hopeful that Varney would do the right thing by making me permanent when he made his decisions.

Mr. Varney was a tall man. He was very tall to be a white man, in my opinion. He was about six feet two six inches tall. He was a thick man and very lanky. His head bounced around and around when he walked. For some reason his head just wouldn't sit still on his shoulders, as if it were too heavy for him to carry. But he was a nice man. He laughed and joked with us. He made us feel comfortable. He made it known that it was okay to work, and have fun in the workplace. He did not give me the impression that he didn't like me as a person. I thought everything was fine. He talked a lot. He shared many things with the group. He shared with us several times, about his previous job; and how he used to be a pilot. We never knew which airline he flew for, perhaps he flew a private jet, I don't know. But if he said he was a pilot, then a pilot he was. Most of us found him amusing. He would get so excited whenever he told us this story. He walked a lot also. He would pace the floor and speak to everyone. He would even come in the break room during our break and talk with us. No one seemed to mind. Even I felt comfortable talking to the boss until realization hit me. One day, realization hit me upside the head like a softball. I felt the pain of fear. I realized something strange about me. I realized I could engage in conversation and not feel afraid whenever I was talking to Varney, and the conversation was not worked related. Until this realization, I was beginning to think that I was overcoming my boss phobia. "Maybe I was overcoming my phobia of bosses in the workplace, and maybe I was beginning to socialize with people at work without them thinking I was so uniquely different." I thought. This would have been a great discovery for me. Instead, I discovered that when it came to talking to the boss about the job, I would freeze up. There was something about talking seriously about the job that made me feel uncomfortable.

I feared saying the wrong things. I never wanted to say the wrong thing in the presence of the boss. I never wanted to say the wrong thing about the job, period. I believed that in the workplace one was supposed to be perfect. I thought it was wrong to express being tired or being sleepy at work. In my mind, one was supposed to express only the positive and good things about work. I didn't want to take a chance of saying the wrong thing and putting myself or my job in jeopardy, so instead of taking the chance of saying the wrong thing and getting in trouble, I chose to be quiet. Being the talkative person I was, and then becoming quiet about work-related topics, probably didn't sit well with the boss. I feel like it gave the wrong impression, perhaps the impression that I was not interested or that I did not know what was going on. Trying to play it safe was probably playing it dangerously. It did not matter if he or she were the nicest person in the world; I was afraid. I was so afraid at times of the boss that I wanted to take myself into the bathroom and give myself an old-fashioned whupping. I wanted to do almost anything to relax and feel confident and comfortable in the workplace. I wanted to show how truly interested I was in the job and in my work, but it never seemed to come out that way. Instead, I appeared aloof and arrogant.

Even though Jeanette had become my best friend at the insurance company, at times I feared her. I would go home after work each day and talk about her to my other friends and family members. I talked about how she intimidated me. I talked about the confidence I believed she had in me on the job and how I hoped I would not be a disappointment. I talked about how arrogant and cocky I thought she was at times. I talked about how I disliked the way she treated some of the other people at work. It was a trip. At times she didn't even treat me nice. And I questioned her motives for trying to get to know me. The ironic thing about being so fearful is that once the bosses or the team leaders got to know me, they all seemed to get along well with me. This happened on almost every job. I usually went to lunch with one of them at least one day out of the week. It wasn't me who had the problem; it was the negative voice inside my head. I knew I was bright and I knew I was intelligent. I knew it was something about God's love that made me believe this.

Jeannette did not pay my insecurities much attention; she accepted me for who I was. Oftentimes she would play on my insecurities by telling me I was acting. She often accused me of acting the fool whenever there was something simple that I could not understand. It was good that she could make light out of the situation.

We had a lot in common. We saw eye to eye on many viewpoints. We had both traveled abroad and lived in Germany. We were both hard workers. I believe it was my strong desire to learn and understand that captivated her. Despite all of this, I feared her. I could go to her anytime and ask questions in general. I could ask questions about other people. I could ask questions like "how is your day." But whenever I had to go to her regarding a work-related question, I felt dumb. I felt like she thought more of me. I felt like I should have known the answers to the questions. Having to ask questions made me feel stupid and dumb all of the time. I felt like the questions I asked were simple ones, I felt like everyone else except me knew the answer to all of the questions I asked.

I didn't feel stupid talking to Varney; I just felt afraid. I knew I needed to ask him about the job despite my fears. I prayed a lot, but my fears and the little voice never seemed to let go of me. I learned to read the Bible, and I had learned some scriptures to support the way I felt. Many times it helped to make me feel better. Many times it was the only thing that helped me to make it through the day. I knew that God did not want his children to fear anything or anybody except him.

For God has not given us the spirit of fear: but of power, and of love, and a sound mind.

2 Timothy 1:7

Every day I prayed for a sound mind. Every day I felt like I was crazy. It had been a great accomplishment having that job at the insurance company. I didn't feel as afraid or as insecure as I had felt so many times before. Before leaving the job at the information center and going to work for the insurance company, I had the opportunity to sit in for the supervisor on an occasion when he had to leave the desk, and I failed. I failed and it was a total embarrassment for me. I tried to play it off the best I could, but when I got home, I cried and beat up on myself; no one would believe. I failed because I couldn't focus. I couldn't concentrate, and on the inside I felt like every organ in my body trembled. I was always consumed with fear. Nothing about me made a whole lot of sense to me. I wanted to shine and I wanted to be great, but that little voice inside told me differently. It fought against my will to live. It fought against my desire to become successful. It fought against my desire to relax and be happy. It fought against my having peace of mind.

The closer it got to our ninety-day probationary period, the less we saw of Varney. He had been spending more time in his office and less time pacing the floor. I missed seeing him pace the floor. Actually, I wanted him to pace the floor because this would have been another opportunity for him to see me dialing those darn numbers, trying to get in touch with those district managers. In other words, it would be a chance for him to see me shine. I knew that I was a good worker, but I wasn't sure if he knew this or not.

One time when I was working at the telephone company, the supervisor asked us to put down three positive things about the person who sat beside us. I sat beside Rosa and Eva sat beside me. I don't remember what I said about Rosa because I was always complimenting others. One of the things that Eva said about me was that I wanted to know the specifics of things. She described me as being the person who wanted to know the how of whatever was to be done; in other words, a show-me-how-to-do-it kind of person. It caught me by surprise to hear someone describe me that way. I had not observed that characteristic about myself. However, it was a big plus for me. It inspired me to have a stronger desire to know how and to understand the know-how.

Two weeks after the probationary period ended, Varney began calling us one by one to come into his office. I was happy that he had started the screening process, but another part of me was scared to death. I feared the worst. Most times when I feared the worst, good things were the result, but not this time. At least I didn't feel the outcome was good. But in the long run, it all worked out fine. "I wanted the job, and needed it, but what if it wasn't for me?" I asked myself.

It was amazing to me how one could become comfortable or uncomfortable in a place in ninety days. I was slowly getting over my experience at the insurance company. But I never forgot my friends. They call me to this day, and I call them. We managed to maintain our friendship. As a matter of fact, a lot of the same people are still working there. We became like family. We had such a close connection. My mother passed away shortly after I was dismissed from the insurance company, a few of them drove four hours to Alabama to attend her funeral. This touched me deeply. They will never understand what that did for me and how much it meant to me. I will never be able to thank Jeanette, Kathy, and Mossey for their acts of love and kindness shown to me during that period of time. We had developed a strong, friendly, family-like relationship. Everyone at the insurance company liked Jan as much as they liked me. No one understood what happened that day. And no one could believe what happened that day. It was a sad day, they say, when Jan and McKenzie went away. It all happened so fast.

The calling process continued. Mr. Varney had apparently gone through his list of names and decided whom he would be keeping and whom he would not be keeping. He called Marian, René, Belinda, Katrina, Tonya, Michael, Terrance, James, and several others to his office. I kept the faith and kept waiting and hoping that he would soon call my name. My heart sink from fear. But since my last name began with W, I thought that maybe he would be calling me last. I knew this wasn't really the case, but this is what I told myself. I kept trying to convince myself not to worry. I watched the others walk in and out of his office. Everyone that walked into his office walked out with a smile on their face. It must have been nice getting the good news. He continued to call name after name until he finally got down to the W's. When he reached the W's, he still had not called my name. My nerves began to work on me. My heart ached. I panicked. Not only did I panic, I was embarrassed and disappointed. Everyone, I felt like, just knew that since Marian and I were such good friends, certainly the boss would hire both of us, and certainly she would put in a word for me. I'm sure she tried. But I knew it was left up to Mr. Varney.

Taking the First Step

Marian and the others kept trying to convince me to be patient. They told me that Varney would call me the next day or the next day. A week passed, and I waited for him to say something. He never said a word to me. After a week of impatiently waiting, which seemed like a month, I finally got the courage to ask him about the job. I was afraid, but I knew if I wanted the job, I had to take the first, and maybe the second, step. It was obvious that Mr. Varney had forgotten all about me. It seemed like he had forgotten that I even worked as one of his employees. "Was I that unimportant?" I wondered. I felt as if I didn't even exist anymore. But I knew I had to make a move. I knew I had to do something soon. I didn't know how to approach him, but I knew I had to do something, that is, if I wanted the job. "I have to take the first step," I told myself.

I was reluctant to go to him because I didn't know how or what to say to him. I didn't even know how to ask the question. I was afraid that my words or my tone would come out all wrong. I didn't want to sound weak or lacking in confidence, and I didn't want to come across too strong. I built up my courage and went to him and asked in a humble but confident tone, "Varney, are you still interviewing for the position?" I couldn't believe I had made the first step. I didn't even wait for an answer, because I was too afraid of what he might say, so I went on to say, "If so, I would really like the position." He smiled and said that they were still hiring and assured me that he would work on it for me. I exhaled and patted myself on the back and walked away feeling hopeful. I thanked him. Thank God, I got over that fear. It was not as difficult as I thought it would be. "I will sit back, relax, and wait to hear something from him," I thought.

I waited patiently. A week later, he had not gotten back with me. I wondered if he had forgotten about me again, or if I had to go through it all over again, inquiring about whether or not there was a job available for me. I dreaded having to ask him again, but he was not moving fast enough. I felt paranoid. Already I had begun to think that maybe I wasn't good enough to work here. Maybe Varney didn't feel like I was bright enough. Maybe he didn't think I was a quick study like Marian. I didn't know what else to do to convince him that I needed the job. I tried to hide my fear, but surely I wasn't doing a good enough job. At this point and time in my life, I didn't think that I showed my fears and insecurity as much, not like I would later in life. I wasn't sure at this time if people noticed how afraid I was. I wasn't sure if people noticed that it took me so much longer to learn and comprehend. Maybe the trainer knew, and maybe she felt my pain, and that is why she gave me the job that didn't require a lot of thinking, or a lot of concentrating in the first place. For some reason she had mercy on me. It was difficult for me to learn anything new. "Maybe they will see me in the manner that Jeanette did, maybe they will think I am just kidding," I thought. Had that been the case, then trying to learn something and actually getting it would not have been as hard for me. I'd kid my way out of it and before you knew it, I would eventually catch on. Yes, that is how it worked for me most times. I had to do things over and over and over again until it clicked. By the time I caught on, others were excelling.

Once I had to cross-train with the others, and I didn't do well at all. I had no idea what was going on and how to dispatch a call to the field. I was afraid to ask questions because it made me look dumb, but what I failed to realize is I was dumber by trying to look smart. I couldn't help myself. I couldn't control the negative thoughts and voices that consumed me whenever I tried to read, or whenever I tried to learn something. My nerves got bad, my breathing got short, and my chest knotted up like a big basketball was sitting in the middle of my lungs. The voice fought against me. There was always a war inside of my head, and the enemy seemed to always have the upper hand. I didn't like it! I resented the way I felt about myself. I hated me for being me. I felt like I wasn't good enough for anything or anybody. I felt so worthless.

Somehow I mustered up the courage to ask Varney again. When I questioned him this time, he said he was still looking into it. I did not feel good about this; I thought by now he would have had a different answer for me. I thought by now he would have called me into the office to let me know something. I wanted to believe him, but I had doubt. By this time, I was beginning to feel uncertain as to whether he was really checking into getting me the job or trying to play me off in a nice way. It made me feel terrible. I felt ostracized. I felt totally left out. One week felt like two months, especially when I felt like all eyes were on me. I felt like all of my coworkers must have wondered what was wrong with me, and why he had left me out. It was shameful that out of all the people in the group, I was the only one that I knew of who had been left out. I was embarrassed. I was terribly embarrassed because it seemed that everyone had started to like me, but because of this situation, I felt it might cause the group to second guess themselves about me. My need to be liked by everyone was important. I desired to be accepted by all, and I wanted to be smart, and bright. I wanted to be in a position where someone would notice me. Being at the insurance company and being recognized was the best thing that could have ever happened to me. But I don't believe it will ever happen again. One thing I have to be is realistic. I am going to be a failure, and I can't help it. This is what the little voice inside my head was telling me, and maybe the little voice was right. I felt certain that being overlooked had given everyone the impression that I was not good enough to do the job. It felt even worse because I had to work so very hard at trying not to let my feelings of disappointment show. I could understand how my insecurities were sometimes mistaken for being cocky, and arrogant. But what was I to do? I was cocky, if it meant hiding my feelings of hurt. Before I would let someone see me hurt, I would rather run and hide.

No Place to Hide

Because of the office layout, I had no place to hide. I sat out on the floor. The feeling that all eyes were on me was becoming stronger and stronger. I felt like everyone was convinced by now, that I was not as bright as they assumed I was. It was not a good feeling. I couldn't hide and I couldn't run. I had been talking to Freda, another coworker. She informed me of some job opportunities elsewhere, which turned out to be a wonderful thing. I was not sure if Varney had called her name either. Perhaps it should have made me feel better knowing that I was not the only one who had been overlooked, but it gave me very little comfort. I was different. I was special. More and more people found me interesting and I had become comfortable talking with others. I was feeling great because everyone seemed to like me. I was starting to trust people. But that wasn't the case, because I didn't trust Varney, and I didn't feel good inside about myself. He was smiling in my face and doing very little to help me behind my back. Why doesn't he want me to work here? I asked myself. Why did he overlook me? Why am I always overlooked? As much as I felt like giving up, I was not going to give up. Because they say good things come to those who wait. I was waiting and waiting and hopeful and hopeful. But the truth was I still felt worthless.

Talking to Freda

Freda told me about this great company that had plenty of jobs available. She gave me the name of the company and the fax number. I went home and began working on my new resume that day, while waiting to hear from Varney. I proofread it. It looked good, it sounded good, and so I faxed it over to the company the next day. Even though I tried to trust Varney, I was losing faith in him. I was beginning to think that he was not doing enough to get me hired. I was becoming more and more upset each day. The treatment I was getting from him was cold. Three weeks had passed, and he had not gotten back with me. He never called me into his office to inform me one way or the other about the job. What was so difficult about calling me into the office, letting me know that there was nothing available? Of course, I would have been disappointed, but I would have respected him for the courtesy.

At the start of the third week, everyone seemed excited about their new job offer. I was trying to smile, but I'm sure the hurt was written all over my face. I was happy for everyone. I only wished that I could have rejoiced for myself as well. I smiled because I knew deep down inside that my day was coming. I had experienced being left out before, and I had also experienced being overlooked. I should have been able to handle this situation much better. I didn't feel as bad today, knowing that I had submitted my resume to another company. I was confident that my resume was pretty impressive. I felt good about it. I felt hopeful that I would be called and I would soon be leaving the computer company. This helped to relieve some of the tension I felt inside.

I continued to do my job each day the best I could. Then one day I couldn't take it anymore. I got the nerves to ask Mr. Varney if I could cross-train to learn my coworkers' job, the ones who sat up front from me. He thought this was a pretty good idea. I was surprised by his quick response. The same day I presented the idea to him, he presented it to them and they agreed to train me. I trained about thirty minutes learning the job. It was easy as pie. It was much easier than getting on the phone calling the same ole people, getting the same ole answers and never making any progress. I loved the way this made me feel. I was doing something new and different and finding the courage to do it. I could do the job! I wished it were mine. I agreed to relieve them one at a time as they went to lunch. This gave me more time to do their job and more time to prove to Mr. Varney that I could do the job. It was important to me that he knew I was a good worker. If only he would give me the opportunity.

I was beginning to feel much better. Every day around eleven thirty, I would go up front to relieve my coworkers for lunch. I felt so good about myself, it was unbelievable. Yes! The floor began to look at me differently. People who never smiled at me before would pass my desk and speak and smile. This felt great. There's something about a moment of fame that draws people to you. I never knew it could feel so good. My new friends seemed happy for me. They hadn't given up hope that I would get the job, especially Marian. She was still insisting that I keep talking to Varney.

One of the young managers who always came by my desk for small talk and laughs would come up front where I was sitting and say, "Girl, I knew you had it in you." I would smile and say, "I thought you knew." He would wink and walk away. It felt great. I had made the first step and the

33

second step, and God took over and turned the messy situation into a wonderful experience. It didn't matter to me anymore whether I became permanent or whether God had bigger and better plans for me. I was loved and it felt good! Trying to work out here is like being black, always trying to prove to others and myself that I am just as good as the next person. It's a constant struggle.

Receiving the Good News

I received a call from the finance company to come in for an interview. I went on the interview and got the job two days later. I was so excited. The next day I hand delivered my resignation to Varney. I did not have to do this, but I wanted to go out with dignity. I thought he deserved the courtesy of being told. He appeared very disappointed and told me he had not forgotten about me. He said, "I was hoping and looking forward to you becoming permanent with us, McKenzie." I thanked him and told him I had found something else and stressed that it had been a pleasure working for him and the company. I wish you could have seen the look on his face.

The interview with the finance company went well. I got the job as a commission analyst. It was such a challenge for me. The finance company certainly had it going on. The company had its own university. I had never seen anything like this before. I thought this was really cool until I was presented with all the material I had to study and learn. Never before had I taken so many tests. Being here was like being in school, except there was no escaping. It was nothing like working for the computer company. Learning that job was a piece of cake. I knew working for the finance company would be different, but I didn't think it would be this much to learn. "I have to be strong and I have to believe in me," I told myself.

My self-esteem and confidence were not as high this time. I had been fired from one job, overlooked on another job, and now was about to be tested to keep this job. "Oh my God, what am I to do?" I thought. I prayed and studied really hard. As new hires, we had been informed that we had three major exams to take, and we had three times to take each test before we would be let go if we didn't pass. This was a very trying time for me. It was a time for my faith in God to be tested and a time for me to test my learning abilities. By the grace and goodness of God, I passed all three tests and passed each of them on the first time. It was difficult, but I did it! As my big brother Joshua Jr. puts it in his sermons whenever he is preaching, "I don't know how God did it! He just did it!" Surely, God had done it for me!

The Finance Company

Six weeks passed, and the job was coming on strong. It was interesting. It was hard. It was all new and different. I liked the idea of all the testing. It gave me the chance to exercise my brain. Oftentimes I felt fearful, but I gradually got over the fear. But I didn't get over the embarrassing moments. And getting over the fear was only temporary. I was embarrassed whenever the teacher asked questions and I didn't know the answers. As much as I studied, one would have thought I knew every answer, but fortunately no one knew how much and how hard I studied. No one probably knew how often I drifted off into the ozone of my mind in the middle of the instructor teaching the class or explaining what and how we were supposed to do whatever she requested us to do. It seemed I always drifted at the time the class or I was called on to demonstrate something. It was really strange. What was even stranger is I thought I was supposed to know the answers, even if no one else knew them. My mind told me I should have known how to answer the questions regardless. It reminded me of how I was supposed to be naturally smart and bright. I had no excuse for not knowing. I could never understand why the little voice chose to beat up on me so much. Sometimes it made me cry, and most times it made me very sad and unhappy.

My mind told me I was brilliant. My mind told me I was smart, yet it went haywire whenever I tried to focus or concentrate for any period of time, then it would get mad and beat up on me because I didn't know how to answer the questions. I would spend the rest of the day beating myself up because I didn't know the answer to the question, and worry about what each and every individual in the class must have thought of me. Surely, they all thought I was smart but I felt like I had made a fool out of myself. It bugged me because I had made myself look so dumb. I worried about this the rest of the day, and only God knows how much I thought about it in my dreams. I could hardly fall asleep at night because the recorder in my mind had to replay the day. It had to remind me how slow and foolish I had been for not doing a better job, and being the best I could be. It told me how smart and bright I should have been. On the other hand, the little voice inside of my head talked so much that I couldn't easily grasp anything. It was a Catch-22, as they say. I tried to look and act interested every day. I did every thing I was supposed to do. I participated in class as much as possible. Every night I studied very long and hard, from the time I got home until I fell asleep. Most nights I didn't feel like dinner. I didn't want to get left behind in class. The good thing about studying was I had met a study partner. Even though he was not an employee of the company, he insisted on helping me learn what I needed to know in order to pass all of my tests and keep my job. At first

I didn't think it was a good idea, him trying to assist me with my studies, since he didn't work at the company and didn't know the job, how on earth was he going to help me? But it turned out to be a lot of fun, and he was a great help to me.

Completing the Training

Once we completed the training, one of the requirements was that each analyst had to be monitored while assisting the field over the phone. I was not excited about this, but it was part of the job. I was monitored twice a week. Every time I was monitored, I was given constructive criticism, as they called it, and very little positive feedback. I had to challenge every one of my calls. Depending on my critiquing score, my job would be lost. I challenged every score under a ninety. I knew I could do better than the quality assurance department was giving me credit for. I believed it in my heart. This was an interesting job, and I had learned a lot in training. It never ceases to amaze me that no matter how much training you get, when you get to the floor, the job appears to be so much different, and the first question you ask yourself is, "Did we learn that in training?" After several challenging discussions, my score began to increase, but not to my satisfaction. I was a perfectionist. My greatest weakness was being a perfectionist. Whenever I learned, I wanted to know it all. I wanted to be perfect, as close to perfect as perfect could be. I wanted to know the job well and wanted to excel. Sometimes I think I tried too hard. Sometimes I wished that I could relax and learn, but that hadn't happened since I had begun my journey in the real world. The fact that I had very little faith in myself made me work three times harder than most. I knew it would be a long journey for me. After all, I had passed all my exams; the extensive training had to count for something.

Yes, six long weeks of hard training had to count for something, but it seemed like the quality assurance group did not feel that way. Something was missing; either they were not getting it or I was missing something. The only thing good about the little voice is it taught me to stand up and defend myself. Then on the other hand, I'm not sure if it was the little voice. It usually did nothing positive for me. Maybe this was the "me" breaking through; if I believed I was right, I stood up for what I believed. I don't know the origin of the saying, but I agree with whoever it was who said, "If you don't stand up for something, you will fall for anything." I always stood up for what I believed in. I also believed in what the late Dr. Martin Luther King Jr. said. "A man cannot ride your back unless you are bent over," so I tried to stand. I would challenge any situation. I did what I had to do. I went to the supervisor and requested to go back into a one-on-one training. Whatever I was missing, I wanted to find. I was convinced that the quality assurance group had chosen me specifically to pick on. Not only was I the new kid on the block, I felt like they sensed my self-doubt and fears.

Back in Training

Going back into training was no surprise to me. I really didn't mind having to go back into training. I found it amazing how happy I was to have requested to go back into training. I found it even more amazing that I didn't feel embarrassed by the fact that I felt the need to go back into training. The manager gave my supervisor the okay to take me back into a one-on-one session, and it went well. I came out feeling only a little better, because I had doubts already. I doubt that I would be able to do anything differently from what I had been doing before. Doubts, doubts, doubts. Doubt is what I had. I went back on the floor, hoping that I could demonstrate a little of what I had learned. The little voice was playing tricks on me again; it had convinced me that I hadn't learned a thing. Oftentimes no matter how much I grasped something, the little voice would tell me that I needed a little bit more, and a little bit more. However, that outside version of me was smiling, telling me I was beautiful, telling me I was bright, and telling me I was next in line.

When I got back on the floor, I understood more than I realized. Thank you, Jesus! But the quality assurance people were still singling me out, and I was still challenging them. Whenever they would score me below a 90 percent, I disputed. I disputed three times and that was the three times they monitored me. I was upset. Whatever they thought I was doing incorrectly, I felt like I was doing it correctly. If I was not doing the job correctly, then it was time for another visit to the supervisor. I resented the fact that I had to do it all over again, but there was no way of getting around it. I spoke to my supervisor again, and asked if it would be okay if we went into training one more time. I explained that the quality assurance group was still giving me a hard time. Of course, she already knew this based on the quality score I received. I promised this time I was not leaving until I understood how to read the financial statement. So there we were again, back into training. It surprises me now how back then I didn't mind pushing and pressing, trying to get a better and clearer understanding of things. But after a while my fears outlived my willingness to go on. I wanted to keep on trying because the Word encourages us to. It was my medicine. It encouraged me to have no fear. It encouraged me keep running the race. The race for me was finding a job, staying on the job, finding myself, and most of all peace of mind. I had gone through this before at the insurance company; I went in and out of training at least three times before I got it! I was too eager to be embarrassed.

Today, if I had to do it all over again, I would be too afraid to be embarrassed. I wouldn't dare let the world see how truly long it took me to grasp something. It would be a difficult thing,

The race is not given to the swift nor the strong but to him that endureth to the end. Ecclesiastes 9:11.

When I finished that last and final one-on-one session, I was good to go. "Those quality assurance people better not bother me anymore," I told myself. I had a better understanding of the job and the whole concept. I learned that financial statement and I learned it well, only to find out that none of the others understood how to read the statement either, not even the quality assurance people. I got it now! As a matter of fact, I had it down pat so well that a few times the quality assurance team came to me for assistance while monitoring someone who was now the new kid on the block. I felt like my mission had been accomplished. I had studied and I had learned. I was doing the job and doing it well. I felt great to be sharing my knowledge. It was ironic because the entire time the little voice had told me I was the only one on the floor who didn't know what I was doing. It was oh so wrong. Most of the team later admitted to me that nobody really knew how to read that statement. As a matter of fact, "they were working on simplifying it," they told me. The quality assurance people did not give me any more headaches. Not only was I making ninety on my monitoring, I moved up to ninety-nine then to the one hundreds. "Maybe I'll be here for a very long time after all," I thought. "Who knows, I might be here long enough to retire? Besides, that is what having a job is all about: working until you are old enough to retire."

The job didn't pay a lot of money, but the benefits were great. I met many nice people on the job. Sometimes it seemed that the only thing that kept me going to the job, especially when the stress was high and the pay low were the people I worked with. I enjoyed people, especially God-fearing people. But I could not believe what God was about to do to test my faith once again.

Bumping Heads

My Lord, what was this bumping heads all about? I had almost completely settled into my new job. Everything was going so well. The department was growing and changes were about to be made. The department had moved from the second floor to the first floor. I was excited about the change once I observed the newness of everything. It didn't seem like a bad idea, moving from one floor to another. I wasn't excited about the change at first, but my feelings about whether or not I liked the changes didn't matter. Management had decided that this was the thing to do, and it was going to be done. It was new and refreshing. I had to get used to it and adjust to the change. I wasn't familiar with the offices downstairs and the people who worked there. I never had a reason to roam the area, so I knew very little about what departments were in the area and the people who worked downstairs. But I soon found out.

I was walking down the hall. I wasn't looking for trouble. I was trying to do my job, but something distracting, terribly distracting, caught my eye. *"It couldn't be!"* I thought to myself. I glanced across the floor to the other department and saw a familiar face. At first I thought it was just someone who looked liked someone I knew. This happened to me quite often. I was notorious for seeing people who looked like other folk and often mistaken them for being someone else. This always seemed to have happened to me. Many times I would end up apologizing, and explaining to the familiar face how I thought they were someone I knew. This time I was not mistaken. As much as I hoped that I was mistaken, I wasn't. It was real. I looked across the floor at the lady I thought I knew, and she looked back. "Does she think she knows me, too?" I wondered. Our eyes caught and for a quick second; I thought I was looking into the eyes of a ghost. I wanted to take off running as fast as I could. "Oh no! Lord, it couldn't be!" I thought. "No, not again; no, that couldn't be Jan." But yes, it was her, Jan from the insurance company. I was not mistaken. For once I was not excited about seeing the long-lost face that I had not seen in awhile. I wasn't sure what I was supposed to do. I wasn't sure if I should run or scream. I tried to keep calm. I didn't want to give anyone any reason to fire me on my new job. It was because of her that I was no longer at the insurance company. It was because of her that I didn't get the experience of working in the new department and getting that big raise. Even though I prayed to be there for three years, I didn't think God would give me only three years and no more. It was all her fault. She was the reason that I was here today and not at the insurance company. I didn't know what seeing Jan's face again was all about. I wished that my eyes had been playing tricks on me because her face wasn't something that I had hoped to see so soon. I must have looked like a zombie walking down the hall after seeing her. I had to do something.

I turned to God. "Dear God, what is this all about? Please speak to me now and speak to me clearly. You have got to talk to me and let me know quickly what this is all about." I prayed. This was not my prayer. I had only prayed and asked you to help me to get over that terrible experience, and let me move forward with my life. I had moved forward with my life and I thought things were working well in my favor. I had been blessed to have found another real job. I had been blessed to pass my exams, and I had been blessed to meet many nice friends. But I could not figure out what seeing Jan in the workplace was all about.

I continued to walk down the hall uncertain as to what to do. Maybe God would give me some directions as to what to do. I was so afraid. By now I had forgotten where I was headed. It took minutes for me to get my head clear. Then I remembered that I was headed upstairs. Instead of going upstairs, I decided to take a detour. I needed to get away for a minute. I needed a few seconds to exhale and allow my brain time to register what my eyes had just witnessed. I had to get it together. For a minute I felt like I was losing it; this must have been some sort of joke or something. "No! We didn't land on the same job again." I laughed. Laughing was the only thing I could do. I had absolutely no control over what was happening. Even though I worked with Jan at the insurance company, I didn't really get to know her well. She was not an outgoing, friendly person, but everyone at the insurance company thought she was cool, so I acted like she was cool also. I never really figured her out; in my opinion, she was too quiet. I didn't laugh and joke with her like I did with everyone else. I had learned that you could not treat all people the same. Because of everyone else, I felt I should befriend her too.

She was a close friend of Jeanette, Mossey, Natasha and some of the other friends I associated with. I tried to treat her as nicely as I could whenever I was around her. I didn't anticipate any trouble, but I had not anticipated any trouble before I lost my job either. I had to get myself together and I had to do it quickly. I didn't want to make the same mistake ever again. I kept walking, even though I wasn't sure where I was going. I wasn't even sure where I would end up.

I ended up outside and found myself taking a breath of fresh air. I needed to spend some time alone with God. He and I really needed to have a talk. I didn't have the good book with me, so I had to pray. He was the only one I could talk to. He was the only one, as far as I knew, who was familiar with this situation. I hoped he was the only one who knew about my ordeal. This wasn't something I was proud of. It was a page in my life that I was turning and leaving behind. I had to deal with this one all by myself. I believed that all things happened for a reason, and I felt like now was the time to talk to God about the reason for seeing Jan.

I didn't get an answer from God right away, but thank God it didn't take long. After spending time talking to him, I felt calm. I lost myself in him. I got so lost in him I almost forgot where I was when I realized I needed to get back to work. I felt all right again. "Things are going to be just fine. Everything is in his hand," I told myself. "Please God don't let her start any trouble," I prayed. "And please don't let me feel any animosity towards her. Please let bygones be bygones." When God and I finished our conversation, I felt peace and calmness embrace me. "Thank you, Jesus Christ!" I knew then that everything was going to be all right. I walked back inside and began working.

Absorbing the Shock

It had only been a couple of hours since I saw Jan. The reality of seeing her had not completely soaked into my brain when I looked up and saw her. She was walking in my direction. My heart started racing, I thought it was going to jump outside of my body and start running out the side door. I breathed in and out slowly several times, trying to take deep breaths to slow my heart rate down. I began to pray again and again. "Dear God, please be with me and be with her too. Why is she approaching me? God, please give me courage." I still had to put my guards up because I didn't know what to expect. I looked up again. I noticed she had a friendly look on her face. I felt calm. "Thank you, God," I thought. My fears subsided. My heartbeat felt normal and I tried to look like I was not afraid.

She walked over to my desk and spoke to me: "Hello Kenzie."

I wasn't sure if my voice would be clear or not, but I spoke back to her in the same friendly manner: "Hello Jan." I am sure she could tell I was nervous.

She said, "I just wanted to drop this note off with you. When you finish reading it, please stop by my desk." I smiled and took the note, not knowing what it would say, and assured her that I would come by her desk once I finished reading it. She acknowledged she heard me, smiled back, and started to walk away. She looked back as she walked away and both of us smiled, as if wishing each other a nice day. Thank you, God.

I watched her walk away. I wanted to make sure she was completely out of sight before I began to read the note. I continued to work a while. I wrapped up the phone call that I had been working on and proceeded to update the account. I had given Jan enough time to reach her desk. Then I opened the note and began to read it.

Dear McKenzie, I can not believe what God has done. He has allowed us to come together again at the same company to work. I ask you to please forgive me for what I did that day. I don't know what came over me. God doesn't make mistakes and I do not believe in coincidences. He purposely placed us on the same job for a reason; if it was just to say I'm sorry.

I accepted her apology and went out to lunch with her a few times before I was fired.

Three years passed and I was still with the finance company. I didn't ask God to allow me to stay here for three years, but somehow it turned out that way. It wasn't Jan who caused me to lose my job this time. It wasn't my prayer. It must have been my fate. Or was it just that the number three had become my lucky number? Who would have thought I was about to lose my job again?

I was getting tired of having to change jobs so much. I couldn't figure it out. I often wondered how others managed to keep jobs, all folk. Folk who had bad attitudes and no personality kept their jobs. Folk who stirred up garbage and chaos were able to keep their jobs. Folk who complained all day long kept their jobs. Why me? Something had to be wrong with this picture. I felt like they knew the secret. But poor me, I felt like I was left out in the cold—working hard, praying hard, and still losing jobs. There must have been some great secret. I wondered if it was a big conspiracy, and I was on the outside. But whenever people talked to me, they all said the same thing like, "Go to work and do your job," as if that wasn't exactly what I was doing. I had heard the words so many times that I had to ask myself, "Am I doing my job?" The answer was always the same: "Yes." So what on earth was I missing?

The severity of my anxiety had not reached its full peak. I had not become too weak to fight. I had not become so weak that I wasn't defensive. I had no problem with defending what I believed. I believed

God had sent me to the company to work, and I believed he was going to teach me how to do the job that had been assigned to me. I knew I had problems concentrating. I knew I had problems understanding, and I knew I may not have been as quick to grasp things as others, but I knew I was bright. I knew God had blessed me with common sense. If I didn't grasp something quickly enough, it was not my fault. And if the message was not clear to me, I quickly requested the instructor to show me how it should be done. It wasn't my fault that the instructor did not teach the class to everyone's understanding.

I knew a part of me was terribly slow, but another part of me was eager to learn. I was eager and I wanted to get it! I ignored the fact that I had to struggle and that it would probably take me longer to comprehend. The stress and anxiety that I felt, I thought everyone experienced. I could never quite understand why the little negative voice inside my head did not appear to be as visible in them and as real as mine was to me. I had to always refer to my Bible. The good book was my way out. The good book was my hope.

Consider it pure joy, my brothers, whenever you face trials of many kinds, because you know that the testing of your faith develops perseverance. Perseverance must finish its work so that you may be mature and complete, not lacking anything.

James 1: 2–4

Perseverance that's right, I was eager to keep trying.

Continuing with the Finance Company

I had been working for the finance company for three years. I had been there long enough to gradually build up my self-esteem and my confidence. I was feeling good. Just knowing that I had passed all my exams, I could not help but feel good. Everything was going well until the company decided to make some managerial changes. How was this wise change about to affect me? Our department received a new manager, Harry, and at that point things changed.

Being me had not been a problem so far with my previous manager at the insurance company. They had gotten used to me. I guess it was okay for me to be me in their presence, whoever I was. Being me was not an easy thing. I had to think about my every action. I studied myself all of the time. I wanted to know who I was. I wanted to know why I spent all of my time worrying. I wanted to know what it was that had a grip so tight on me that there was hardly anything left in me to squeeze out. I had to think about the way I should look whenever I approached a manager or supervisor; should I smile or should I look serious? Should I compliment today or shouldn't I? Should I try to engage in small talk or shouldn't I? Will I react the way I'm supposed to react? It completely wore me out.

I was tired. I was tired of everything, but most of all I was tired of trying to be me. It was better for me if one looked at my attire and judged me. It was just great for one to assume that if you knew how to dress, you knew how to act. I never desired being approached by anyone with authority; I knew I would be a disappointment. There wasn't any doubt that he or she would see straight through me like a clear glass of water. If

I chose to engage in small talk, I knew I would end up daydreaming and missing the whole conversation. *Lord, have mercy,* if someone tried to tell a joke, I would always miss the punch line worrying whether or not I would get it before the joke was finished. Whenever I tried to engage in small talk, I always got lost. God, I hated this. I never understood what it was the person was saying because the entire time they would be talking, I would be worried wondering if I looked like I understood.

I never looked in the eyes of anyone. That was another one of my great fears. I knew they would see my fear, and I was afraid. I was afraid one would see how sad and worthless I really felt on the inside. Before people would finish whatever it was they were talking about, I was already trying to figure out what was I going to say? I wanted to comment intelligently on whatever it was they were saying without looking stupid or dumb. Somehow I always ended up looking dumb and stupid because I had daydreamed during the entire time, and when they finished talking, I didn't know what to say. I would look at the expression on their face and make my judgment. If they were smiling, then I would smile; if they made a comment of disgust, I would shake my head in disgust. I must have been doing a good job by following suit because the people never stopped talking to me. Whenever it came to friends and family, it was a different story. I didn't get away with drifting as easily. They would interrupt my drift and verify whether or not I was listening or ignoring them.

It was so hard to be me. It was just as hard trying to discover who I was. I hated that I could not give anyone a few minutes of time without drifting. I hated that I could not listen. This made it extra hard for me because I had so much to worry about. Most times I tried to put on a happy face. I tried to carry myself as if I didn't have a worry in the world, and that my life was a fresh dozen of roses. This must have been the arrogant side of me. This must have been the side of me that a lot of people didn't like. But this was the part of me that kept me going. It kept me moving. I had to have something to keep me afloat. "She is so happy; she is so carefree, what is it about her that makes her smile all of time?" This side of me seemed to have angered many. But the reality of it all is, I was so full of pain and disappointment. All day long I worried, wondering if I had said or done something that may have hurt someone's feelings. I never got a moment of peace. That little voice on the inside made sure of that. It was surprising to me that I had even lasted this long on the job. I had survived for three long years. No one knew except God and me how happy and blessed I felt because I still had a job. I constantly prayed for a moment, just a moment, of peace. I prayed constantly that the logs on my shoulder would just ease up for a minute; yes, just one minute would have been heaven to me. I wanted to know what it felt like to sit at my desk for one minute and not feel like I was enclosed in a small box. I wanted to breathe for just one moment, one minute. The only relief I received was the fact that I knew the job well. I knew that going in and out of training had paid off. I still had not managed how to communicate with the supervisor. I still had not managed how to utilize my time well in doing my job. I didn't know how to act or react to most situations.

The good thing about it all was I felt accepted by most of the people in the workplace. I even believed at times they didn't notice my fears or insecurities. I was happy that they had gotten used to me or had accepted me for who I was. Whenever I didn't feel accepted, sometimes I could break that by making people laugh. I could always make people laugh; it came natural for me. That was one good thing about me, and I was too insecure to see that I had that God-given ability. I wanted everyone to be happy even if I never found the happiness I sought. I hoped that Harry would accept me. I hoped that knowing my job—not my insecure feelings and self-doubt—would be enough for him to keep me. But it wasn't. We did not hit it off. I was already getting negative energy from him. I am sure the feelings of fear that lived inside me were not portraying a pretty picture of me. "God, I wish I could look normal," I thought. "I wish I could look happy and confident like everyone else. I wish he couldn't see the true feelings of what I was thinking behind my smile." I had to deal with these feeling every time I was faced with a new situation. I knew they were not normal feelings because they never went away, they never relented themselves from me. I was consumed. I was overloaded with stress, fear, and anxiety every day. "Lord, will he notice how strange I am?" I worried. "Will he think I am weird? Will he take the time to get to know me and accept me for the insecure, lonely-at-heart, fearful individual I am? God knows I need my job." It wouldn't have been so bad if I had felt this way on the inside and somehow been able to camouflage the feelings on the outside. My insecurities worked well against me. I was always fighting against myself, trying not to look like a wimp, trying not to come across as weak, fearful or timid; and even this was working against me. I was considered arrogant, thinking I was all of that, egotistical and Ms. Sophisticated Lady. My ego was all I had, and I wanted to hang on to it for as long as I could before the little voice tore me down completely.

It's interesting how the mind has a way of letting you know at first glance when meeting someone for the very first time whether you like that person or not. It also amazes me how often the one that you thought you wouldn't like, sometimes turn out to be your best friend. Many times I experienced this. It may have turned out this way with Mr. Harry, but he didn't allow himself or me the time to find out. He didn't come across as a friendly person. He didn't come across as a person who had worked with and around people at all. He had no personality.

He was short and had blonde hair, blue eyes, and pale skin. He didn't come across as a people person at all. There was no indication that he had ever been in management before. "I'm sure he will not be taking any time trying to get to know me," I thought. And I really didn't care for him. His personality was definitely conflicting with mine. On top of it all, I believed he was prejudiced; he believed he wasn't. He often talked about his heritage. He told us about the strong Indian blood he possessed in his family. He seemed proud to share this pertinent information, so proud that it had almost become to the point of bragging. I don't know why he felt like it was so important to discuss this with the group. There was nothing about him or his family portrait that gave anyone any idea that he was Indian unless he told you. I supposed it was his way of letting us know that he was not racist or prejudiced.

Harry had been the department manager for about three months now. We clashed. It was unfortunate. I knew I would have to work harder than the rest, knowing that at any given time he could kick me out of the door. Already Harry was beginning to trip. It didn't take long.

Shortly, I began to receive e-mails from him telling me that I had been returning from breaks late. It wasn't unusual for me to return from break a little late. I didn't goof off a lot, and it must have been okay with the previous boss, but Harry was obviously not having it. So for the first time on the job in quite some time, I had to begin watching the clock again. I had to get in touch with time, unless I wanted to receive more e-mail. The first e-mail stated that I had been three minutes late, then another one stated I had been one minute late. I knew that trouble was starting. I knew that I had to do something quick to keep this man off my back. I couldn't believe he was whining over one minute, but the truth is one minute counts; I learned that too. So I did what I had to do; I decided that I wasn't going to be late anymore. I decided that I would take ten-minute breaks instead of my scheduled fifteen-minute breaks. This way I would never be late again. This seemed to be working well for me but disappointing Harry. No more tardiness for me. It was almost too good to be true. I took my breaks and rushed back to my desk as fast as I could. I was doing well. I had conquered my first test. I would rush out, and rush back so quickly I'm not even sure if anyone in the group missed me. But one day, I was late again.

Two weeks later, I took my break and time flew right past me. I was two minutes late. How could I have let this happen? I knew this was a terrible thing. But it just happened. God knows, I had no intentions of ever being late again. The next thing I knew I was being asked to come into his office. I was being written up, with the statement that I had been warned not to be late anymore. I had no problem with this, except for being disappointed in myself. He was exactly right. Even though I knew it was just his way of picking on me, I was late. I had no defense except I was never going to be late again. I had no desire to go into his office anymore.

Three weeks later I would find myself sitting in his office once again. I hoped it would be a pleasant visit. I hoped he would compliment me on how well I had been doing my job. I thought he would tell me what a good job I had continued to do. After all, I was doing all I could to keep my job. I worked very hard. I gave up breaks and worked around the clock. It was okay because I wanted to stick around till retirement age. I wanted to make my parents proud. I knew this would have made Mama and Daddy very proud. I wanted to stick around for a very long time, too, and be proud, but in my heart I was desperately trying to outdo three years.

Yes, I was hoping Harry would have something good to say, even though I knew it was not likely. Trying to make my way to his office was dreadful. We didn't get along. He was the big boss, and I was the fearful kid in the office trying hard to be cool. But it didn't seem to be working that way, so here I was walking to his office. It felt like a double dose of stress, with anxiety, anger, and fear all in one. Everything was attacking me at the same time. I was nervous. I was scared. I could feel my throat slowly closing up on me. The tightening of my chest was beginning to feel like two fists instead of one, and the feeling that all of the blood in my body was rushing to my head made me think twice about my job. It frightened me. It frightened me because I already feared the boss, and I was experiencing greater fear of having to deal with a boss whom I resented. I struggled making my way to his office.

I walked into his office trying to look pleasant. I wasn't smiling like I normally did. I felt tensed, and it was difficult to smile. It was as if the elastic in the facial muscles of my face had frozen, and I needed some time to let it thaw out. But apart from all of that, despite it being my nature to smile a lot, I was not feeling like my jovial self anymore. I wasn't smiling like myself anymore. I didn't know if anyone recognized how my spirit wasn't as uplifted as usual.

So in his office I sat. I could hear my heart beating. It was beating so loud, I thought he could hear it too. "Have a seat, McKenzie," he said. "How are you today?"

"I am doing fine," with a trembling voice I responded. "How are you?"

"I am fine," he answered. "I have been noticing you lately, McKenzie, and you no longer seem happy working here. Are you happy working here?" he asked.

"Yes sir, I am," I replied. I knew exactly what he was trying to do. He was on a mission and he was starting to work on it pretty darn quick. The man was trying to fire me. I was certain that he knew I didn't think the best of him, and I was certain that he knew that trying to intimidate me would make it that much easier for him to get rid of me. I tried to listen closely to what he had to say, but the little voice inside my head had begun to talk. It reassured me that I was not good enough for my job or anything else. I was born to be a failure, and a failure I was. He didn't like me and no one else liked me either. It reminded me of all the negative experiences I had encountered. It assured me I was about to lose another job.

It was still my hope that he would surprise me and have something nice to say to me. What I needed to hear was something positive. I thought that maybe, just maybe, hearing something positive for a change would be a good thing. But on the other hand, I wasn't too sure about that. Hearing positive things said to me were something I wasn't too familiar with. The thought almost frightened me. But inside I longed to hear something nice said to me, like being told that I was a great person, a loved person, and most of all a hard worker, by the boss. I longed to hear those things, but on the other hand, the thought of hearing such things was scary. I'm not sure if I would have been able to handle it; me, hearing something good being said to me—not likely. It was a thought and the thought made me smile inwardly. I had become accustomed to hearing negative things. But the irony of hearing negative things taught me. It taught me the importance of saying nice things to others. It taught me how to say positive things to others.

I learned the importance of showing kindness and encouraging others. Often I found myself saying things to others that I wished had been said to me. It taught me love for mankind, and most of all it taught me unselfishness. Being positive is the most important thing that you can do for your children and for your loved ones. Be kind, be positive, and show some love. Negative words create negative people, and positive words create positive people. I learned that no matter who you are, you have some good in you. And it is good to do good. Let us encourage one another:

Your Love has given me great joy and encouragement, because you, brother, have refreshed the hearts of saints. Philemon 1:7.

Snapping Back

So much was going through my mind while sitting there in his office. I had to snap back. I had to shake myself to wake up from the daydreaming. When I woke up, I had no idea where he had left off. I didn't remember exactly what he had been saying before I drifted away. When I snapped back, I began talking, telling him how I had always enjoyed my work, and how working for such a great company had been a great opportunity for me. I reminded him that I had been on the job for three years and had never had any problem. "Don't this account for anything?" I asked.

He seemed to ignore my comments and proceeded to say to me, "But you do not seem very happy here anymore, McKenzie. It seems like you no longer enjoy being here."

"But Harry, what about my work?" I asked.

"Your work is fine."

"Then why am I sitting here in your office?" I asked.

"I would like to see you smile more, McKenzie. You're no longer perky." He said.

"So, you noticed?" I asked myself. I wanted to fight back at him, but instead I held my tongue. But the look in my eyes I could not hide. The look must have said to him, "Sir, I think you are the problem." But there is no doubt that he already knew that. I felt my patience growing short, so I asked if I could please be excused from his office now.

"Yes, McKenzie," he said.

I smiled and walked out of the office. I was not going to hang around any longer going back and forth with someone telling me I didn't look happy when indeed I wasn't feeling very happy. He made it very unpleasant for me. I believed it made him happy seeing me becoming so miserable. It was becoming harder and harder for me to smile. It was becoming harder for me to avoid him. I wished there were some way I could ignore him all day every day and just concentrate on my work. Why in the world was he picking on me so much? I had enough problems of my own without him. Having to live with myself was difficult enough for me. I couldn't understand why others felt the need to insist on making things harder for me. If it wasn't the boss, it was my family. Someone all the time seemed to putting me down!

The Day I Was Let Go

I will never forget the day he fired me. We had just come back to work on Tuesday, the Tuesday after Labor Day. We were having a department meeting, and I was doing all I could to show that I was interested in what was going on. I participated in the meeting by asking questions to show that I was well abreast of what was going on. I was careful not to ask anything stupid; looking stupid was the last thing I needed. I hadn't noticed the look on their faces, Harry and his boss, Ellie. But later I noticed how the two of them looked at each other whenever I spoke. And neither of them seemed very impressed or interested in what I had to say. It just so happened that both of them had transferred together from the same department, and they seemed to be working together hand in hand. They looked at each other in such a way that their eye contact should have been my clue that I was about to be fired. But with a little prayer and positive thinking, I thought everything was going to work out. Things did eventually work out, but my days at the finance company were counting down. I hoped to be there for the long haul, but I had to face reality, and reality was that Harry was the department manager, and he was out to get rid of me. I couldn't help the fact that I didn't care much for him as the boss; personality conflict I guess is what you call it. Things were just fine the way they were for me. I didn't understand why he wanted to get rid of me if I was coming back from breaks on time, coming to work everyday and doing my job? I am sure I am not the only person who has worked under his supervision that he didn't like or who didn't like him. Besides, is this a reason to fire anyone? I couldn't understand why this was happening to me—first Jan, now Mr. Harry.

I made one more visit to his office weeks later, and it was my final visit to his office. After this visit, he informed me that I had been fired. I was accused of no longer showing interest in the job. I could not believe what I was hearing that day. I was angry. I was hurt, mad, angry, hurt, furious, and had too much pride to let him see me cry. I held back the tears and asked God, "Why me?" My mind drifted, thinking about how hard I had tried. I had done everything in the world I could do to keep my job. I wasn't ready to leave, but I guess it was time for me to go. I felt like God had let me down by allowing Harry to fire me. I was a Christian. I had always been a Christian, but I couldn't understand what kind of test I was always going through. I was beginning to feel like God didn't like me anymore either.

I was a babe in Christ and obviously did not understand the power of the Almighty. I didn't realize that I could have asked God to move my mountain, and he would have done just that; he may have just let Harry go instead of me. But I didn't know what to do. It would be later that I would grow and grow and face more challenges, more hard times, and many disappointments, only to find out how much God really loved and cared for me.

All things work together for good, for those who love the Lord.

Romans 8:28

I loved the Lord and things were working out for my good, but I didn't know it. I learned that you don't always realize what you're going through is working out for your good. It would be years later that I discovered just how much he loved me, and how much I needed him in my daily walk. It would be years later that I would realize like the Apostle Paul that the less I had, the more I depended on him. It would be years later that I could appreciate him in big blessings and little ones, too.

All I knew is that I wanted my job. I wanted to be there for a long time. I knew how hard it was for me to be accepted. I knew how long it would take me to learn something new if I had to start all over again. I would have to prove to myself and everyone else that I could first, learn the job, and then second, do the job, and third, there was no use in trying to defeat the fears; it was impossible. I could only hope that they would go away. I was always praying to be normal. I always prayed that God would take away my worries and my fears. I was always praying that I could like me for me. All I wanted was to be normal and to be happy. I often wondered if it was too much to ask for. I hated myself. I hated myself because I had let me down again. I hated myself because I had let my family down. And I hated myself because I had let the boss down. I felt dumb.

My God, my God, why hast thou forsaken me? Why art thou so far from helping me, and from the words of my roaring?

Psalms 22:1

I prayed a lot. Praying was one thing that I believed in. I had witnessed God doing some awesome things throughout my life. I believed it was the prayers of my mother and father that held me up many times when I felt incomplete. Whether or not they knew I felt down and out didn't seem to matter; I felt blessed because of them. I felt blessed by them even in my fears.

Confiding in a Friend

Before I was terminated from the company, I had the opportunity to speak with another supervisor about Harry. I wasn't trying to badmouth him or anything; I just wanted to get someone else's insight on him. Besides, the person I chose to go to was a man in the company whom I trusted. I shared with him my thoughts of Mr. Harry in hope that he would give me some advice that would ease the stress in our working environment. More than anything, I wanted to keep my job. I also hoped that he would be able to give me some good advice on what I needed to do to make myself a better employee. He was the manager of another department. He worked on the opposite side of the building, and I occasionally saw him in passing. He was tall, dark, and very conservative. Just to look at him one might have thought he was not very friendly, but that was just his look. He was one of the few black managers at the company, and seemed very dedicated to his work. He had also become a friend of mine. I thought it might do my heart good to talk with someone else outside of my department about the stress and anxiety I was experiencing. I didn't know what I was going through at the time. I knew very little or nothing about stress and anxiety. It would be years later when I learned that stress was real, and that stress could be deadly. I learned that it could cause high blood pressure, stomach ulcers, thyroid problems, heart diseases, and many other illnesses. Stress is hell. I once heard a man say that stress could burst a still drum. I can attest to that. Many people unknowingly suffer from anxiety, stress, and depression, and just like me; they don't know why their lives are so miserable and unhappy.

I trusted Arthur. I hoped he would not misunderstand and turn his back on me. I wanted to know his thoughts about Harry. Even if our opinions differed, it didn't mean I had to see things his way. He thought Harry was okay but complex. I shared my thoughts with him. I told him how Harry was always singling me out and I never understood why. Then he wanted to know what I was doing? I paused and looked at him. I could never figure out why folk were always asking me what I was doing whenever I discussed my experiences on the job. I told him I was working, doing my job and doing it well. Then he wanted to know if I was participating wholeheartedly with the group. At first, I did not understand the question. I asked. "Do you mean am I doing my job, working hard, and getting along with everyone?" Then the answer is yes. He didn't seem impressed with my answer, and I was very disappointed. I wondered what else was I to do. My face must have looked baffled. I was confused. Then he asked if I was a team player. I wasn't following him. I was not quite sure what being a team player really meant. I thought I knew. I thought it meant that I was supposed to like everyone and get along with them. I knew I was doing that. However, I wasn't totally committing myself to go along with the flow. He looked at me. Then he asked me about some game and wanted to know if I was playing the game? I looked at him strangely and asked what game he was referring to. I thought he was going to say the game of life. I was about to freeze up and began thinking to myself, no wonder I am so confused, life is not for real, it is only a silly game.

He said, "McKenzie, you have got to play the game." I listened. I was anxious to hear what he had to say, and hopefully learn some tips on how to play the game, whatever game I needed to be playing. "It is the game of the corporate world," he said. "When you are on the field, you have got to play the game, and you have got to play with the team." I didn't understand because I wasn't playing any games. I was real, about as real as real could get. Then he broke it down, saying, "When in China, you do as the China men do." I looked baffled again, because I was guilty. I was guilty because sometimes I felt so left out of the group. I felt like I was playing alone. I was my own person with my own thoughts and ideals. He paused and looked at me. He wanted to make sure I understood. "You have got to play the same game that everyone else plays in order to fit in Kenzie," he stressed. "You cannot be on the field playing soccer if everyone else is playing football. You have got to play the game," he said. I knew then that I was in trouble. Then things started to make a little sense to me. I didn't fit in; I was in a world of my own. As much as I wanted to fit in I felt left out. But how did he know that I acted that way? Was it that obvious? I thought. I never felt like I fit in because of my crazy fear of the boss. I never felt like I fit in because of the fear of not being liked or accepted by others. This is the game I was trying to conquer. All I wanted was to be well-received by others. I wanted to feel good and confident about myself and do a good job. But the little voice inside my head made me feel like I would never reach that goal. Most times I knew before I began the work that I wouldn't last. But I kept trying because that was all I knew to do. I kept trying because I was expected to succeed. I was expected to grow up, be somebody, and make something out of myself. I knew all of this, but I also knew that deep inside I was nothing more than a big disappointment. I was a disappointment to life, to my bosses, and to my family. My name should have been disappointment. Everything was becoming nothing more than a disappointment.

I couldn't share these feelings with anyone; they wouldn't understand. I didn't understand. The few times I tried to explain to my friends about my boss phobia, they would tell me how they experienced the same kind of fear in the presence of their boss. I knew they did not understand. I knew their fear was not paralyzing them. I believed their fear was the common fears that all of us experience periodically. I had heard about that type of fear. I had been to school, and at one time psychology was my major. Most of my classes were about abnormality. I knew about the fear they spoke of, but did they know about the fear I experienced? No. No one normal could possibly feel the way I felt. Not one of them had ever had fears so badly that they walked out on the job. Not one of them had fears so badly that they lost sleep night after night or felt like they were carrying logs on their back all day, everyday. Even after I arrived home each day, the fears didn't dissipate. I found myself worrying whether others had sensed my pain and suffering. I worried if I had said or done anything to hurt anyone. I never wanted to purposely hurt a soul. That is why it was so hurtful when others would describe me as a trip or outspoken. Sometimes they described me as purposely saying things to make others feel bad. I was constantly analyzing myself, trying to see myself the way others saw me, or the way I thought they saw me. If anything, I wanted to do for others just to make them like me. But the recording played inside my head over and over and over again. Only God knows how I fell asleep at night. Falling asleep was the only escape I had. Sometimes I hated to wake up because I knew the recorder would start playing in my head all over again. I could never find peace of mind. Being at work was no escape. I worried the most at work, trying hard to be perfect, trying hard to relax, concentrate, and do my job.

There was still life after leaving the finance company. I had acquired lots of knowledge. I had met new people, and we kept in touch for years. Losing my job was more like a transfer. I immediately found another job less than two miles away. It was with the help of Zoey, who had become a friend at the finance company. I confided in Zoey. I hoped that in some way she could have bridged a closer relationship between Harry and me. She had the privilege of working with him prior to transferring to the department I worked in. But nothing seemed to help develop the perfect boss–employee relationship between us. She could not convince Harry to change his mind about me. It was just one of those things. Thank God for friends.

Discovering My True Friend

It wasn't a big deal for me to approach managers or supervisors, as long as I was not under their supervision. I didn't feel intimidated by speaking with Arthur about Harry. I attracted managers, because of my professionalism. I tried to be professional at all times. I knew how to look like a manager. It seemed to be the only thing I could do to take the focus off of all my fears and self-doubt. I must have been looking pretty important on most days, based upon what my best friend, Naomi, once said to me.

It was meant to be an insult, the comment she made to me on that day. But because I felt so low about myself, it turned out to be a compliment. One day Naomi out of her anger told me that the only thing I had going for me was the way I dressed. She had no idea how I felt inside. My jobs had been rough on me and my best friend was no longer acting like a friend but a stranger who had turned her back on me. Precious, who I called my half sister, was my other best friend, and my first cousin. We had grown up together. It was almost scary how our lives seemed to have paralleled each others. She was away and I couldn't talk to her. I imagined she was experiencing problems of her own. She couldn't seem to get herself together either. She was bright, highly intelligent, and educated. Unlike me, Precious took her education very seriously. She knew from our childhood what she wanted to be when she grew up. She wanted to be a teacher. I remember when we were growing up how

I would get so tired of playing school. It seemed every chance we got to play on the inside because of rain or heat she always wanted to play school; she would be the teacher. Lynn, Delinda, Dexter, and sometimes Baby Brother, and I would be the students. I, on the other hand, always wanted to play church. I would be the preacher. I would stand up in front of everyone and preach. I preached the sermons I had heard playing at home on our stereo. I had heard them so many times that I knew them by heart. Precious would amen me on. The others would shout and sing, encouraging me to preach! "Preach, girl, preach," they would say.

I believed friends were forever. I never imagined the day would come when Naomi and I would hardly be speaking to each other. But she had turned her back on me, and I didn't think I would ever get over the hurt. My trying to cope with losing my best friend was about as difficult as trying to live with excessive stress and anxiety. She was the only one I could count on when no one else was there for me. I didn't known of any friends who were as loyal to each other as she and I, with the exception of Gail and Oprah. I felt blessed to have had a best friend such as Naomi. There were times when we disobeyed our parents' trying to look out for each other. When I traveled out of the country, I didn't have any close friends to talk to. I wrote to Naomi and asked her to call me. She knew she would face trouble making long distance phone calls on her parents' phone, but that didn't stop her. I didn't even have a phone. I had to depend on the neighbor allowing me to use their phone. Once she received my letter, she called and we talked. Of course when the phone bill came out we were both in trouble. Her mother quickly contacted my parents and told them they needed to come up with half the money to pay for her phone bill. It wasn't funny then but we laugh at it now. But losing Naomi as a friend was better than losing her for life; this was my consolation. I had to deal with this on top of all the fear and anxiety of trying to hold on to a job. At times it felt like a part of me had been snatched away, leaving me handicapped. Who was I going to talk to about my stress at work? Who was I going to go out on the town with?

Moving to Atlanta was the greatest thing that had happened to me, and I wanted Naomi to experience a piece of heaven. I knew she would find that being in Atlanta was much better than living in our small hometown. It didn't take a lot to convince her that Atlanta, Georgia, was the place to be. I had never seen so many black people in all my life. I had never seen so many black people working in almost every business I went to. If I went to the bank, blacks were working there. If I went to the telephone company to pay a bill, blacks were working there too. We were in every business, and I loved it. I had not realized before now how prejudiced my hometown was until I went home to visit my parents. There were no blacks working in any well-established business. They were hardly working in clothing stores. It was a wonderful change. The people, the atmosphere, the tall buildings, and all the bright lights I loved it. She moved up to the Big City months after I did.

Naomi had a place to live waiting on her when she arrived. As fate would have it, our friend from college, Sherita, and her best friend from home were living in the same city. This was unbelievable! And even more unbelievable, we lived on the same side of town. I wanted Naomi to come and get the taste of Atlanta because it had so much to offer. Jobs came a dime a dozen. If I lost a job one day, the next day I would have found another one. I had not seen anything like this in my life. But her ultimate goal was to find herself a husband. We all had high hopes for her to get married and become that housewife that she had always dreamed of being. She was one of the few people out of the gang other than Precious who knew exactly what they wanted out of life. Men were plentiful. They were about as plentiful as the jobs. The problem was trying to choose the right one. The other problem was trying to figure out which ones were actually interested in females.

I had spoken with Sherita and told her about Naomi's plans to move here; the gang would be reunited once again. She thought it was a good idea, and in a few weeks Naomi was here in the Big City. It wasn't long after she moved here that our friendship started to fizzle. I had no idea that moving to a new city would change our friendship. I knew my inviting her here was the best thing for her; besides, the city had so much to offer. It had more than jobs. It had theaters; you could see a play like on Broadway. It had art museums. It had tall, beautiful buildings and big, bright lights. It had almost everything you needed. It had more malls than I could count. It was clean and it was beautiful. Most of the people were friendly. I couldn't imagine our friendship falling apart. It was almost immediately that I started to see changes in her. Never before had I witnessed her talking about me negatively to others. Never before had I witnessed her expecting me to do things for her that I normally did for her as a friend without a thought, and now I was feeling pressured to do these things. She became demanding. What was happening? My Lord, what had gotten into my friend? I couldn't help but wonder if maybe the big city and the bright lights turned out to be more than she could handle. It was definitely a difference from our hometown. I was fortunate to have had Sizzie.

I had Sizzie, so I wasn't alone. She wasn't only my sister, but she was also my best friend. In reality she was my best friend of all friends. It was easy to see that we got along well. It was obvious that I confided in her and likewise. But her schedule was so busy; I had to make an appointment most times just to update her on what was going on with me. But most days we caught up on things when she got to work. At one point we worked the same part-time job for about two years, and boy, we were too tired to talk when we got home. I shared everything with her, except the way in which Naomi was acting. I was too embarrassed to let her know that my best friend had changed so quickly. We argued about everything. We argued about religion. She swore she wanted to change over to become a Jehovah's Witness. She swore I didn't know what I was talking about whenever we went to the Bible. She then swore she wanted to be Holiness, then one time it was Seventh Day Adventist. She wanted to be any denomination except what we were familiar with. The funny thing about it all is that neither one of us read the Bible that often at the time to discover what religion was right or best for us. The truth is neither one of us knew anymore than the other. One time we even fought over a man. It turned out neither one of us ended up talking to him. As it turned out neither one of us dated him, which was the best thing. "This was a no-no! This was definitely something that didn't happen between friends.

I valued friendship more than anything in the world. At one point in my life, I believed a best friend was all that a person needed, next to God and family. I believed a best friend was the one who would take you in when no one else would, and pick you up from work when no one else felt like it. I believed best friends were the ones who would wake up out of their sleep anytime of the day or night and come pick your butt up if you were stranded on the side of the road. I believed this so much that I ended a relationship when the guy I was dating told me he was too busy to come to my rescue. Needless to say, that relationship quickly ended. I believed a best friend was the one who would listen to you talk all day and all night about your good experiences and your bad ones when no one else cared to hear about your story. But the day Naomi told me she didn't have a best friend, I felt like someone had jagged me in my heart. I felt like such a fool because she expressed this in front of my family and other close friends of mine. They knew that Naomi and I went way back. They knew the story of how we walked home from school each day, and how we double dated whenever her boyfriend was able to find me a date. But this day I felt betrayed. I always spoke highly of my best friend. I trusted her with everything. I trusted her to drive my vehicle anytime she needed it, I trusted her to baby-sit my house if I had to leave to go out of town, I trusted her with my bank account, and most of all I trusted her with my man. I had come to know many other people in my life, and some of them became close friends, very good friends, but I couldn't say that I trusted them with all of the above.

Everyone who knew me knew she was my best friend. We met in junior high school. We had a lot in common. We both grew up in church. I liked talking, she liked listening. I liked singing, she liked dancing. She was a great singer but unlike me, she could dance too. Both of us were blessed with a reasonable amount of commonsense. But after not speaking to each other on a daily basis and visiting as we once did, time brought about a change. I had to get used to not talking to her everyday. I had to get used to not having anyone to call a best friend except Sizzie. I missed the laughs; I missed having someone to go out with. Actually, my life had been put on hold. I wasn't as outgoing as Naomi. She had no problems driving or traveling long distances. Many times I wanted to go places but didn't, because I didn't have anyone to come along with me.

Years passed and we were finally mature and could sit down and talk civilly to each other once again. It must have been her ultimate goal to express her feelings about friendship. But I felt like such a fool that day. I wanted to dismiss myself from the Memorial Day cookout. Was it my depression that made me believe I had this special friend? Or was it my strong need to be liked? Right now I am not exactly sure. Maybe she was right; maybe she didn't have a best friend. Maybe I didn't have a best friend. Life was all an illusion. Maybe I was all-wrong to believe that we were the only two *best friends* left in the world besides Oprah and Gayle. Maybe she was right in saying that she didn't believe it was right to label friends as best. Maybe she was right to say that classifying a friend *as best made others feel less important.* Maybe today was the day for me to learn something new. I was dumbfounded and I was so embarrassed when she made the statement at the cookout that she didn't have a best friend. She practically said that she didn't even believe in best friends. Had I not been hosting the party; I would have left it.

The good thing about living is that you live and you learn. I learned why Naomi had no best friend. She explained that labeling a person as a best friend would take away from all the other friends she had come to know. She stressed that fact. I had come to accept the fact that the friend I once knew vanished the day she moved to the big city. I had come to accept the fact that my life would go on, and whatever friend to her I could be was the way it was. But I could not digest the fact that she had not valued our friendship that much at all.

Friends Helping Friends

Zoey had a friend who worked for the telephone company. She had mentioned this to me earlier, and I hoped that she would mention my situation to her friend. I was not surprised when she told me she had told her friend about my job search. I was excited to know that the company her friend worked for was hiring and there was a strong possibility that

I would get the job. Zoey felt confident that her friend would be able to help me. When I arrived home from work, I immediately started working on my new resume. I certainly had to add all I had learned at the finance company to the list. Surely, I had learned something with all of the extensive training I had gone through. Surely it would be impressive. Zoey's friend was not just a regular employee at the telephone company. She was one of the managers in the Human Resources Department. I was excited to know that my chances of getting the job were certain. I got my resume together and I was ready for a new job. I knew that, despite it all, God was on my side. It was not by coincidence that Zoey was there for me. Even though she may not have been able to change Harry's mind, she was more helpful in finding me a new job. I knew God put her there. I got the job at the telephone company.

God who watches over the birds, the trees and the seas will surely watch over me.

When I left the finance company, I left good friends behind. We continued to keep in touch with each other. It was only about four weeks after leaving the finance company, that I received telephone calls from several of my coworkers. They informed me that Harry and Ellie were no longer with the company. I was told that both of them had been fired. I smiled. I did not rejoice in their loss of jobs, but I believed in God and I rejoiced in him. I believed he was watching over me. I believe that what you do to others shall be done unto you. I never knew why they disliked me so much. They disliked me enough to cost me my job and my livelihood. Daddy would say, "*You can't do wrong and get away; you might get by, but you won't get away*".

For with the same measure that ye mete withal, it shall be measured to you again.

Luke 6:38

Daddy would have referred me to the Bible had he known at the time what I was going through. I imagined him referring me to the scripture below.

I have been young and now am old; yet have I not seen the righteous forsaken, nor his seed begging for bread.

Psalm 37:25

Because of my faith, I knew that I had not been forsaken. Because of my faith, I know that I will never be forsaken. I knew that as long as I had life, strength, health, and a sound mind, God would continue to enable me to work and to find a decent job. Finding a job had not been a problem for me, just trying to keep them. I wanted to find peace. I wanted to experience peace in the workplace, and peace of mind because of his word.

Thou wilt keep him in perfect peace, whose mind is stayed on thee: because he trusted in thee.

Isaiah 26:3

I trusted God and I wanted peace. I tried to keep my mind on him. But there were many times when that seemed too difficult. I wanted to work at a telephone company. It used to be my dream. I was grateful that my dream had finally come true. "Yes, I am going to work here and stay here until I am old and gray," I said to myself. I am going to retire here!

Working at the Telephone Company

Working at the telephone company was another venture. The experience I got from working here was great. There was a lot to learn about the job. We had a six-week training period. The training was just as long and intense as the training at the finance company. This training was different. We did not get to take our tests as many times as we did at the finance company. We had quizzes a few days out of the week. The good thing about our quizzes is if we flunked, we were allowed to put in the correct answers and go home and study for the big final. I studied every night. I felt certain that things would work out. After all, being a telephone operator was one of my longtime dreams. Whenever I saw commercials with folk wearing headsets across their heads, I thought to myself, that is what I want to be when I grow up. The opportunity had presented itself to me, and I was ready to work!

We had a large training class. I am not exactly sure how many of us there were, but it seemed like each week the group became smaller and smaller. I wasn't sure why, and we were not always told why, but people were disappearing by the numbers. Maybe they decided to quit because it was more information than they could grasp, or maybe the trainer was requesting them to go, or maybe the potential employees changed their mind. I didn't know. The disappearing acts were making me nervous. I tried to have faith, trying to convince myself that if I could do well at the finance company, I could succeed here. The truth is I knew in my heart

I wouldn't succeed. I knew deep down inside no matter how happy I appeared on the outside, inside it was impossible to succeed. Outwardly, I appeared perfect, but on the inside there wasn't a day that I didn't hurt. There wasn't a day that I didn't experience the same hurt in the same manner. I hurt in training each day.

It all started when I reached twenty-five years old. There was something about turning twenty-five that told me by then that I should have had it together. Something told me I should have landed that perfect man, and that perfect job. Something told me I was supposed to be happy and I was supposed to succeed. I fought and struggled because inside I had no way of knowing how I would succeed. I had managed to get a high school diploma and went on to further my education as a college graduate, and the sad thing about it all, I never got the opportunity not once to work in my field. For the rest of my life I would learn to settle. I learned to settle for this and settle for that. This was the best I could do with my life. But my dream of becoming a telephone operator was happening. "Maybe I will be like Sizzie; I always admired her job working for the telephone company," I thought. I don't know if it was because of her that I wanted to be an operator, or was it the fact that I was pleasant and I believed I had a pleasant voice.

I experienced difficulties shortly after accepting the position. Even though I wanted the job, my mind was not as alert as it should have been. I worried more on this job. I did not want to be a failure, and I did not want to be judged cruelly anymore. I didn't want to be judged period. I didn't want to be a disappointment.

I spent the entire six weeks of training not understanding anything that was going on. I spent most of the entire eight hours a day wondering.

I wondered if I would be able to do the job once I got out of training. I wondered if they would escort me out of training before the training period was over. I didn't know where the other people were going. But I knew; I just knew they were going to be terminating me next. I tried very hard to look interested. I befriended as many people in the training class as I possibly could. I didn't know if getting to know people was a good thing or not, it was just a part of me. The more people liked me and accepted me, the more I felt good about myself. The feeling of being accepted and liked by others was so important to me. Sometimes it made me feel guilty having them accept me because I did not believe that I was as bright and smart as they probably thought I was. My mind wouldn't let me. It was telling me more and more each day that I was going to fail. It told me that I would be working under the same kind of supervision as the finance company. It told me that I would probably have to end up going in and out of training before I would be able to do the job. Last but not least, it told me I would be let go like so many times before.

The day came for us to take our final exam and I passed. I was excited about passing, but I was uncertain about anything that I was supposed to do. Once I made it to the floor, I was more afraid than the first day I came to work. I was on the floor answering calls, troubleshooting, and assisting customers with all their billing inquiries and technical problems. I had far more work here than I had at the finance company. I had over fifty screens of information to refer to whenever I needed to answer the customer's questions or whenever I needed to review a customer's account. I didn't feel confident in what I was doing. I was afraid to put the caller on hold because I thought I was supposed to know the answers. Looking back, I think of how silly I was. How are you supposed to know something if you've never done it before? I didn't know the secret to being smart was reading and studying. Somehow I was led to believe that smart people were just born that way. If only I could sit down and read and comprehend, I might be a sharper and smarter person, I thought. If only someone would have a little faith in me, I might do better. What difference does it make? Failure, yes a failure.

It was so ironic, because I still had my might to fight. I felt confident enough to challenge those quality assurance people. They had already picked me out. "Here we go again," I thought. It seemed everyone in the workplace always chose me to pick on. They had begun the same thing on this job, picking on the new kid on the block. They monitored me and I challenged them. I knew what I was doing may not have been exactly right, but surely I wasn't doing everything wrong. All I could think of was the fact that I had passed my final and I was going by the book, doing what I was supposed to do. I didn't have to go in and out of training again here, and that was a good thing. So far this had been the first time. I kept challenging them until things finally ironed out. I converted to doing things their way but not without a fight. My ability to fight was all I had. I couldn't give in to these feelings. I knew I could do better. I knew I was born to do better. I knew I was born to achieve; that is what God wants for all of his children. I didn't know how, but I knew God must have a plan for me. I had been unhappy and miserable for too long. When I look back, this is when I believe the beginning of my strongest and greatest fears begin to hit me. My worrying was beginning to surface above my head. My worrying would never stop. The worries were greater than they were at the computer company; they were greater than they were at the finance company. When I look back, most things seemed to have centered on work. This is where I got the opportunity to exercise my skills and abilities, and only God knows what they were. To me, I had no skills and had no talents. I just couldn't get it together. It didn't matter how many jobs or how many new and different opportunities confronted me. I just couldn't get it right. The problem with not knowing your talents, gifts, or abilities is you feel like you should try everything. Every job opportunity advertised in the paper I felt was the job for me. I believed that everybody had gifts from God and I longed to know what mine were; if not two, than just one gift would have been sufficient. But if I had skills, I didn't know it.

Being away from work was quite different. I could choose to be around people, and I could choose whether to talk or be quiet. Most times I chose to talk because I didn't want to give anyone the wrong impression. I didn't want anyone to think I was ignorant. I learned that it would have been all right to have sat there and not said a word. If I was around folk I knew, I took the lead in the conversation, which made me feel like I was bright. It made me feel like I was intelligent. But this didn't last long. It wouldn't be long before they would recognize my insecurities. Things just seemed to get harder and harder for me. The hardest thing for me is I didn't have anyone to talk to about these feelings. I didn't know if they were normal feelings, and I didn't know how to deal with them. I didn't know if maybe something was wrong with me.

The weight I carried from being so worried was about to take me under. It was slowly but surely weighing me down. I could feel the stress on my face becoming tighter and tighter; and on my shoulders, across my back, I would be stiff as a piece of iron. It hurt me deeply. I didn't know what was happening to me. Getting out of bed each morning was dreadful. It was hard for me to be on time. It was harder for me to leave on time. I felt like eight hours were not enough to give the company. I felt like I owed them more. In my mind they were doing me a favor allowing me to work. Despite the long hours, the hard work, and the little pay, I was not feeling good about my life and myself. All I could think about was how long are they going to allow me to work here before they come up with some excuse or reason to let me go.

Proud Parents

My parents had not begun to worry much about me in the work world. They knew I was responsible. They knew that I would try to do whatever I could to meet all of my obligations or die trying. It fascinates me to this day how parents know their children. True parents always want the best for their children. And good children always strive to do whatever they can to make their parents proud.

At first I could not understand my parents' enthusiasm. As a child growing up and as a young adult, it embarrassed me to hear them share their joy and excitement with everyone. But as I grew older, I grew out of the embarrassment. I realized it was gratitude. So now when I hear my daddy cheer, I sit and smile. Daddy is always speaking out at his churches whenever an opportunity presents itself to talk about his children. He is so proud. First, it was Mother who was so elated and proud. She always shared this joy with everyone, especially in church. Whenever there was an opportunity to speak about love and being proud, she talked about how proud she was of her children. Now that Mama is no longer with us in body to express how happy and proud she is about her children, Daddy has picked up the pieces. He is always talking about his children and how proud he is of all of us. Even though Daddy is not exactly sure what my profession is, he always associates me with the insurance company. I never worked as a social worker. However. I spent long hours in school preparing to be one.

He talks about how the Lord made it possible for all of his children to go to college on his and Mama's little income. At every church event that Daddy has, and we attend, Daddy makes all of us stand up like it's our first time being recognized. I know the people are probably tired of hearing Daddy's story. But he has told his story so many times, it has just become a part of him. He is eighty-six year old and still going strong by the goodness and grace of God. He still preaches the Word every Sunday. Daddy has coined the phrase, "If you get sick, call my daughter, the doctor; if you get in trouble, call my son, the lawyer." He is a humorous man and a proud parent.

Keeping On at the Telephone Company

We had to continue our learning process at the telephone company by taking continuing education courses. I took many classes. I took my classes very seriously. I focused mainly on self-improvement courses: courses like how to build up your confidence, how to be successful in the workplace, and how to win your boss over, and courses like the seven steps to success. I took advantage of the opportunity. I was amazed at how much you could learn from a book and how a little inspirational reading could benefit a person so much. It was giving me the strength and courage I needed. I was no longer feeling down and out. I had begun to feel a sense of peace, joy, and happiness. Hallelujah!

The self-help courses helped me so much that I felt brave enough to step up to the plate. I began to e-mail my boss suggestions on how I thought we could better serve our customers, and what I believed would make the department flow much more easily. I began to smile again. The heavy weight from the tons of sandbags I was carrying on my back and the twenty-pound weights I was wearing around my ankles seemed to be losing its strength. It seemed like the bags of sand had begun to seep through the air holes and the load was becoming lighter and lighter. Thank God, I was beginning to feel my burdens being lifted. When I took my hour lunch I would spend half the hour in the study room, and the rest of the time sleeping in my car. I was doing so well that Amanda, the supervisor, approached me. She asked if it would be okay if she forwarded some of my suggestions to her manager, Judy. I was impressed by the thought—the thought that she considered my suggestions to be that great made me feel even better. I feared the manager and felt very uncomfortable whenever I was in her presence. Those same uninviting feelings of anxiety would come over me. The attacks would come stronger and more forceful than before. I was unable to control the unwelcome feelings. The fears of self-doubt and lack of self-love were overpowering me. I rarely saw the manager, and that was a good thing. Her office was in the rear of the building, and I only saw her in passing or when I went to the rear of the office to fax a document or to pick up a fax.

We didn't see a whole lot of her, but she knew most of us. It was amazing how she knew all of us when she had very little interaction with the people on the floor, but she did. She even knew me. It was hard not to know me. If you had seen this face with this fear, you couldn't forget it either. It was almost impossible to hide the way I felt on my face from day to day. I could feel the fear and tension very strongly. It felt like cement drying into the pores of my face. It was as if I had put on a mask for Halloween, except I could not take it off when it was time to take it off and put it away for the next year. I'm sure she thought that I was the most insecure person she had ever seen. The look of distress and fear was painted all over my face. Sometimes it can be disappointing how the way we feel shows on our face. Sometimes I wish the way we felt in our hearts were just as visible. I knew deep down inside it was that little voice that talked to me all day and most of the night until I would fall asleep that made me look this way. I wondered so many times, Lord, why don't it ever tell me anything good? It might have told me something good that cold day on campus. I am not blaming the little voice for sending me on a car chase. That was by choice. I thought it was a good day to car chase.

On Campus at TSU

I'll never forget the day I chased behind that little red car. Something about that car caught my eye. I had just left the business office and had received good news that would help me to continue my education. I was on a natural high. I was excited and so were my friends. We were walking down the sidewalk to my car, Sherita, Naomi, and I. I was looking down at the information that I had just received, verifying that everything was correct. Everything was perfect. It was the good news I needed because I was only a few months shy of my graduation date. We were walking, laughing, talking, and happy that it was Friday and I had just gotten paid.

It was a beautiful winter day. It was cold but we didn't mind the coldness, because the excitement from the day seemed to have taken some of the chill away. We slowly walked to the car, shaking and shivering. I had my own vehicle. The car had been passed down to me from Joshua Jr. It was a classic. It was a 1968 Volkswagen Bug. The car was old and it was cold. It had only one headlight. It had no back-seat floor on the passenger side, but there was nothing wrong with the engine except that the heater operated from the engine and it took a very long time for the car to get warm in the wintertime; most of the time it never got hot.

The strangest thing about driving a Volkswagen Bug to me was the fact that no heat blew from the heater into the car. The other strange thing about it was I didn't believe the car had any vents inside it for the heat to blow from. Well, supposedly whenever you pressed on the accelerator, the heat was to come from beneath the seat. It was all so strange to me. Most winters I froze. But apart from all of that, it got me where I wanted to go. It even got me where I needed to go, most times. I never needed to travel very far. Every weekend when I got off work, I would drive forty miles from school to my hometown. I didn't have much to do when I arrived home. In my little town, there wasn't very much to do at all. Naomi was still there, and I got the chance to visit with her. It was better than sticking around campus and being home alone at my apartment, because most students had gone home for the summer.

I worked at the university library. I was fortunate that I worked early on Saturday morning and was free in the afternoon. I would leave Saturday afternoon when the library closed to go home and spend the night. Mama and Daddy were always glad to see me, if only for one night. I would leave on Sunday afternoon and head back to school in order to get to work on time. It was during the summer, and most of my friends had gone home for the summer. I liked the idea of being close enough to drive home from school whenever I felt the need, which was every weekend. It got very lonely being the only one of the gang left in town. I had to go to summer school if I wanted to graduate in the summer.

Overall, it was a good day. Before we reached the car, I looked up toward the street and saw the cutest and the *baddest* sports car I had ever seen in my life. Usually I was not impressed by cars, but for some reason, the car caught my attention. Apart from it being Friday and cold outside, I don't know what got into me. But that day, that car caught my eye. I yelled to Sherita and Naomi, "Look! Look! Did y'all see that?" They both looked up and one of us suggested that we follow the car. We didn't discuss it or negotiate whether we should or shouldn't; we start running as fast as we could to the Bug. We jumped in. All three of us got in the front seat. We were smooched up together trying to keep warm, and off we went chasing behind the cute, little red sports car.

Staying on the Same Job

From the way things were going in my life, I never knew from day to day how long I would last on a job. I wasn't sure if my acting and dressing professionally was going to be enough to carry me through the day. By now the bosses knew I wasn't as intelligent as I appeared to be. By now the bosses knew I was going to fail, and inside I knew it too. I felt guilty. My father did not do this. He worked hard and he was successful. He worked on one of his three jobs about thirty years before he retired. My older sisters and brothers didn't do this. They were fortunate enough to have landed the perfect job, whatever it means to have a perfect job. They lasted for such a long time on their jobs. Sizzie had one major job in her life after graduating from college, and she stayed there almost thirty years. Lots of people did this, but I didn't know how in the world they managed it.

My other sister, Sarah Jean, has been on one job for almost all of her life. She went to school to become a doctor. Yes, she became a black female doctor from my little hometown, Ozark, Alabama. She did private practice in a town just outside of our hometown for almost twelve years. She transferred to another city after our mother passed away. We hated to see her leave, but she had greater opportunities knocking on her door.

Somewhere in another town there was a great demand for doctors to treat a specific illness and she ventured out. She is a very good physician. I say that because she is such a hard worker. In all the years that I have known her to be a family practitioner, I have never once heard her complain about having to go to the hospital whenever she was on call. I never heard her complain about not being able to spend holidays with us because of her work. Surely, she must have missed being at some of the celebrations.

We all seemed to be very hard workers. "What's up?" I ask myself sometimes. "Did I choose the wrong profession?" Once I got a job, I worked it well. I worked so hard and such long hours that I was fired twice because I worked overtime and the company didn't want to pay me for it. I agreed not to be paid. I just wanted to stay on top of things. I wanted to be perfect; if being perfect meant working overtime, then overtime it would be. I was willing to accept no pay but that was too unbelievable for the company to receive. I agreed to accept comp time, but that was asking for too much and they fired me!

Joshua Jr. seemed to have landed the perfect job as well. He became a minister at a very young age. He has been preaching since age seventeen. Actually, he said the Lord called him years earlier. But he was discouraged by some of the older ministers about going into ministry. They told him he was too young. They encouraged him to enjoy his life as a teen and have fun. He sadly postponed his preaching, but didn't seem to be as happy anymore. It seemed as if something in his life was missing. The calling never ceased. He struggled. He questioned Mama about his relationship with God. He tells the story of how God never stopped speaking to him. He tells the story of how he prayed and prayed; asking

God if this is what God really wanted him to do. Twenty plus years have passed, and Joshua Jr. is still a full-time pastor.

When I was younger, I used to think of him having his own business. I admired him having his own job. But I later realized that he didn't have his own business, he was working for the Lord. This is God's business, and God never sleeps or slumbers, which was similar to him and Daddy. They were always on the go. When people needed help and assistance, they called on God, then the preacher. Sometimes I think they may have called on the preacher first, then God. I remember how they tried to always be there. Now that Daddy has retired, he is more available to go to visit the sick. I never knew of anyone sick whom Daddy didn't try to visit. Daddy even visited people he didn't know. If they desired prayer, Daddy prayed. I soon learned that Daddy and Joshua Jr. were not their own bosses. God is the boss and the church is their primary responsibility. I learned that being a full-time pastor and minister was a full-time job.

My other brother, Harvey Lee, who Mama adopted, refuses to work for anyone now. He said he served and worked long enough. Even today you cannot hand deliver him a job. He has served his country. He retired after twenty-two and a half years in the army. He fought in two wars, the Vietnam War and the Persian Gulf War. He retired from the military three months before Mother passed away. She got the chance to attend his graduation.

Last but not least, Baby Brother. Baby Brother has been working with one company for about as long as I have been looking for a job. Even though he has many different jobs, he still managed to stay on one job for twenty-plus years. His education seems to have paid off for him, especially after going to school and majoring in criminal justice. Baby Brother really made us all proud when he went on to further his education. He recently passed the bar, and practices law.

Baby Brother and I were similar in having many different jobs, but I just did not know how to hold on to the job. I once asked Baby Brother to tell me the secret of keeping a job. Since he was my twin (that's what we call ourselves), I knew he would give me the best advice. He said the secret is to always look busy. I worked hard all day long on the job, but it seemed the minute I would stop to exhale, the boss would inhale and walk right by my desk or come inside my cubical. He gave me tips on how to work hard even when I wasn't sitting at my desk. He said, "If you are walking around, walk with a pen and paper in your hand, even if you are making a trip to the restroom." The objective is to always look busy. I tried this many times. It actually worked for a while until someone discovered my insecurities, and I was back at square one.

Keeping on at the Telephone Company

Amanda forwarded copies of the e-mail with the wonderful suggestions and bright ideas to Judy and carbon copied me. She was pleased. She was certain that her boss would be just as impressed as she was. I tried to act calm, but I was so happy. I knew it could go either way. I knew that Judy could approve or disapprove, but whatever the response was, I would still remain proud of myself. "The employee with the big eyes and the scared look on her face is doing well." "She looks weak and fearful but she has bright ideas." "She is an asset to the telephone company." "We will implement these suggestions ASAP," I imagined hearing these words coming from Judy's mouth. It wasn't long before I was made aware that Judy had received her copy. Well, Ms. Judy wasn't impressed at all. I was not surprised when she responded in a negative way. The only comment she made regarding the learning I obtained from the continuing education courses was, "She misspelled a word." There were no words of encouragement. There was no recognition of improvement. There was no reason for me to be motivated. Here I go again, I thought. She gave me what one might call constructive criticism. Her exact words were, "Before McKenzie sends out an e-mail, she needs to make sure she turns on spell check." *Tanks a lot. I thought to myself." Tank you!"* No comments on the suggestions I made. No complimenting words such as "that was good, or she did a good job, or very nice suggestions, just make sure she turns on spell check." Those were her words. I didn't want something like this to hurt my feelings. But it did. I was highly upset. "What could I have expected from her anyway? It didn't matter if I did a great job or if customers complimented me for great customer service. I was still a failure." I thought. Was she trying to keep me down? Did she expect more from me, or did she expect nothing from me? I never figured it out.

Oftentimes I would get requests from the customers to speak with my supervisor, because they thought I had assisted them well. They would compliment me from time to time for doing such a fantastic job. They complimented me on how pleasant I came across over the phone. I knew I was great. I had a pleasant voice, I had personality, and I loved making the customers happy. But what good would this do me if I didn't believe it in my heart? What good did it do me if the confidence did not show on my face? I needed the support of others to make me feel good about myself. It would be years later that I learned I don't need anyone to feel as good about me as I feel about myself. I learned to be appreciative for whatever good thought or kind deed that anyone did or showed me.

I learned that it is the small things we sometimes take for granted, and sometimes it is those small things that make us the happiest. Most of all I learned that if I feel good about me, others will automatically feel good about me. But if they do not, that is all right, I will still feel good. I learned that you should continue to feel good about yourself despite the odds. Be faithful and be confident.

Because he which hath begun a good work in you will perform it
until the day of Jesus Christ.

Philippians 1:6

Leaving the Telephone Company

Leaving this job was different from leaving my previous jobs, yes, it was quite different. Actually, I feared myself out of this position. I felt so much tension I thought I was about to have a heart attack. I thought I would die. I knew if I didn't quit the job, the job was going to quit me. I didn't want to go through it again. There was no way I could face the rejection. There was no way I could handle being dismissed. Everyday I waited for them to tell me that I was no longer needed. I knew in my heart, that no matter what I did or how hard I tried to do what I did, it was a matter of time before someone would tell me, "You are no longer needed here. You do not look happy, or You do not seem to enjoy working here any longer." I was lacking faith and confidence and whatever else I needed to keep myself together.

One day I went to lunch and never came back. I called the office to let them know I was not feeling well. I also went to the doctor that day, and he informed me that my blood pressure was high. I was in pretty good health. I had never had a problem with high blood pressure; to me that was very serious. I knew if I did not go back, it was possible that I would suffer from high blood pressure, but I was certain that if I went back, I would have high blood pressure.

After two years of working at the telephone company, I didn't go back. I made several attempts to get up every morning to go back to work. I could not get myself to do it. I was scared of what might happen to me if I decided not to go back to work. I had never done anything like this before. "People don't walk off jobs, jobs let them go," I told myself. I knew I was in absolutely no position to walk off anybody's job; that only meant starting all over again for me, something I had no desire to do again. I worried and I worried. I cried and I cried. I prayed and I prayed. I didn't know what to do or how to do. I thought that sooner or later I would get a breakthrough and have whatever I needed to get myself together, but it didn't happen. The worrying and worrying that I was experiencing was not strong enough to get me out of bed, or carry me to the shower, or force me to drive to work, for I was weak. My whole body ached. I had no energy. I had no strength. Whatever the problem was, it had a tight grip on me, so tight that finally I was too weak to fight. It felt as though I were slipping down a greased pole, unable to get a grip. I had become used to feeling this way, and I thought it was normal. But as normal as it was, it hurt. Feeling uptight, unloved, unneeded, unwanted, helpless, worthless, and plain on miserable was just a part of me, and the feeling was becoming stronger and more powerful than ever. Ever since I lost the job at the finance company, I felt weight on my shoulders. But over time, the weight became more and more unbearable. I had experienced these feelings before. I felt this way the day I was hired at the insurance company, but I must have been able to play my feelings off pretty well. Most of my coworkers there called me crazy. They said I was intentionally slow. They told me my wanting to learn and my requesting to go in and out of training was just a tease. They swore that I did it just to aggravate the instructors. I loved this. I loved the fact that they felt that way about me. Truly it had to be that way; I was too bright, too smart, and too intelligent for it to be any other way.

I received calls from my coworkers from time to time. Sometimes I would answer the phone; other times I couldn't. I didn't know what to tell them. All I could say to them was I was not feeling well. I could not tell them how fearful I felt on the job. I could not tell them how I ached all day long on the job. Every day my muscles felt like they were tied into knots. After I left work each day, I felt very little relief. Many days I drove home with tears rolling down my face. I knew something was not right, but I didn't know what was wrong. The only thing I believed kept me alive was the fact that I slept. I was able to lie down, and after the little voice got tired of replaying what took place during the course of my day, I would fall asleep.

One day while I was lying in bed, the doorbell rang. I mustered up enough energy to get out of bed to see who was knocking on my door. I was not expecting anyone. I slid my feet into my house shoes, tied my scarf around my head, and went to the door. It was the postman. He was delivering me a certified letter from the telephone company. I had no idea what it might say. I thought they were sending me a letter to tell me I was fired. Instead, when I opened the letter, it was a letter stating that I had twenty-four hours to get back to work. I looked at the time; it was two o'clock in the afternoon. I had until two o'clock the next day to return to work. Since my deadline was in the afternoon, I thought maybe, just maybe, I would be able to get back to work.

I woke up early the next morning. I showered, ate breakfast, and laid everything I planned to wear to work out on the bed. I felt good. I felt like I had been given another chance, and I didn't want to miss out on the opportunity. Once I had all of this done, I had nothing else to do but lie down. I tried to stay awake and alert, but the little voice inside of my head was trying to convince me how terrible I was. It began to drain me of what little strength I had mustered up. All I could do was lie there and wonder what it would be like if I went back to work. Every time I tried to pull myself out of the bed, something else forced me back in the bed. I fought, I cried, and I begged God to help me; but I could not do it. There was the fear, along with the little voice that had kept me up all night telling me if I went back, the same thing would happen all over again. The little voice told me this over and over again. It told me how I was not good enough to work there any longer. It reminded me about how my ideas were shot down like a bird. It nagged me all night long. It nagged me throughout the day whenever I was awake. Thank God for my friend Jackson. He must have been heaven-sent to me.

My Chocolate Man

My friend Jackson (Chocolate) thought I had myself together. He had no idea how I ached, and how I worried about my career. I certainly thought he had himself together. It wasn't until he got to know me better that he would talk to me and tell me how crazy it was for the companies to fire me. He believed I worked hard, and I did. But like me, he could not understand the logic behind my changing jobs so often. He could not understand the sense of letting someone like me go. He thought this was downright crazy. He used to ask, "McKenzie, tell me what are you doing at work?" As much as I liked his accent, I felt no need to answer such a question. It had to have been rhetorical. I thought to myself. Surely, he was not waiting for an answer. I would just look at him like he was crazy, about as crazy as the company was for always letting me go.

I met him shortly after I lost my job at the insurance company. He had been there for me. As a matter of fact, he was my study partner. At first, I would get so mad at him. I told him he could not help me study. "How are you going to help me study when you do not work there?" I would ask. But he was finally able to convince me that he could indeed help. He helped, especially with the math part and that thing about the rule twenty-one. We studied well together; actually we got along well from the day I first met him until eight years later.

Love at First Sight

It was love at first sight the day I met him. I will never forget. It was on a hot summer Saturday afternoon. I had decided I was going to get myself better. I didn't know I was about to venture out on an experience that would become the experience of a lifetime. I was about to go somewhere I had never gone before, and about to do something I had never done before. I had looked up a number in the phone book where you could go and get the massage of a lifetime, and it would help to relieve you from all of your stress. I called and made an appointment.

On the day I was scheduled to go to Excellent Masseuse, I almost did not go. I was not feeling well, even though it was Saturday. Unlike most people I was not happy it was the weekend; everyday was like Saturday to me. I was not feeling happy. I was not feeling good. I did not feel like getting up out of bed. I did not feel like going anywhere. All I felt like doing was staying home and lying in bed. My sister told me I would probably feel much better if I got up and got out; she thought it might do my heart good to walk around a bit to keep my blood flowing in my body. I had mentioned my appointment to her days earlier. I took her advice. I gave it some thought, and at the last minute I made up my mind that I would go. Despite the way I was feeling, I am glad I decided to go. I had begun to feel better already. Something about getting up out of the bed and walking from room to room somehow seemed to have made me feel better. Maybe it was the fact that I was not home alone today. Maybe it was the fact that someone other than me knew I needed to do more than just lie in bed. I had gotten tired of lying in bed day after day and night after night, but I had no reason to get up. I had no reason to feel like living. I got myself together and decided to go along with my day as scheduled.

I reached the spa with no problem. When I got to the parking lot, I could not find a parking space very close to the store. What the heck was I thinking, I needed the exercise anyway. I needed all the walking I could get, especially if it's as good for you as the doctor orders. I drove around the parking lot one more time and found a parking space. It was the parking space that I had passed by several times earlier. I pulled into the parking space. It was the space right in front of the door. Even though I was near the end of the parking spaces, I was fortunate to have found the space that seemed to be lined up with the spa.

The Excellent Masseuse Spa was located next to the nail shop in the Atlanta strip mall. Before getting out of the car, I put on fresh lipstick, blotted my lips, and made sure no lipstick was on my teeth. I looked in the mirror to make sure my hair was in place. I was wearing my hair very short at the time, and it wasn't likely that the wind would have blown it out of place, but I wanted to make sure. It was a short, sassy, black, and curly with a natural look, and I liked it. I was used to changing my hairstyles so frequently that the color and style I wore that morning was subject to change to another color by evening. I had learned to take advantage of the versatility of being black and being me. I appreciated God for making me black. Every now and then, I would actually feel good about myself. I believe that was the God in me still shining beneath all of the hurt, the pain, and disappointment. As it turned out, someone else also thought the style was becoming.

After I got myself together, I got out of the car with my long skinny legs and 130-pound body weight and start walking toward the building. Being five feet eight inches tall, I looked much smaller than I was. The good thing about being tall and skinny is people didn't seem to be focusing much on my weight anymore. I wasn't hearing it a lot from people that my legs were so skinny. I didn't even hear a lot of people criticizing me about how big my eyes were; in fact, I had begun to get compliments from some of the people, telling me how big and beautiful my eyes were. I can't say that I believed them, but it was nice to hear something positive every once in a while. No one seemed to think being skinny was the worst thing in the world anymore. What is the world and the people living in it coming to?

Were they beginning to accept me for who I was, or was I beginning to feel good about myself more often? Whatever it was, I was glad to be feeling good.

Before I reached the store, I looked in the direction where I thought the store might have been. I could see from a distance a tall, dark, thin man standing at the front check-in counter. "Thank God for big eyes," I thought. I was looking in his direction, but I wasn't sure if he was looking in my direction; even though it appeared he was, there was no way to tell for certain. I was feeling little vibes as I walked. I couldn't help but wonder if he was looking at me in the way I was looking at him. "What a way to start the day," I was thinking and smiling underneath my breath. He was still looking in my direction. I was not sure if this was the place I was supposed to be going, but I hoped so. The closer I got to the door, the greater the vibes hit me. I had butterflies by now flying crazily around in my stomach. "What is going on here?" I asked myself. When I got close enough to the door, I could read the sign on the window; then I realized this was the place. And yes! He was looking at me too. God help me to keep cool.

When I walked into the store, I had pretty much composed myself. I walked in and I saw people sitting in chairs lined up against the wall. I looked at them and spoke. Those who heard me spoke back. "What do I do now?" I thought. I walked over to the front counter where the tall, thin man was. "Hello," I said. "My name is McKenzie Lee, and I have a two o'clock appointment."

"Yes, McKenzie, I see that you have an appointment," he said in a deep sexy tone. He smiled at me in such a way that I could feel myself melting on the inside. It was like hot chocolate syrup melting on vanilla ice cream.

"How could I possibly be feeling this way over someone I don't know?" I thought. I was feeling him, and he was feeling me back. There was something in the air that told me he felt the same way too. There was something in me that told me "this man belongs to you." I felt so certain about this. Could it be love at first sight, does it really happens this way? Oh my Jesus! For a second I forgot there were others who were sitting there. I forgot about everything. I almost forgot what I had come here for. Oh my God! I thought to myself. Not only does he look good, he sounds good. It was something about that accent. It was nice and unique and the funniest thing about it—I could understand every word.

"Please be seated and someone will be with you shortly, McKenzie."

"Thank you," I said. I looked around for a vacant seat and sat down. My mind started wondering. I wondered if he was single and available. I wondered what I would do if he tried to converse with me, what would I say? I wondered if he would be the one to give me the massage. I hoped it would not be him. Then I prayed that it would not be him. It would not be fair. I would not have allowed this thin chocolate man to give me a massage that was way overdue. I wouldn't feel comfortable with a stranger who I had a crush on rubbing the aches and stiffness from my poor, pitiful muscles. My body probably felt like a premature elderly woman.

I sat down, picked up a magazine, and tried my best to look cool and calm. I told myself that I did not like him. I told myself he was probably a married man. I told myself that I was probably reading this all wrong, until I looked up and he was looking at me. Our eyes caught. I did not want to look too long because I did not want him to see my fear. Even though for the moment I had forgotten all about my fears and doubts. I didn't want the man to discover right away that I didn't feel good about myself. I didn't want the man to discover right away that I was unemployed and broke. He looked up at me, and our eyes locked again. I was getting a little nervous, but something about him also made me feel calm. I told myself I was going to relax and not worry. After all, I came here with the intention of getting some relief. When I looked back up at the counter, he called my name. I loved the way he called my name. I could hear every syllable.

He asked me to come back to the counter and fill out some paperwork. I wanted to jump up out of my seat and run to the front counter. I slowly got up out of my seat, walked over to the desk, and filled out all the information. While I was filling out my personal information, I wondered if he was trying to remember my phone number, and if he did, would he have the nerves to call me. After I finished the paperwork, I went back to be seated. I picked up the magazine I had been staring at, and pretended to be reading. It was hard trying to stay focused on reading, because I was thinking about him. It was hard to focus and concentrate, period. I was trying hard not to draw attention to myself. I didn't want anyone to read me in the way I was supposed to be reading the magazine. I did not want anyone to know how excited I was and how good I was feeling for the moment. I did not want anyone to look at me and tell that I had fallen in love with this man. I did everything I could to appear cool, calm, and collected. The only way I knew how to do this was to sit still and continue to stare at the magazine.

I could relax and enjoy my pleasant thoughts. For the moment I was floating in the clouds. I thought about how down and out I was feeling before I left home to begin this journey, then I met him and how uplifted I had begun to feel. I wasn't anticipating meeting anyone today, but it happened and I was glad it did.

I had only been sitting for about five minutes when the gentleman called my name again. I stood up and walked over to the counter. Someone from the back came out front to meet me. "Thank you, Jesus, for not letting the man at the counter be my masseuse," I thought. As much as I liked him, I did not want him to be the one to give me a massage. I walked to the back as instructed. I walked inside the dimly lit room. It smelled so good. The ambience alone made me feel like my burdens were being taken away from me and someone was laying them on the floor. The soft music they were playing and the scented candles that were burning were enough to relax my mind before the massage began. The fragrance from the hot oil and the candles was so soothing. I could feel my muscles and my mind already beginning to relax. I knew that this was exactly what I needed. Then the massage began. I knew I needed someone or something to press deep down into the body to help to release some of the tension that had been suffocating me from day to day. I never knew this could feel so good.

The massage did wonders for me. I felt pounds lighter when I left the place. However, I did not leave the place before saying goodbye to the chocolate man. He was waiting for me when I came out. I couldn't help but admire his courage. There was no beating around the bush. He asked for my phone number, and he asked if it would be okay for him to call me sometime. I gave him my number and said, "Nice meeting you, and I look forward to hearing from you."

We dated several years. I don't know why we didn't get married, but again as much as I had hoped to be his girl forever; it did not turn out that way. I thought I was in love for a lifetime. For the first few years of getting to know him, I think we saw each other everyday. He was my soul mate. He was the man God had put on earth just for me. We never seemed to get enough of seeing each other. If he did not visit me after work, I would visit him at work. He worked long hours. Whenever he could not get a break from the job to visit me, I would go to the job and wait for him to get off work. Sometimes he would assign me duties at the office, like answering the phones and taking messages or scheduling appointments. On the weekend, my day to be off I would visit him at the job I didn't mind. Neither one of us seemed to mind. We both wanted to be in each other's presence as often and as much as we could.

On the weekdays it would sometimes be slow at his office, and he would come to take me to lunch. He came to my job at least three days a week and we would go to lunch. It did not matter which job I was on. He stuck with me through thick and thin. He saw me through some of my many jobs. He followed me from job to job. It did not matter to him that it took him forty-five minutes to reach my job sometimes, depending on where I was working at the time. It did not bother me that we saw each other so often. I was in love and I believed I would be in love with this man forever. If love could cause rapid heartbreaking, anxiety, and stress to dissipate, then this was my time.

Deep Thoughts

It was four months before I found another job. Life for me looked very gloomy. I felt worthless, like a complete failure once again. I was convinced that I was no good. I was convinced that my college education had not done a thing for me. How could I tell my parents, family members, and my friends that I had lost another job? What would I tell them was the reason for my being told that my service after two years was no longer needed? This time it wasn't the voice from the supervisor telling me I wasn't interested enough or proactive enough, it was the little voice inside of my head that would not stop talking. The little voice that was forcefully fighting its way through my mind had won again. How could I explain to them my incompetence after being on one job for three years and another for three years that I had to leave? How could I tell them the truth, which was that I was too afraid to work, and that being there made me feel like my life would come to a quick end because of the

</>
100

fear? I knew that sounded too ridiculous for anyone to believe. I was in no way receptive to hearing what they would have to say about my fears. I am certain beyond doubt that I would have been considered lazy, crazy, or just making excuses for not wanting to work. I did not feel strong enough to deal with their feelings and thoughts of me. I had heard it said too many times about other folk. I had heard old folk say, "I wonder why that man or woman won't get them a job somewhere." I had heard them question, "What is wrong with him or her, just lazy, or just want the government to take care of them." I wonder now if it was depression or their weakness keeping them from working. I wonder if they had the desire I had but gave up trying because of fears of falling and failing. I wonder if embarrassment outweighed their strength in attempting to overcome their fears and self-doubt. I wonder if in their weakness, they had too much pride to admit that something in life was terribly wrong. I wonder if they were too afraid of being labeled weak, that they became strong by bragging about not having to work in order to survive. Where was God? Where was all the peace and joy that he had promised me?" I wondered. Where are you now, God?

Turning My Back on God

I had become so frustrated that I became angry with God. I could not understand why he would not let me get a job and keep a job. I could not understand why he would not let me experience peace. All I wanted was to be happy and to work. I wanted him to love me. Since I felt like he no longer cared, I got mad. Yes, I got mad at God, and God put me in my proper place. He gave me the wake-up call of a lifetime. You wouldn't believe what I experienced in one day. I was involved in three auto accidents.

I had told God that I was going on this interview, and I wanted him to give me this particular job. This was my first mistake, telling God and not asking him. I got into my car driving on 285 westbound. I was felling burnt out, but I was still going on the interview. Traffic was bad, but this wasn't unusual for Atlanta. I was still angry and mad at God. I continued to drive. I was headed to my interview and determined that I would get the job. I was driving in the thick traffic, driving a stick, shifting gears, looking ahead, and then looking back at traffic. It required a lot of looking and moving, driving in the big city; driving here was nothing like driving in the small cities back home in Alabama. Sometimes there you didn't even have to look; you knew nothing was traveling on certain streets at certain times. If you've ever lived in a small town, then you know what I mean.

I was driving right along and trying to maneuver my way over to the next lane. I was holding my foot down on my clutch instead of my brake and looking back to make sure that I could move over to the right lane; before I could move over, I rear-ended the back of the car in front of me. Not only was I late for the interview, I did not get the job. I became angrier with God.

I drove back home. When I got home, I tried to relax, but I realized I was too angry to relax. I decided that I would go down the street to The Winery. I thought if I had a tall glass of wine, I would be able to sit down and relax. I put my shoes back on, walked outside, got into my car, and headed down the street to the wine store. Just before I made my left turn to go to the store, the car in the ongoing traffic lane decided to stop and give me the right of way. I thanked the gentleman and proceeded to cross over to the next lane to get to where I was going. I looked toward the ongoing traffic lane and the car beside him had yielded the right of way for me also. I thanked him and continued to drive. I did not look at the next lane to notice if anything was coming. Actually, I had forgotten all about the extra lane; I just pulled right out to cross over, and the fast-moving car hit the passenger side of my car. Boom! Thank God, I did not get hurt, but it scared me to death. It also made me angrier. I asked God, what he was doing to me. "Why are you picking on me? Don't I already have enough going on?" I asked. God had to show me once and for all who is.

I finally made it across the road to the wine store. By now I had no desire to drink anybody's wine. I wanted to go straight home and sit down. I wanted to take a nap, but I wasn't sleepy. I was too angry to sleep. I was too angry to do anything. Again, I didn't know what to do with myself. When I got home, it was time for my brother to come home from school. He had been visiting with us during the week while working on his doctorate degree. Shortly afterward my girlfriend, a family friend, came by to visit us. She was from Alabama also, and she was going to school here in Atlanta, at the AU Center. She was like family to us. All of us knew Annie. She was a few years younger, but she thought she was as old as my sister and I.

When I attended TSU, she would often come to visit me. She and I would sit on the front porch, watch traffic go by, and talk like two very old people chilling out on the front porch. She was a member of the church where Joshua Jr. was the pastor. I knew her and her entire family very well. They were good people. Annie would come over every Sunday, if no other day of the week, to have Sunday dinner with us. We tried to make sure she got one decent meal while in school working on her masters' degree. She surprised us when she received her degree, left town, got married, had a few kids, and for years we never heard from her. It surprised me even more when moved back to the big city and hired me to baby-sit for her every once in a while. She is still family. True friendships never die.

It would happen that as soon as Annie got to my house, she wanted my brother and me to ride out with her. She was trying to locate a building where she was scheduled to attend a meeting the next day. I did not hesitate to go with her. I was not driving this time, so surely I would not be running into the rear end of anybody's car. I would not have to be bombarded with stuff on my mind and neglecting to look in both directions, so off we went. The three of us jumped into her car and went looking for the building.

We rode down Roswell Road, into Sandy Springs when we noticed the building to our left. It was the building she was looking for so we drove into the parking lot. Surely we would be safe off the highway and off the main street. Unfortunately, that wasn't the case. We were driving through the parking lot trying to find the front entrance of the building when a car speeding through the parking lot slammed into our car. Bang!!! It had happened again. I had been in three accidents in one day. Lord, have mercy! I give up!

I began to pray immediately, "Lord, I surrender." It is because of me, I know, that this accident had occurred.

Before I could speak, my big brother said, "Kenzie, we got to take you home. Sorry, little sister, but I do not want to be in a car with you anytime soon. What's up with you?" he asked me. He even suggested that I catch a cab home. I was just as confused as he was, but only for a minute. I didn't know what to say. Being a man of God, a minister, and not wanting to ride in the car with me really made me think twice about myself. I knew he was kidding, but I was thinking seriously, "I think I better straighten up." I knew God was trying to tell me something and I knew I had better straighten up my act and surrender myself to Him.

"God, I cannot win without you," I prayed. "God, I am sorry for acting the way I have been acting. Please forgive me," I asked. I do not remember ever getting mad or angry with God ever again in my life. I had learned my lesson. Who was I to get mad at God? I will never get angry with God again.

My dear brothers, take note of this: Everyone should be quick to listen, slow to speak and slow to become angry, for man's anger does not bring about the righteous life that God desires

(James 1:19–20).

A fool gives full vent to his anger, but a wise man keeps himself under control

(Proverbs 29:11).

From that day forward, I tried to control my anger. I prayed to God to help me not to become angry. There will be times, I'm sure, when I will question God. To me this is quite all right. How will I know if I don't ask?

We have not because we ask not.

(James 4:2)

Several weeks had passed and I was trying to adjust to being home and out of work again. I started answering the telephone. My friends had begun to call me at home and vent about their day at work. I would listen to their stories, and say to myself; at least it's the people who were getting on their nerves, and not their own fears. My pain was different. It was me who was causing all of my pain. If I could have relieved myself from all of my own accusations of not being competent or capable, I believe I would have been able to deal with the other situations. I tried to encourage them to hang on in there, assuring them that things would get better. Just because it wasn't my pain didn't mean it wasn't pain. I learned that your hurt might seem small to me, but it might be big or greater than mine to you, because hurt is hurt. I was hurting but I wasn't going to turn my back on God anymore!

Going to Church

I never stopped going to church because that is where my roots lie, and I never became angry at God again. Everyone in my family is some church-going, God-fearing, Christian-believing people, and church was all I knew. Somewhere down the road a few of us strayed, but somehow we found our way back to the Lord. I hoped that one day the Lord would give a word to the minister to help me discover who I was and explain why my life was so miserable. I wanted to know the purpose God had for me. I thought being in the church would help me to find my place in life. I thought being in church would help me to find love, peace, and joy. But often I would leave church disappointed. It upset me dearly when the minister would preach and say, "Whatever is keeping you back, let it go!" "Don't let life, depression, and your circumstances keep you down." "Get over it! Whatever happened way back then, you need to let go of it now."

I don't remember a certain circumstance that caused me to fear so much. I didn't know why I hated myself so much. I didn't know why I was never happy. All I knew is that I had felt this way for most of my life, and things weren't getting any better; they were getting worse. All of the phrases sounded good. They sounded real good. For a minute and for most of my life, I believed in the phrases. I believed I could let it go. I had tried many times to reprogram my brain and think on positive things. I would pray, read the Bible, and go to church every Sunday, praying that the little voice would leave me. But the little voice never went away. Instead as I grew older, it grew worse.

It even tried to drown the preacher out. Sometimes, I would drift off into never never land while the preacher preached. It told me that all of the people in church thought they were better than I was. It told me how no one else in church was trying to live right except my family and me. But most of all, it told me how God was never going to cure me of my little negative voice. I had come to believe that it was never going to go away. But I was not going to turn my back on God. I was not going to become angry anymore. Even though I had come to believe that it was more than just a little negative voice, but a monster, and eventually it was going to destroy me.

Why was the preacher standing up in the pulpit saying these things? He obviously had not gone through what I was going through. He obviously didn't know anyone else in the world who felt the way I did. I felt sorry for me and sorrier for others who were experiencing the same pain. I wanted to get up and find my way to the nearest door. I needed help! I cried for myself. I cried for others. He obviously didn't recognize it was an illness. He obviously didn't know it needed to be treated in order to

107

overcome. Things had gotten so bad that I realized I needed a physician. I needed help! I knew God was helping me, because for me to want to see a physician voluntarily had to be God speaking to me.

I never had any doubt that God would not deliver me or any person from any illness. What is too hard for God? Nothing, absolutely *nothing*! It doesn't matter if its cancer, AIDS, high blood pressure, diabetes, or depression, God can deliver you. Even though there were times when I didn't always call on him first, it turned out he was still the first to come and rescue me. I knew the power of prayer. That is why I eventually realized I needed more than a word from the minister. I needed a doctor. You cannot let go until you know exactly what you are letting go of. You've got to know the source of the condition. You have got to treat the condition. This is the beginning of your letting go and letting God. I was letting go. I felt like I should let someone in my family know how I felt. Maybe they didn't like me, but they had to love me.

Behold I am the Lord, the God of all flesh: Is there anything too hard for me?

Jeremiah 32:27

Is there anything too hard for God?

Genesis 18:14

Broken Spirit

I unconsciously longed for the love of my family members. One thing I discovered is that coming from a happy home doesn't always mean you are going to feel loved. I didn't feel family members gave me much attention or love. My aunt always fussed at me. She seemed to intentionally do things to make me feel bad. I loved her so much. Mama told me that she had to quit her job one time because I was beginning to think that Auntee was my mother.

It wasn't until she died that I realized the possibility of her disliking me too. When she died, all of the nieces and nephews thought they were her favorite niece or nephew. There was no doubt in my mind that I was her favorite niece. I took more abuse from her than anyone in the world. It didn't matter that she fussed at me all the time. It didn't matter that I couldn't do anything right in her eyesight. I couldn't even write or speak well according to her. I think she influenced Mother to think negatively about me. I believe it had a lot to do with me becoming the person I became. After a while, I became defiant and sassy, as the old folk would call it (hard headed). Yes! I became defiant and defensive. I was always on the defense to speak up and speak out whenever she or any grown person said something ugly to me. It made me mad and angry to hear them say bad things about me seemingly all of the time. They would call me grown, and I wasn't sure what that meant, but it certainly did not sound like something nice to say about a small child. It was the look on their faces whenever they would call me grown that convinced me that it wasn't anything nice.

My other aunts and uncles talked about me too. They would talk about me being so skinny. No one had ever seen a person as skinny as I was. They talked about my hair and wondered why it would never grow. My first cousins would compare my hair with their newly born nieces who were blessed to be born with naturally curly and long hair. When I would come around, they would laugh and ask how could it be that the baby's hair was longer than mine. I'm not sure if they knew it hurt my feelings, I'm not sure if they even cared. I tried to ignore them. But being a kid, it was hard not to hear such harsh words being said to you. They said I had big eyes and they were always asking where I got the big eyes. If they didn't know, why on earth did they think I would know? They convinced me that having big eyes and being skinny with skinny legs was not a good thing. When the heat became more than I could bear, I began to talk back to defend myself. Whenever they would say something ugly to me, I would say something-sassy back to them. I didn't know I was being sassy, but this is what they told me. But I wonder if they knew what they were doing. I wonder if they knew that the words that came from their mouths would haunt me for the rest of my life. I wonder if they knew how to say kind things to anyone. I wonder if they knew how my feelings hurt. I don't think grown folk realize the things that they say can hurt children in the way they do, and have a lifelong effect on them. They couldn't possibly know. They couldn't possibly know the deep hurt that I felt deep inside. Because of this, I became the worst child that Mother ever had. Mama would often say I was the only one of her five children that talked back to her. I believe that, because I've never heard any of my siblings mention to each other or me a word about verbal abuse. I became so defiant my cousin told me that my mama was going to send me to the reformatory school. I didn't know what that was and I didn't understand why they thought I was so bad, but I knew I didn't want to be sent away from Mama to go anywhere unknown to me. Mama never said a word about sending me away. Besides, I couldn't have been that bad. I couldn't have been as bad as they were mean.

Mama and my aunt always called me lazy. I never knew why they called me lazy. It could have been because I was often tired and didn't have a lot of energy. It might have been because I enjoyed sleeping every

110

chance I got, or it may have been because I never volunteered to do any chores. I only did what Mama told me to do. When I was growing up, parents didn't know and didn't care about the stages of development. It was a phase that I didn't understand and certainly not one that Mama understood. I didn't know I was supposed to volunteer to do things; besides, the first time I volunteered to do something, it got me in big trouble.

Big Trouble

I will never forget the time I wanted to surprise Mama and Sizzie. We had just finished supper the three of us. I only remember the three of us eating supper. Mama and Sizzie got up from the table and walked down the hall, carrying their conversation with them. We had a long hallway. It seemed long to me, and the room straight up the hallway was the upper room. This was the girls' room, and this is where Mama and Sizzie went to talk. I didn't follow them, because I wanted to surprise them. I wanted to do something that I thought would make Mama very happy and proud of me. When they were out of sight and down the hall talking, I came up with a bright idea to surprise them and make them happy, especially Mama. I pulled a chair from the table and put it in front of the kitchen sink. I began to run hot, soapy water into the white porcelain sink. I stepped down from the chair and got each plate off the table one by one, each glass, and all of the silverware and started to wash the dishes. I was so excited about this; it felt good doing it. When I was finished, I ran down the hall shouting to Mama and my big sister to come, take a look and see what I'd done! When Mama got to the kitchen, all she could do was smile. I am sure she told me what a good job I had done, and from that night on I had to get up in the chair and wash dishes. A monster I had created. I called it trouble because on nights that I didn't feel like washing the dirty dishes, I got in trouble. Mama said that I had done such a great job that I should do it all of the time.

Strange Kind of Love

It was unusual reaching out to family. I thought they should have been reaching out to me long before I got to this point. I believed that they were well aware of my condition. I believed they chose not to help me for their own gain that is what the little voice told me. I resented them. If they wanted to help in anyway, they knew how. At least this is what my mind told me .I was not sure if this was the negative or the positive side of my mind talking to me. But I knew the little negative voice told me throughout my life that none of my family members really cared that much about me. I knew they loved me because Mama and Daddy wouldn't have had it any other way.

Until today none of them really seemed to have cared about me anyway, except Sissy. I sometimes call her Sizzie and other times I call her Sissy. She answers to both. She always seemed to have cared, but it was usually when she was out of the presence of the other family members. It seemed their impression of me affected her. She was definitely influenced by them. Before they came around, she and I had a perfect sister–best friend relationship. I always felt like they wanted Sissy to dislike me as much as they did. My other sister and her husband always wanted to know how she was able to deal with me. They wanted to know if I was good for anything. She would answer in her own subtle way. One time when they asked her how she could get along with me, she came out and said, "I do not know." I believe she felt compelled to give them the answer they probed for. I was so hurt and disappointed by that, I couldn't laugh with her for days. I'm sure she noticed what they were trying to do, and I am sure she wanted to tell them I was not the monster they thought I was. Instead she never said anything. My relationship with her went a long way back. She was my big sister; she was Mama's first born.

Every time she called home I would answer the phone, say hello to her, and then call for Mommy and Daddy to come to the phone. I wanted her to speak with them first because she and I usually had a lot to say to each other once our parents finished talking. When she finished talking to our parents, she would ask to speak with me again. We had so much to catch up on. She and I would talk for several minutes and sometimes an hour before hanging up the phone. I would tell her about my week at school. We would talk about other family members and all sorts of things in general. She would share with me what was going on in Atlanta. Sometimes Mama would hold the phone on the other line, trying to listen to what we had to say. I can remember many times saying, "Mama, hang up." She would then hang up the phone. I suppose she was wondering what in the world did little ole me and my big sister have to talk about. She was the oldest but she got along with all of us. She gets along well with Baby Brother, my big brothers, and even my sister Sarah Jean, who was quieter than all of us. I didn't feel like I got the chance to know her that well, because she didn't say a lot. When Sarah Jean was home, before leaving to go off to college, the only thing that I remembered about her was studying and cleaning up. She would clean the house spotless everyday before Mama came home from work, and dare my friends and me to come inside the house and track up her freshly mopped kitchen floor, or dare us to come through the front door and run up and down the hallway. She was adamant about that. This was one of the things that made me think she was a mean big sister. I will never forget the time I went to visit Sarah Jean after she graduated from college and got married. I was fourteen years old. She had recently informed the family that she was pregnant and expecting a baby girl. I was so ecstatic. Mama and Daddy had no grandchildren, and I had no nieces or nephews. My sister was about to bring a new member into the family, and, boy, we were oh so happy. I went to visit my sister and her husband for the summer. I don't remember whether she invited me or if I asked to come. What I remember is she sent a plane ticket for Baby Brother and me, and the next thing I knew, we were flying high in the sky headed to Nashville, Tennessee. Yes, we were going to the big city. This was not the first time we had visited with her and her husband, but this time would be different because we were having a baby!

Once I got to the big city, I was bored to death. I had no friends to call on the telephone. I had nowhere to go. I missed my friends back home so much, but I did not want to let them know how much I missed them. I wanted them to think I was in the big city and having big fun. At times I got so bored, I wished to go back home. The only outing Baby Brother and I would get would be a trip to Baskin-Robbins to get some ice cream. My sister would be craving ice cream, and the four of us would jump into the car and go get some ice cream. Sometimes we were lucky enough to go out two nights of the week. We would drive downtown to the post office. It was always exciting to go downtown. The buildings were tall. The lights were bright, but the streets were almost empty. Most people I assumed had retired for the evening. They were probably doing like Sarah Jean and Lil G getting ready for the next day. I had to prepare for the next day, but it was all so different for me. Instead of going to bed early; I tried to stay up as late as possible without disturbing anyone.

I was a big girl; I could not be calling back home telling Mama and Daddy I was homesick. Instead, I chose to play it off. I made the best of my vacation by working my buns off trying to make my sister and her husband proud. Everyday I would get up and clean up. I had my routine. I would start downstairs. I would dust the furniture, and then I would vacuum the den and the living room and sweep the kitchen floor. If there were any dishes left over, I would wash them. Some days I would make breakfast, but most days I didn't. I tried to sleep as late as possible so that my day would go by fast. I didn't like being bored, and of course, I was not a TV kind of person. When I did all of this, I was finished with my work downstairs. The hard job was cleaning upstairs. It was a big job, but I felt like I owed them that much.

Each morning I would go into their bedroom and make up that big huge bed. It seemed extra big to me because I was so small, and besides, I was not used to making up a bed that was so big. I had never seen a bed so big. Mama and Daddy didn't have a bed that huge and if we did it probably would not fit any of our bedrooms. I would put away clothes; some I would fold, and others I would put away in the dirty clothes hamper. I had everything neat and in order. I wasn't sure if my sister and her husband appreciated my hard work or not. Because everyday I would place things on the dresser and on the countertop in the bathroom in their proper places, and everyday when I would go to clean up, everything would be out of its place, which required me to do the same thing over and over again. The hardest part of my job was trying to clean the bathroom. It seemed that toothpaste always splashed on the mirror, and water splashed everywhere. Maybe they thought I enjoyed doing this, or had they figured out I was bored and needed something to do.

I did not want to tell my sister or my brother-in-law how bored I was. I had Little Brother there to keep me company. He would watch TV and sometimes help with the cleaning. I taught him how to do everything. He knew how to wash dishes, he knew how to clean. After I finished the cleaning I could hardly wait for my sister and brother-in-law to come home. My brother-in-law was a great cook. I knew if I did not have fun cleaning and washing clothes, I would have a good time eating his home-cooked meals. His meals were so good that neither Baby Brother nor I missed Mama's good ole cooking back home. He cooked so well that whenever he and my sister would come home to visit, Mama would retire herself from the kitchen. We knew Little "G" would be cooking up some good stuff. But his great cooking cost me my visit with them. I really didn't know that my summer vacation in the big city was about to be over. I felt so bad when I learned it was time to go. I felt like I had been used. I felt like all of my hard work had gone unappreciated. My brother-in-law's timing was perfect. His planning to kick Baby Brother and me out of the house was perfect.

It was approximately three days before the baby was born. We knew that my sister's time was getting closer and closer. She would let us touch her stomach and feel the baby moving. Her stomach had gotten so big it looked like two basketballs; the baby looked like she would come at any minute. I was becoming more and more excited. I was concerned about how my sister would look once she went into the hospital and had the baby. I wanted her to look pretty. I wanted her hair to be pretty. I had braided her hair. It was so beautifully braided; I had done one thing right. I thought to myself. I thought the style complemented her face well. I had almost forgotten how bored I had been. I could not concentrate on anything but the baby. My brother-in-law was getting excited too, except he was getting excited about planning a way to get Baby Brother and me out of the house.

Days before the baby was scheduled to come, Lil G started acting funny. He made comments about me eating too much food. He accused me of beating him to my sister's plate to eat her leftovers. I thought it was all fun and games at first, but this man was serious. It had become a game to me trying to race to my sister's plate to grab her leftovers. She did not eat a lot of food to be pregnant; she didn't eat a lot of food at any time really, and I didn't eat much either, but maybe because Lil G's food was so tasty, I ate more than usual. But to my brother-in-law, I had a pretty good appetite. He used my appetite as a way to send Little Brother and me back home.

I didn't know my brother-in-law had called Mama. Yes, he had already told her that I was eating too much food and that it was time for me to come home. I can laugh at this now, but the day it happened I was too naïve to know I had been overeating. I was too naïve to know that I had been eating so much food I was about to be sent back home to Mama and Daddy. Mama called the next morning while Sarah Jean and Lil G were at work. I was so glad to hear from her and had no idea I was in trouble. She asked how I was doing and what I had been doing. I told her. I told her I had been a good girl and all I did was clean-up, eat, and sleep. She listened, and then said, "McKenzie, we are coming to get you and Little Brother tomorrow."

I began to cry and ask why, "Mama, why are y'all coming to get us?" I asked. "It is time for the baby to come." I said. Today was Thursday. Mama meant Friday, when my brother and my Daddy got off work, she would be coming to Nashville, Tennessee, to pick up her children. Mama said that Lil G had called and told her I was eating all of the food. He said he could not get enough to eat before I would be grabbing food off of my sister's plate. I did not understand what Mama was saying; all I knew is she was planning to come and take me home and I was not ready to leave. I knew that the baby was about to come any day, any minute. Oh God, I did not want to leave before I could see her, kiss her, and hold her. I begged and pleaded with Mama and Daddy not to come and take us away.

It was around midnight. Mama, Daddy, and my big brother Joshua Jr. were leaving Alabama, and my sister was on her way to the hospital to have our first baby. The baby arrived before the family made it to the city. It was a beautiful baby girl. She was one of the most beautiful babies I had ever seen. She had a long, beautiful caramel face. She had a head full of black, curly, silky, beautiful hair. She would never wake up long enough for us to see her eyes. But when she did open her eyes, they were big. She had big, brown, beautiful eyes just like me. She looked like a beautiful black baby doll. For the moment my parents had forgotten that they were supposed to be picking Baby Brother and me up to go back home.

She was so beautiful that Mama and Daddy could not turn around and go back home. They stayed around for a few more days. They stayed around long enough for my sister to be discharged from the hospital. Daddy prayed over the baby. He thanked God for letting her come into the world healthy and happy. Daddy had the privilege of bringing his first and only grandchild home from the hospital. For a while I thought Daddy would never get over the joy and excitement of being a Grandpa and how he was the first to bring her home. Before we said our good-byes, Daddy, Mama, Joshua Jr., Sarah Jean, Lil G, Baby Brother and I blessed the baby, and Daddy gave her back to God. I think giving a child back to God is what they call christening in today's terms. I was too young to understand its full meaning, but I knew it was a good thing. I also knew that I did not want to leave without spending more time with her. I didn't know and couldn't understand why my sister and brother-in-law disliked me so much. I liked being around them, especially now that they had the baby. I could visit and not be bored. It would be years later that I came to realize that their attitude and actions toward me hadn't changed. I was convinced that they really did not like me. As far as I could tell no one liked me, not even me. It was just a strange kind of love.

As a young adult, I still did things to try to win them over. I did it unconsciously. It would be years later that I discovered that I didn't have to do anything to win the love of others. It would be years later that I discovered that I do not have to do anything to win the love of others to make me happy. It would be years later that I discovered that all I had to do was love me and I could be happy. It would be years later that I discovered that I had to love me before I could truly love others. But before that time I felt lonely. I felt sad and unloved. I had fought hard to win their love and they hadn't paid any attention to me. I used to wonder why children with unloving parents fought so hard to win the love of their mother or their father. It is just natural for a child to be loved by his or her parents. Life without the love of a mother or father can make life feel so incomplete. But even this we can overcome, but it takes time.

When they moved from Tennessee to Alabama, I found myself doing the same thing. Whenever we would visit them, Mama, Daddy, Little Brother, and me, I found myself doing the same things. Maybe, just maybe, I could squeeze a little love out of them for me. We often visited their new home. It was bigger and it was beautiful. We entered the house from the side door, which led us into a big, huge kitchen. Around the corner was a separate room, which led into a huge den. Since the kitchen was the first thing you saw, I would walk into the house, smile, shake my head at the dirty dishes, papers, notebooks, and color crayons which greeted me with a welcome and a smile. I would put my purse down and all of my dread of having to clean up, and walk straight to the kitchen sink and begin washing dirty dishes. Then I began picking up schoolbooks, and color crayons, and sweeping the kitchen floor. I never waited for Sarah Jean or Lil G to ask me to clean. I felt their pain from their busy schedule. I wanted to help out, but more than that I think I was unconsciously trying to win their love. By this time they had two more kids and three times as much work to do. I would follow the same routine, starting downstairs and going upstairs, except the house was much larger and the workload had tripled. In hindsight I am not sure if any of this really mattered to them. I think they would have been happier not seeing me. It wasn't until I requested pay for my service that they realized the hard work I was doing for them. Neither one of them seemed to mind paying me for my service. I'm not sure if they would have ever noticed my hard labor had I not begun requesting pay. I was a newly legally separated young woman by then, and I needed some funds in my pockets. I had no problem asking them for pay for my hard earned work. The situation with my sister didn't seem to get better. I couldn't make her love me, or even like me. Why was she so mean? I finally had to let it go and address this to Mama. I knew she would take care of it, once and for all. Then I had my brothers to deal with.

I felt like my brothers loved me but disliked me too. I knew they loved me because Mother would not have had it any other way. I admired my brothers. I thought the world of them. I thought they were cool, and even more, I thought they were some sharp brothers. They loved to dress, and

120

I admired that. I admired any man who knew how to dress, especially those who knew how to dress themselves. I had dated guys before who knew nothing about dressing. I once dated a guy who dressed so poorly he made a suit look bad. Do you realize how difficult that is to do? It is very difficult for a black man. There's an old saying, "*No man can wear a suit like a black man.*" But this one guy, it was unbelievable, because he made a suit look bad. I thought the world of my brothers. My brothers could be conservative; they could be yuppie, or just plain sharp. They were humorous, fun, and alive. I did not realize how much I admired them until I noticed how they never said anything nice about me. They never said how nice or how cute my outfit looked. They knew fashion and they knew style. Evidently, I did not have fashion or style in their eyes. I felt like they had gotten together and decided that they were not going to compliment Kenzie. It didn't matter what I was wearing or how well I wore it, they were not going to compliment me. It would be years later, many years later, when I started trying to put the pieces of my life together, that I realized the cold treatment I was getting from them. I did not know if it was real or if it was the little voice that brought it to recognition, but in my eyes and in my life it was real. The bottom line was my brothers didn't even love me. No one loved Kenzie. Once I was asked to be on a program to speak and to sing for a special occasion. Little Brother and Joshua Jr. attended the event. Once the service was dismissed and people were greeting, meeting, and socializing, many people came to me and told me how well I had done. I thanked them. I felt good about this. I thanked God for those people who thought well of me, but something was missing. Neither one of my brothers had said a word to me. This made me wonder, this concerned me. I wondered if I should believe the people who hardly knew me, or should I believe my brothers, who said nothing. I wondered if not saying anything to me meant being nice. The old folk used to say, "If you can't say anything nice, then don't say anything at all." Were they taking heed to what the old folk advised them? Was I supposed to believe that I had done a good job, despite my brothers not commenting? Or was I going to believe the strangers? I chose to believe the strangers because for the time being they boosted my ego. They encouraged me; they gave me what I needed when I needed it. But in the long term I gave up, because my family knew best and they must have believed I was terrible. Maybe this was their nice and silent way of telling me that I was terrible. I was just like that little voice inside my head that said, "a failure."

It didn't stop there. Daddy got hipped too. He was sharp. Everyone says the same thing about my Daddy. I enjoy seeing him look so sharp at eighty-six years old and going strong with the grace and goodness of the Good Lord. I love him so much. The young folk, the old folk, and everyone seems to admire him. I think he gets a kick out of that. I thank God for Mama and myself. We used to get on his case all the time because he loved his old work clothes. Daddy would wear them everywhere. If it were left up to him, he would wear his old work clothes every day of the week except Sunday. I can remember when he thought it was all right to wear his work clothes to the hospital to visit the sick, if it was not on a Sunday. I remember when he thought it was all right to wear his old work clothes downtown on Saturdays and to the mall. He thought it was all right to wear his work clothes if we went out to eat dinner. Mama and I worked hard on changing Daddy's idea about looking all right. It is good to know that it all paid off.

I give myself credit for teaching Baby Brother to be a sharp dresser. I learned that when I went off to college. There was something about college that made me want to look better. Like a lot of others, I didn't have much, but it was okay. I learned to mix and match and put what

I had together well. I had two outfits in my wardrobe and whenever I put on my burgundy shoes with my khaki pants with my orange, green, and brown striped colored sweater, I was sharper than sharp. Every time I wore the outfit someone complimented me. I learned how to wear neckties. It was the thing. I would not have fathomed a female wearing a necktie to be a sharp and pizzazz thing to do, but I wore it well. I even learned how to tie neckties. I impressed my daddy so much when I went home for spring break by tying his necktie before he went to church. I even taught Little Brother how to tie a necktie and wear the shoes and shirts that the college guys were wearing, so when it was time for him to go off to school, he would have a jump start on the college attire. My adopted brother, Harvey Lee, didn't care a lot about everyday dressing. But he dressed well on Sunday. He had one suit his entire life, it was black. He had one shirt—it was pink—and one necktie, which was multicolored. When he put the suit on, no one could convince him that he was not the Bum. He wore this suit every Sunday for as long as I can remember. And every Sunday he wore it like it was his first time wearing it. He swore that all the ladies had to wave their fans when he walked into the church; a ladies' man he was.

Harvey Lee, he was a trip too. He was selfish. He didn't want anyone to drive his car. I couldn't understand what was so special about a car, that he didn't want anyone to drive it. He didn't share his money either. He was extra stingy. I didn't believe he liked me either.

He attended church in the city, and the rest of us attended church in the country. Joshua Jr., Little Brother, and I attended church in the country where Daddy and Joshua Jr. pastored. My sisters were away. Mama, Little Brother and I were members of the good ole Baptist Church. Daddy and Joshua Jr. were Methodist, and the rest of the family was Baptist. I supposed it was all good going to church and spending the long hours, but I still didn't feel loved. We attended both churches equally. Once we left Daddy's church for the morning service and afternoon dinner, we had to attend our church for evening service. We did this every Sunday. We never got home from church on Sundays before dark. It did not matter to Mama and Daddy that the evening service did not start until five o'clock in the evening. We waited until church started. It was a good thing that Uncle Toot and Aunt Mae had moved back to the country. We would go to their house eat a big dinner and wait around until it was time for church to start. The only good thing about being gone all day long was I got the chance to visit with Precious. Apart from that, I thought we would never get home. Sundays were our longest day of the week. All of the neighborhood kids had gradually begun to stop going to church with us. There were so many of us at one time that we formed a choir and sang for Daddy's and for Joshua Jr.'s church. One Sunday we would sing at Daddy's church, and the other Sunday we sang at Joshua Jr.'s church. As my friends got older and older, the choir got smaller and smaller. I could not talk Valeria, Cissley, Rita, or her brother Randy into going to church with me anymore. Precious and James, her brother, even stopped going. Baboo stopped going. There was no one left but Baby Brother and me.

Mother, on the other hand, I knew she loved me. She encouraged me to speak. She was a great speaker herself. I would love to be able to speak half as well as her. She later became a minister. She made sure I sang, spoke, and prayed. But I believed Mother used to think, I was the worst child she had. This is what the little voice inside of my head told me. Strange kind of love, I thought to myself. Because my Auntee was so critical of me, I became defensive. I did what I felt was necessary to keep the hot heat off my back. I got tired of hearing bad, ugly, and negative things being said about me. I resented those comments. Mama accused me of having a sassy mouth. Mama said I "always talked back to her." She always reminded me that none of the other kids ever talked back. I was so happy when I grew up and grew older. Some things changed. I remember the time my mother said something nice to me. Was she changing the way she felt about me? She had begun to say to me that I "was a sweet girl," or "a sweet child." She said, I "was the child that stood up for her." Yes that I was. No one was in a position to speak unruly to my Mama, not her sisters, not her brothers, nor her in-laws. What she meant was that if I felt that anyone misunderstood her in any way, I took a stand. Sometimes I think Mother was misunderstood like me at times because she loved so hard. In the end, the one that she loved and trusted the most outside of the family ended up letting her down. It was the same with me. The people I thought the world of let me down. I was accustomed to my family members putting me down. They thought I was tough. They thought I was loud and tough. They felt that since I was outspoken, I must have been the most insensitive person that God had created. The strange love that my family had for me did not stop there. It affected their offspring.

Passing the Torch

It was evident that the feelings my siblings had for me affected the way their children treated me. I wanted to be the aunt to them that my aunt was to me. I tried to be like Auntee. I wanted to inherit the loving, kind, and giving side of her and extend that love and kindness to my nieces and nephews. It did not happen that way. The kids thought little of me, mainly because of their parents.

Mama was crazy about her youngest sister; and so were all of my siblings and me. But things are different with my nieces. The difference is, my mother respected my aunt, and I obeyed and respected her too. Whatever my aunt or any adult told me to do, I did it. Unfortunately, I do not get that same respect from my nieces. I am reminded of the experiences I've had with them. Like the times I tried to discipline Simone, and her parents would defend her and tell me how wrong I was. They accused me of picking on her. "Kenzie, why are you always picking on Simone?" They would ask. Surprised and disappointed I was. Many times I was lost for words. I couldn't believe it. I used to wonder who the adult was and who the child was. Things have changed a lot from the time I was growing up. Respect meant everything. Children would quickly stand up to let the adults sit down. When family members would visit, children had to give up their beds for the family member. But today it doesn't happen that way. Parents don't even ask their child to sleep on the floor or air mattress and offer the adult the sofa or the bed. It's a new generation. It is more like first come first serve. Today you will be SOOL. (so out of luck.) It's a different world as Grandma used to say.

Simone was not a bad kid. At times she could be the sweetest child in the world. To this day I don't know if her parents realize who the adult is.

My niece Sophie is very similar to Simone. She has respect for me whenever it is convenient for her. I discipline her, and she talks back. It's nothing like my upbringing. The difference here is I don't have to worry about her parents defending her. Actually, I think they appreciate the help. Sometimes, I feel they refuse to discipline her to avoid her tone and her attitude. She knows where to draw the line because she doesn't disrespect any of my siblings; it's just me she seems to have the problem with. Oh my God, sometimes I wonder if she has internal turmoil going on inside of her head like I did for so many years. I've never seen her talking back to any of her aunts or uncles on her father's side of the family. She certainly knows where to draw the line. The truth is she knows how to act but she refuses to give me any respect. I used to worry about this, but now I pray. I pray that I am not the mirror that reflects who she is inside that makes her resents me so much. "Could it be my inability to hold on to a job?" I ask myself. If I have nothing else, I have a heart full of love and that was the best thing Auntee could have passed on to me.

My other niece, Noel, is an exception. She is respectful towards me. She never says an unkind word. She is a respectful child. She has always been respectful to everyone. If I ask her to do something for me, she will. Usually she hides herself in her books. She is never without a book. Whenever it is time to cook, she is studying. Whenever it is time to clean, she is studying. When it is time to eat, she takes a break, and then continues to study. She kids about her sister Sophie being naturally smart and a fast learner. They're both extremely smart and have their own personalities.

Guys, on the other hand are different. I may have used some of my aunt's disciplinary tactics on them, but it did not cause them to lose their respect for me. They never rebelled. The other nephews are great-nephews. They are great too. The others are young'uns. They are beautiful. One pretends to be very shy; the others are more like me, friendly and outgoing. I believe they will obey. They already know who the adult is. The good thing is their parents never stand in the way whenever I discipline them. It makes all the difference. Someone once said it takes a community to rear a child. I agree.

My Dearest Auntee

My Auntee was one of my favorite people. Auntee never had children of her own. But she was like a mother to all of her nieces and nephews. But it was a disappointing discovery when I learned that all the nieces and nephews thought they were her favorite. As nice as she was; she could be just as fussy. It didn't matter that much to me because I was certain that she loved me. I learned to accept her for whom she was. The fact that she did not have children was unfortunate because she tried once to have children. Mama said the child died at birth. Therefore all of us became her children. Auntee was single all of my life. But she married three different times to three different men whose names were Lee. She married Lee Williams, Lee Coleman, and Leland Thomas. It seems Auntee loved the name Lee.

It was another shocker when Auntee died; my older sisters and brothers thought they were her favorite. This was interesting to me because of the big age gap between us. I guess Auntee just had that type of spirit; even though all of them questioned her love for me after her death. It surprised me to hear my siblings discussing how she stayed on McKenzie's case. "Didn't she?" One of them asked; then looked directly at me. I looked at them acknowledging that I heard the statement but I was unable to mumble a word. I was speechless. I never knew anyone noticed how hard she was on me. I couldn't believe what my ears were hearing. I thought the way Auntee treated me was the way she treated everyone; hearing this almost brought tears to my eyes. I was shocked. I was devastated. It was not until then that I realized she had not been the monster to them that she had been to me. She was always on Precious and my case. But I knew she loved me. I believed deep down in her heart she meant well. She did a lot to help people.

She Had A Heart Full of Love

Auntee always had a heart full of love. She was always doing things to help others. When my aunt was working for the city, she went inside this family's home and they were sleeping on pallets on the floor. They had no beds and very little furniture. After work, my aunt went to the furniture store and bought the family a bed, a sofa, and some food. She had a big heart.

Precious and I caught hell as the ole folk say from Auntee. I don't believe Precious ever got over it. She was never able to shake off the hurt. Precious and I were two peas in a pod. Whenever you saw me, you saw her. We were best friends, cousins, and we called ourselves twins. One major difference between us was that everyone liked Precious. They called her Chocolate Doll. She was dark as a Hershey's candy bar, and pretty as a doll. She had long, shinny, thick, black, curly hair, thick eyebrows, and big pink lips and a big round nose. I think she got the nose from Auntee. All of the cousins thought she was pretty, even Auntee. Sizzie liked her too; she gave her the nickname Chocolate Doll. Sometimes we called her Hershey. Everyone thought that because she was dark and pretty, she had to be as sweet as a chocolate bar. Auntee always talked about how she helped to save Precious's life when she was born. The story was that Precious was very sick when she was born. She only weighted a couple of pounds and she had a twin sister who did not survive. Her name was Princess. I am sure that had she lived she would have been as black and pretty as Precious. As we grew older we proclaimed to be sisters. I was the twin she never had. Our lives seemed to parallel each other's so much. Even though Precious got complements from our cousins, she never thought she was pretty. All she could remember was the insults by Auntee and the face that she saw when she looked into the mirror. All she could remember is that she was the fourth child out of five who never got special attention and so was I. Her life story was so similar to mine it was almost unreal. She came from a loving home but somehow she felt left out. She had dreams, big dreams but no one seemed to have supported her dreams. Many times she and I felt we were on our own. I didn't have big dreams. The things that happened in my life just kind of happened that way. Unlike Precious, I never knew for certain exactly what it was I wanted to be when I grew up. The one profession I held on to the longest was my desire to become a nurse. A part from this, our lives seemed so similar. I don't know what it was about us that made Auntee talk so negative to us and I loved her so much. Mother loved all of her siblings but I believed Auntee was her favorite; she was definitely my favorite aunt. I am sure all of her siblings felt like they were just as close to Auntee as mama was, but I know she and Mama were as close as Sizzie and I.

Auntee was bossy, and she talked to us like we didn't matter. I started out that way when I was old enough to baby-sit, but thank God for deliverance. One time a friend asked me to baby-sit for her, and I agreed that I would. Auntie had told me not to jive and play with the kids but to be strong and discipline them. I took the job, and I yelled and screamed and told them "no!" demanding that they sit and stay. This did not work. They told their mom that I was mean and I spanked them, and they did not want me to be their baby-sitter anymore. The lesson learned here is that you do not have to yell, scream, or shout to make a child obey. You can say what you mean, and mean what you say in a nice way, and believe me, that child will obey. Auntee never asked me to do anything. She harshly gave me orders and commanded me to do things. "Go *git* this, and go *git* that." She would say. Everything was always in a nasty and demanding tone. Bring me my purse. Go *git* me that broom out of the kitchen!" "Shut yo mouth, you too grown!" she would say. "Can't you say anything nice to me sometimes?" I asked myself. It was not the fact that I minded doing what she asked me to; it was that ugly tone. But back in the day, this is just the way adults did things. Adults did not value your thoughts. They were the adults, you were the child; you listened and obeyed. You didn't get many chances to make many choices. Whenever they ordered you to do something, you had to jump right then and there. I really don't believe they knew any better. I really don't believe they knew children were little people, with feelings, ideas, and common sense. I know they didn't know any better. They really didn't mean any harm. Auntee was notorious for this. It was years later that I could no longer tolerate the tone of her voice and the way she spoke to me. The commanding, the demanding, and the derogative tone had run its term. I resented that and I began to sass her, as the old folk called it, talking back. This was a no-no, and I got plenty of *whuppings* behind my mouth. I'm sorry, I just couldn't help it. I became my aunt. It was so ironic because everyone who loved her seemed to have hated me. I never understood that. None of this mattered back then, because whenever she was nice, she was extremely nice. I loved her so much, and she always had money to give and a heart of love.

A Happy Disappointment

Auntee was always doing something thoughtful for others. It didn't matter that she fussed and treated us so mean she still had a big heart. When everyone else was screaming broke, Auntee always had money.

She didn't mind sharing her money either. Lots of time Auntee would have to give Mama and Daddy money too. Sometimes when she would come to our house I would go into her purse and take me some nickels, dimes, and quarters. Somehow she always knew I had gone into her purse, but this never seemed to have bothered her. This was one of the few things that I did that I thought might have deserved punishment, but Auntee never got mad. There were times I would ask her for more money and she would ask if I had already been in her purse. Some times I would tell the truth and some times I would tell a sweet little lie in order to get more money.

I loved Auntee. Precious may have loved her too, but was not as trusting as I. She really never felt as close to Auntee as I did. I don't believe she ever felt close to anyone. But because of my love for Auntee, I wanted Precious to like her just as much. Because of me she trusted, and it failed. I convinced her how nice Auntee was. Auntee tried to do as much for Precious as she did for me. She gave Precious as much money as she gave me. The only difference was I spent more time around her and Grandma so obviously I got more. Since Auntee was always doing for others; I felt like Auntie deserved someone to do something nice for her. But what I chose to do wasn't the exact thing that she needed.

I thought it was a fantastic idea. Auntee never had to want for anything. Everything she needed she had. Everything she wanted, she bought. Whenever we needed money she gave it to us, most times. She deserved something nice in her life. I thought. I decided to clean up her house for her. I asked Precious to help me and she agreed. Auntee had left home to go and run errands. She may have even gone to visit some of her friends. She had lots of friends. She was youthful and fun to be around. She took me out with her when I was fourteen to play bingo. I won. I won a float. I never got the chance to use it, because none of us were allowed to get into the swimming pool. I even had my first drink with Auntee. It was non-alcoholic, but it was a drink and I felt like an adult for the first time in my life. I'll never forget having my first Shirley Temple. I knew my idea would make Auntee very happy.

We dust, emptied ashtrays, straighten the chair covers on the chair, and swept the living room and kitchen floor. We did all we could to make Auntee proud of us. After we finished cleaning up, we left her house and ran home. I went to my house and Precious went to hers. We had worked so hard we were tired. "We were *woe* out!" as the old folk would say. We were too tired to play from all the cleaning we had done. Before we left her house, we checked to make sure that everything was neat and clean. We had no idea that Auntee wouldn't be happy about the good job we had done.

When Auntee arrived home, we were not there to see the expression on her face. We assumed she was happy. We thought she would brag about the good job we had done and compensate us too. Shortly after we got home Auntee called. She called my house first and talked to me. She asked if I would go and get Precious and come down to her house. "Yes ma'am, we'll be right there." I assured her. I didn't notice anything unusual in her voice. I hung up the phone and ran next door to get Precious. I told her that Auntee had called and wanted us to come to her house. I told her she wanted to reward us for doing such a good job cleaning. We grinned with joy and excitement as we ran across the street to see what she had for us. We knew Auntee was going to reward us well, because she always did. We couldn't wait.

We ran across the street and down to Auntee's house we went. When we arrived she was not smiling. I could not understand why she had such look on her face. Why would she be looking so mad and dissatisfied after all we had done to make her smile? "What is wrong with her? I thought. She told us to come inside and have a seat. We sat in the living room on the sofa and waited patiently for her to come back from the backroom. Suddenly, I was no longer feeling good about all the work we had done. Precious and I were sensing that something must have been wrong. We were no longer excited. When Auntee came from the back, she had Grandma's black belt in her hand. Precious and I began to cry. We were full of disappointment. We had time to jump up and run out of the front door but we knew the beating we would face from running, would be worst than the one we were about to receive right now. Auntee wanted to know what on earth, had we done to her house? She asked question after question as her hand swung back and forth with the belt hitting me across my legs and my arms. She wanted to know why had we rearranged her whatnots? She wanted to know why we had thrown out her cigarette butts. We could only tell her the truth. The truth is "We thought we were cleaning up the house for you." "We thought we were going to make you happy. We cried. She did not believe a word we said. Then on the other hand, she may not have even heard a word we said. She continued hitting me across my legs spanking me good ole fashion. When she finished up with me she went to Precious and started spanking her too. We cried and cried and when she was finished spanking both of us, we ran back across the street and went home. We were so disappointed. Auntee never had to worry about Precious and me ever cleaning up her house again.

She Showed Me Love

The lady of my life was my Grandmother. I often wonder what I would have done without my Grandmother. Grandmother showed me love. She showed me the kind of love and attention I longed for. She took time out to notice me. She would ask, "How was school today?" God must have sent her to me. She was in my life for only a brief moment, and I have more memories of her closeness and love, almost more, than anyone who spent time and took interest in me. I loved Grandmother. I love my mother dearly, and I loved her for having a mother like Grandma Dora. They say mothers love you, and grandmas spoil you. My grandmother loved me and spoiled me.

I looked forward to getting out of school each day so that I could go see her. I was five years old, and my grandmother died when I was eight. It was an abbreviated time for me, but some of the greatest times. I would run home from school, put my books on the table, and run across the street to sit with my grandmother. She lived only a few feet from us, but I had to cross the street to get to her house. Mama had taught me to look both ways before crossing the street, but no doubt there were days I ran straight across the street without looking, trying to get to Grandmother's house. God was with me, I say to myself. Grandmother lived with my Auntee. Auntee worked everyday, and Grandma would be home alone. I could hardly wait to see her. I knew she was just as excited to see me each day as I was to see her, even though Grandmother could not physically see.

Grandmother was a very pretty lady. Mama and Auntee looked more like her than any of grandma's other children. I am told most of them looked like my grandpa. I never met grandpa he died before I was born. The other children were all high yellow just like Grandpa. More than anything, Grandma had a beautiful heart. She was average height, about five feet five or maybe five feet six. She was a thin woman. I would give her about one hundred and thirty-five pounds. I'm not exactly sure, because I was so short and so young. She was dark skinned, with long, fine, silky, black hair. I can imagine that her eyes must have been brown like mine. I never saw Grandmother's eyes because she wore dark glasses all the time. Grandma was blind. Mama said when Grandma was sick in the hospital recuperating, she fell down some stairs while trying to maneuver her way around, and as a result of her fall, she injured herself and became blind. But I always believed Grandma could somehow see me. The smile she had on her face whenever my face met her face convinced me that my Grandma could see me. Oh, how I loved and adored her.

Everyday after school I would run to her house. When I knocked on the door, she would make her way to the door and let me in. Grandma would greet me with a kiss and a hug. After her greeting, I would go inside the house and sit down right beside her on the sofa. When we finished talking about my day, Grandma never failed to ask me, "Kenzie, do you feel like going to the store today?"

"Yes, ma'am," I would always say. I knew exactly what I was going to buy before Grandma even told me. Everyday after school when I went to Grandma Dora's house she sent me to the store. I always knew what I was going to buy even before she told me. I always bought the same thing. I would buy an apple. She would go into her little change purse, get a dime out of it, hand it to me, and I would run down the street to the store to buy us a juicy apple. Grandma and I never had a bad apple. Our apple was just like our days, always sweet and good.

The store manager knew me. He was a family friend. My brother Joshua Jr. worked for him whenever it got real busy. He was blind also, just like my Grandma Dora. He would always choose the biggest, the sweetest, and the prettiest red apple in the bin for Grandma and me. I don't know how he did it, he just did it. "Frank Lee, I would like to buy an apple, please," I would say.

"Kenz, is that you?" he would ask.

"Yes, sir. It's me." He must have known immediately that I was visiting with Grandma, because had I been coming to the store for myself, I would have been buying a honey bun. Frank Lee would laugh and wish me a good day. I'm sure he was laughing because he knew how much I loved honey buns. He knew if I got my hands on a dime, the first thing I would do was run like a track star to the store to buy a honey bun. Frank Lee was definitely a family friend. He is a part of our family. He remembers the day and year of all of our birthdays. He even knew Mama's and Daddy's birthdays. I often kid him about having a memory like an elephant. He never forgets a thing. We all love him so much. We sometimes call him our big brother. I wish I could say it was only my family that he knew so well, but he knew many families. He seemed just as close to the other families as he did mine. He had that kind of spirit. Sometimes I would get jealous when I would hear him talk about other families that he knew so well. They would call him Dad, some would call him their big brother; he is a likeable kind of guy.

Whenever he talks to us about others, we can easily see that they love him just as much. I saw him only a few days ago, and like always, I was glad to see him. He always kids me about eating honey buns, and I always kid in general. I always had jokes. I would joke with him about dating. I even joked with him about being able to see. Just like my Grandma, I believed he could somehow see all of us. His I.Q is unbelievable!

When I got back to Grandma Dora's house, she would find her way back to the door, open it for me, and let me back into the house. Grandma

Dora would have me wash the apple and ask me to bring her a knife from the kitchen so she could peel the apple. I would sit patiently on the sofa beside my grandmother and wait for her to peel the apple, and we would eat it together. Each bite seemed to get juicer and juicer, just like the kind of love I had for her. This was our daily routine. I enjoyed spending time with her until her death. I'm sure there were no indications to Grandma that my life would end up this way.

When Did It All Begin?

I woke up early one morning and walked down our long dark hallway. I could hear Mother sniffing. I walked into her bedroom, and she was crying. I was so afraid. I didn't know what to do. I could not believe my mother was crying. What was she crying about? I didn't even know to ask her, "What is the matter, Mama?" I ran out the room as quickly as I could, and ran next door to my Aunt Mae Lee house to get help. My Aunt Mae Lee and Uncle Toot lived next door to us. Uncle Toot was Mother's brother, her baby brother in fact. I ran out the backdoor as fast as I could, screaming and shouting, "Aunt Mae Lee, Aunt Mae Lee, something is wrong with Mama! Something is wrong with Mama! She is crying! Come help! Come help to see about her!"

I didn't have to knock on the door, because folk normally kept their doors unlocked. Besides, most of the neighbors didn't knock for long anyway. They would knock on your door one time, then they would say, "comin' in" and walk right into your house before you could turn your head. The only time we had to lock our doors was when the bad kids came outside to play. Sometimes they would be mischievous and walk into your house and borrow some of your toys without you knowing until you saw them outside playing with them. Sometimes they would be so mischievous they would break them. Sometimes they would sneak in the backdoor and take the last two biscuits out of the pan and run home. Mama and Daddy never worried much about the missing biscuits, but I did. It seemed I always got hungry after I discovered they were missing. But most of the time we felt very safe and secure in our neighborhood. Everyone knew each other.

Sometimes we had to plan our outdoor time around the bad kids. Because the kids would snatch our bike, ride it all day, and then bring it back to our house with two flat tires. Baby Brother and I would be so mad that we would cry. We could hardly wait for Joshua Jr. to take our bike to the store and get it fixed for us. Other than that, we loved everybody and got along well with everybody.

When I reached Uncle Toot and Aunt Mae Lee's house, I could see through the back screen door that my aunt was home. I ran straight into the house, yelling for my aunt to come and help! Aunt Mae Lee did not say a word or attempt to ask me any questions; she just came running straight to the house. She ran into the house and went into Mother's room. I was standing outside of the door. I was scared to go inside the room and scared to stay outside of the room. I could not stand the thought of my mother crying. It was a feeling that is hard to explain. As Aunt Mae Lee entered the room, I could hear Mother's cry getting a little louder and then a little softer. I heard words, but I could not make out what was being said. I started to cry, too. I didn't know what to think. In a few short minutes it seemed everything was calm. I didn't hear anymore talking except "okay, it is going to be all right."

When Aunt Mae Lee came outside of the room, I was still standing outside the door. I am sure I looked very lonely and helpless. I didn't know what to say. All I could do was hold up my head with my big red eyes and look to Aunt Mae Lee for answers. She said Mother would be okay. She assured me that Mama would be all right and that she was okay.

I don't remember where anyone else in the family was at the time. Daddy was gone to work, I assume. Baby Brother must have been asleep. I don't remember where my other siblings were. I suppose my big brother Joshua Jr. was in school. I suppose my sisters were away in college. Mama had not adopted my other brother yet, who became parentless as a teenager. He was my big brother's best friend. When his grandparents died and he had no one to care for him, Mama took him in. Harvey Lee became my big brother. I believe he was seventeen years old at the time. He was almost grown but not grown; besides, he was a boy and you know they don't become grown at legal age. At least most of them don't, in my opinion.

I never questioned Mama about why she was crying. It saddened me to think of my mother crying. I am convinced that she was crying because she felt lonely. As much as Mama and Daddy wanted their children to grow up and go off to college, they missed us so much. Every time one of the kids would leave home to go to school, Mother cried. She cried a lot. I felt my mother's pain. I still feel my mother's pain.

Starting the Family

This is how it started. When Mother gave birth to my older sisters and brother, she was young and beautiful. She was patience. She was vigorous. She was vibrant and vivacious. She had energy out of this world.

She had almost as much energy as Daddy. She loved children; they were her heart. But it was after many years of marriage before Mama became pregnant. I can only imagine what it must have felt like being unable to have children and start a family as soon as she and Daddy had desired. They had to wait. It wasn't by choice. According to Mama; it was God's will.

They loved children and family so much. This was probably why it was easy for them to take in many of their relatives. Mama and Daddy played a vital role in the life of Daddy's younger siblings because he lost his parents at such a young age. Out of the thirteen siblings, all of them are deceased now except Daddy. Family meant everything to Mama and Daddy.

It was nine years of marriage before they had their first child. Even though Mama and Daddy desired children must sooner; the Lord did not open Mama's womb to receive the gift of life until the time was right. Mama had almost given up hope of becoming pregnant, and then it finally happened. They had waited patiently and prayed. Then the day came and they were blessed with a beautiful baby girl. I can only imagine the joy they felt inside.

My parents thought she was so wonderful and beautiful that they called her Cooter. It would be years before I understood what was supposed to have been so special about the name Cooter. One day Cooter explained the name to me.

"First, it was Daddy who named me," she said.

"Humm, umm." I waited with a look of anticipation on my face, impatient to her what she had to say about the name. I didn't find the

141

name to be so great at this point, even if Daddy had named her. I kept waiting for her to tell me more about the name. I kept wondering what could be so significant about the name Cooter. It seemed Mother had no problem with the name Daddy had given their firstborn. To her it was a cute and catchy little nickname.

Nicknames were the thing. Everyone had one. The problem with having a nickname was the fact that only a few people knew you by your given name. People like your teachers and maybe your boyfriend or girlfriend knew, but no one else knew you by any other name, and if they did, most of them never used it.

My first cousin, whom I refer to as my rich cousin told me how he went to enlist for the military. He listed the names of close friends and relatives who knew him well as references. He said when the people were contacted, they all denied knowing him. No one knew him by the name on his birth certificate. Everyone knew him by Kyle. Kyle was certainly the only name I ever knew him by and I had known him all of my life. I never knew him as Jefferson. "*Jefferson?*" Everyone asked. "*I ain't ever heard of him,*" A favorite Uncle said. He failed his background check because no one knew him. He was much luckier the second time around. By then he had told everyone his given name. Everyone had nicknames. Some of the names I could identify with, but I could not understand the name Cooter. I understood my nickname. There was no question about it. Mama named me McKenzie Lee, and everyone knew me as Kenzie. That made a lot of sense to me. But what was up with this name Cooter? No one else in the family had an unusual name like Sizzie, whom Daddy called Cooter.

My father had always been a man who spoke very fast, and sometimes he stuttered. It didn't seem to matter to *Cooter*. When Daddy called her by her nickname, she knew exactly what Daddy was saying. I never asked Mama or Daddy about the name, but one-day Sizzie took it upon herself to explain the significance of such a funny name.

One day she asked Daddy where he got the name. Daddy explained, he had gotten it from her. He said, "When I looked down into your crib that day, and saw your smile and big bright eyes, I thought you were the cutest thing I'd ever seen. From that day on, I started calling you 'Cute un.' In other words, I thought you were one of the cutest young'uns I had ever seen, and the name just seemed to have fit you."

When she finished telling me the story, I smiled and smiled. It was one of the cutest stories I had ever heard. We all figured out eventually what Daddy was saying all of this time in a fast kind of way, "Cute One?" "Cute Un." Yes, this is what he meant, that my baby girl was a cute one! Yes, that was an eye opener for me and, all I could do was smile with amazement, "You are telling me that all of these years, Daddy was trying to say 'Cute One,'" and we all started to call her by her nickname once again *Cooter*.

Once Mama and Daddy started their family, it wasn't hard for her to conceive, however, she did experience some grief. Some time during the pregnancies, Mama lost one of her children, which was a baby boy. I don't remember if Mama said he was the first child she and Daddy had or the third child. I didn't want to remind Daddy of their loss. Even though many years have passed, I still find it difficult to talk about. I've heard the old folk talk about how sad it was to deliver a stillborn child. The thought saddens me.

Mama had three beautiful kids, almost back to back; they were only two years apart. She had her oldest child, Cooter; then Sarah Jean and then her baby boy, Joshua Jr. It seemed as if Mama and Daddy had it all planned. It also seemed that after the third child, they were finished with the babies; after all, neither Mama nor Daddy was getting any younger, and they had the ideal family, two girls and a boy.

Who Would Have Thought

It was years later that Mama and Daddy decided to have another child, and that child was *me*. Nine years after getting over the dirty diapers, cleaning up the spilled milk, and getting over the interrupted sleep, they did it all over again, just for me. I'm not sure if this was exactly how it happened, but it happened. I'm not sure if this was a good idea. Since Mama is no longer with us in body, I didn't want to ask Daddy. I didn't want to put him on the spot like that. Besides, I had been asking him a lot of questions lately. I wanted to give him a break, and on the other hand, I wasn't sure if I really wanted an answer. The knowledge of my existence was disturbing for Joshua Jr. There wasn't any doubt about how he felt about me. I was not well received I was told. This may have been a mark for life on me. Being the blessed and precious child to come nine years later may not have been a good thing after all. "Maybe the child would blossom," or "Maybe the child would become a burden." *I don't know* but I am certain that Mama and Daddy would say I was a blessing. Then maybe it was a thin line for Mama and Daddy. Nine years of marriage before becoming pregnant, then nine years after being finished and done, here comes another one. Who would have thought?

According to Mama, if Joshua Jr. had to choose, there may not have been any more babies. Mama always gave props to her baby of nine years. She bragged about how he was such a humble, sweet, and perfect child. I agreed with her; he was a nice, humorous, and humble child. I was crazy about my brother. He defended Baby Brother and me when the other kids tried to jump on us. He would go looking for our bike once they accidentally took off with it without our permission. But trying to understand that a baby was on the way was not good news to his ears.

He didn't get it. He couldn't grasp and fully understand the thought of another child, another person in the picture taking his birthright. It wasn't sitting very well with him and probably wouldn't have set well with me either. "What will my life be like, if I am no longer going to be the baby?" he must have thought. How can you ask a nine-year-old to understand something like this? Back in my day, a nine-year-old did not grow up as fast and knowledgeable and aware of things as the nine-year-olds today. He cried. Whether Joshua Jr. was crying because he didn't want to give up his rights of being the baby, or whether he feared the workload that was about to be placed upon him, no one seemed to know. Mama said the only thing that consoled him was her promise and the promise of Auntee that the baby would be a boy. They told him this so often that having a new baby on the way was not so bad after all. His disappointment had become excitement. He had much anticipation. The thought of having a little brother turned out to be a good thing, even if it meant giving up his birthright of being the baby. The thought of having a baby brother to play with, and one who would look up to him, made things much easier·

for him. I can only imagine how his days went, thinking and planning on all the fun he would have with his little brother. Little brother would learn to skate, ride a bike, play sports, play in the band, and do all the things that big brother did. It must have been the shock of a lifetime the day the baby was born. Mama and Auntee were unable to keep their promise. There's no doubt that his mind must have been blown away when Mama came home from the hospital with a little baby girl. I'm sure his brown eyes must have turned red. The little brother he had waited and hoped for turned out to be a little girl; what a surprise. It was definitely a surprise but more of a disappointment. I am sure he questioned why Mama and Auntee had broken their promise. As beautiful as his little sister was, he was disappointed. Mama said the disappointment didn't last for long; in just days Joshua Jr. was enjoying his bright-eyed, big-eyed little sister. It didn't take nine more years for Mama and Daddy to try this thing again. Four years later they happened upon another. This time it was that baby boy that they had promised Joshua Jr.

Feeling Fear As A Child

I always feared. I feared the daytime, I feared the nighttime. I feared the lights on and I feared the lights off. I'm not sure if it was fear that I feared or if fear existed deep down inside of me. Even when I was too young to worry, I worried. Somehow fear and doubt seem to have consumed me from the beginning. I feared the thought of my mom hurting. I feared she might cry again. Then on top of fearing her hurts, I feared everything else around me. I feared getting sick, I feared my mom getting sick; I feared what one thought of me. I feared the dark and the monsters that came along with the darkness.

I was not allowed to sit around adults when they were talking, but it never failed that I would overhear bits and pieces of their conversation. Whenever my parents would talk about someone they knew who was sick or suffering from an illness, I feared getting sick. I became so afraid; I could not sleep at night. I felt as though I was experiencing the same illness. I became sick. I would feel so sick that Mother would come to my room and sleep beside me until I fell asleep. Some nights Mother would tell me the story about Chicken Little who witnessed the sky falling down. Mama would go through the names so quickly when she told me the story that I never learned all the characters' names. All I could remember was Chicken Little, Henny Penny, and Turkey Lurkey. These were the characters in the story that my Mama told me. Whenever she would tell me the story, I would fall fast asleep. Sleep came so easily knowing that she was right there by my side. But whenever Mother would get up to go back to her bed, I would immediately wake up again. Many nights Mother would end up sleeping by my side just to make sure that I would be able to get a good night's sleep.

The next day when I awakened, I would worry myself again concerning the sick person that I had overheard Mama and the other adults talking about. Whatever they said was ailing the sick person they spoke about seemed to ail me. I never told Mama why I was afraid. Many times I do not believe I knew why I was afraid. It just seemed like fear and doubt was out to get me. I didn't share these feelings a lot with others. I'm sure if I felt afraid; I thought they were afraid also. I shared this information with Lynn one day. She lived two houses above where we lived, and we played almost every day. Lynn was not only a friend, but she was my cousin also. She seemed like a worry-free person. Whenever Lynn visited me, I would share with her sometimes how I thought my head or chest had been hurting like the person I had heard mama and the other adults talking about. I would ask her to look down my throat to see if she could see anything wrong with me. Sometimes it even felt like my stomach would hurt, just like the person I had overheard them talking about. Lynn would always tell me that nothing was wrong with me. She sounded convincing, too. She would tell me that that was just something in my head. She told me I shouldn't worry or think about crazy stuff like that. Whenever she said this to me, I felt fine. I would be able to play for hours without worrying that something might be wrong with me. But when night fell upon the earth, I would become fearful all over again.

I don't remember as a little girl whether or not my heart raced or my throat closed up or blood rushed to my head in the way that it did as an adult. I only remember that when President John F. Kennedy got shot in 1963, Mama had to take me to the doctor. Then I remember Mama having to take me back to the doctor again six years later, when Dr. Martin Luther King Jr. was assassinated. The doctors never diagnosed me as being sick or ill, to my knowledge. Mama never told me that anything was wrong. She told me that the incidences were tragedies and that the country had suffered great losses. She did not give me any reason to believe that I was not okay. Back in the day lots of kids were scary cats as they called it. In some ways I am sure Mama thought this was normal. Some kids were just scary cats.

Innocent Neglect

One day Mommy, Daddy, my aunt, and other neighbors were sitting on the back porch, and I disappeared. Yes, I disappeared. I was about six or seven years old. Mommy, Daddy, and all of the neighbors would sit out on the porch in the evenings when the sun went down. It would be so hot during the day we couldn't wait till evening and night when it would cool off and the children would go outside to play. The parents would sit on the porch and watch the children. We could run all over the neighborhood because every family knew who lived in every apartment. Everyone felt safe. Somehow I had wandered away down the street when my uncle saw me and asked me to get into the car with him. I was excited to be going somewhere with my uncle, even though I didn't know where I was going and it never crossed my mind to ask Mother if I could go. I jumped into the car. He was my uncle and I knew he wouldn't harm me. I hopped into the car and we drove away. He took me to what would become one of the most fascinating and memorable places in my life. He took me to the fair—the carnival is what they call it now. I remember the bright lights, the Ferris wheel going round and round high into the sky, and for the first time I ate some good ole cotton candy. I don't know what made my uncle take me here, but it was great fun.

It must have been Mother's motherly instinct that told her I was missing. Soon Mother and every parent in the neighborhood were looking for me. They were yelling, shouting, and calling my name. "Has anyone seen Kenzie? Where did she go to so quickly?"

"I just saw her a minute ago," one neighbor said.

Another said, "She was just here."

When the word got to my grandmother, she was highly upset. My mother told me that Grandma was very upset with her. Mother said this was the only time she could remember her mother ever becoming angry with her. Grandma was so upset she accused Mother of not being

149

attentive to me. She accused Mama of sitting outside half watching them children. "What is wrong with you, Parrot? You better find my baby, or we are going to have to call the police." Grandma sometimes called Mama by her nickname, too. Shortly there after here came my uncle and me, he with popcorn and a soda and me with cotton candy. I can imagine the relief my mother and all the other mothers must have felt when they saw us getting out of the car. My mommy was so happy to see me; I think it was minutes later that she questioned my uncle about why he took her child away without her consent. My grandmother was so happy her baby was found. I knew how much she loved me. I knew Mama loved me too, but my grandmother's love was so special and it meant so much to *me*.

Section II School Days

Attending Grade School

Going to school as a child was a great thing at first. I loved it. We only had one big school. Classes started from kindergarten and went through the twelfth grade. Age and classification were the only things that separated us, and an imaginary line in the hallway that showed where the little kids section was cut off. Our classrooms were at the front of the long hall; depending on which door you entered. The junior high students were in the middle section of the long hallway, just past the high hump in the middle of the hall. I liked the high hump; it was like a thrill hill. It was one of the highlights when going to the cafeteria. We knew we were close to the lunchroom once we crossed over the high hump. And just before we got to the exit doors we would turn to the left, walk down all the stairs and into the big lunchroom we would be. The high school students had all the other classrooms. Before you reached the big exit doors, you could turn right and go up another hallway. The high school students had classes up that hall also. Just before the end of the hallway, was the principal's office. It was on the left hand side. I loved the school before it was taken away from us and the name changed.

My First Performance

I will never forget my fist experience of having to perform. I was seven years old and in the second grade. I had to go on stage to say a poem. My teacher saw something in me that others hadn't discovered yet. I was bright. Any poem or speech that I had to learn, I learned it quickly. When I observe little kids today, I see the same brightness in them;

the brain sitting on ready and receptive to receive all types of learning. I'm amazed how sharp and quick their brain is. If there is someone to teach, they are ready to learn. It saddens me when one doesn't get the opportunity for various reasons to be taught. The sad thing is, if around age four or five, the child has not gotten it, the road ahead is going to be rough and difficult. But the good thing is that it is never too late!

I enjoyed going to school until one day I got my feelings hurt. The teachers sponsored a program for the elementary class. I was one of the students selected to be on the program to do a poem. I will never forget how my cousin and my other classmates and I were so excited about being on stage in front of a large audience. We had practiced reciting our poem over and over again to each other so many times that we knew each other's poem by heart. Lynn's poem was called "The Swing." I remembered so much of her poem; it's a wonder that I didn't mistake it for my own. I will never forget my poem either titled "My Shadow," written by Robert Louis Stevenson. I still remember the poem as if it were yesterday when I had to recite it to the huge audience.

The day before I was supposed to say my poem, Mama combed my hair to make me look pretty. She laid out my outfit the day before so that there would be no problem with me getting dressed the next morning. I wore a pretty yellow sunshine dress with what Mama called a *cancan*. A cancan was starched stiff, slip-like underwear that you wore to make your dress stand out far away from your legs and your body. I remember feeling so pretty until the show began.

When the show began, I was excited about walking on the stage in front of such a huge audience. There were lots of people sitting out in the bleachers. I walked out on the stage and began reciting my poem.

I recited my poem very loud and clear just like Ms. Bell, my second-grade teacher, had told us to do and I got a standing ovation. All of the teachers and the other kids clapped loud and long. I was happy. I felt good and smart, just like a little girl who had just done a marvelous job. The attention I got, the claps, and the standing ovation, made me feel great. I can hardly explain the feeling of excitement and love that I felt. But the moment of fame did not last very long, because later that day, my spirit was broken, and the feeling of love and appreciation disappeared. The thrill turned into a fiasco when we were asked to perform again by our teacher for the high school students. We were asked to recite our same poems for the big kids, and this is when the hurt fell upon me like heavy raindrops.

I had rehearsed again. I looked in the mirror, patted my hair, looked down at my pretty, shiny black patent leather shoes, and made sure that my big bow in my hair was on the braid that Mama had put it on before I left home to go to school. I felt pretty and brave all over again. In my mind, I thought the second time around would be much easier. I thought the second time around would be much better. What went wrong? Before I went out to say my poem, Lynn did hers; she did a good job and got handclaps and yells. Then Vanessa went out to recite her poem; she did a great job and everyone clapped and yelled. Last but not least, they called my name, and I went out to say my poem. Before I could get through the first few lines of the poem, everyone started to laugh. The big students were laughing so loud; I didn't get the chance to finish my poem before I ran off the stage in tears. I didn't know why they were laughing so loud and hard at me. I loved my poem, and I wanted to share it with them. The poem went something like this:

I have a little shadow that goes in and out with me, and what can be the use of him is more than I can see. He is very, very like me from the heels up to the head; and I see him jump before me when I jump into my bed.

(Robert Louis Stevenson)

For years I remembered that moment like it was yesterday. I was not sure if the audience heard any of my poem, because they were laughing so loud. It was a *Carrie* moment for me, thinking back. I couldn't understand. "What on earth could have been so funny? Why were they laughing at me?" I wondered. I looked out into the audience, and I saw Joshua Jr. Everyone was laughing except him. He just sat there, and when my eyes caught his, he bowed his head down and tucked his chin to his chest, and only God knows what he must have been feeling. He was probably feeling more hurt for me than I was feeling for myself. I'm sure he felt embarrassment and shame for his little sister. I think he wanted to cry for me. I took off running from the stage. I ran so fast off the stage, I left imaginary dust behind, but I still got a standing ovation.

Joshua Jr. did not share this experience with Mama, and neither did I. I knew he had not.

If Joshua Jr. had told Mama about this incident, the big kids would have never had the opportunity to laugh at an innocent kid again. Even though Mama was a sweet lady, she was a lady who stood up for what she believed in. Mama would have gone to the school and spoken with the principal and demanded an explanation as to why the big kids were acting like a bunch of little kids. It may have been a good thing had Joshua Jr. told Mom about how the big kids were acting, but he probably wanted to get over that experience as much as I did. The lesson learned is we must go on. As long as we have a support team in our corner we will be able to go on. It is good that we support and encourage our children.

Becoming Independent

Many days Mother would not be feeling well. She didn't seem to have the energy that she once had. Some days her energy level would be so high she could work all day, nonstop. And other times her energy level would be so low, she barely felt like walking through the house. She managed to do what she had to do, but it was obvious that she was not feeling well. It is so ironic how my life seems to parallel Mother's. Many days and probably more days than Mama, I didn't feel like getting out of bed. "My Lord, where did all my strength and energy go?" I wondered. Many days I didn't know what to do with myself once I was awake and had forced myself out of bed. I would desire to clean up the house, throw out some old clothes or papers that I knew I no longer needed, but I could not push myself to do it. I could hardly push myself to do anything. I would spend the whole day planning. There were times I had letters that needed to be mailed, and I didn't have the willpower or energy to walk to the mailbox. There were days I needed to go to the bank and check the status of my overdraft account, but I had no willpower; nothing would get me energized to take care of the important business that I needed to take care of. I procrastinated. Eventually and by the grace of God the Almighty, I always managed to meet the deadlines on whatever it was I was putting off.

When I turned ten, it seemed Mother's energy level fluctuated. She did things differently, when it came to preparations and organization.

She would plan and prepare in advance for what needed to be done. She would have Auntee braid my hair the night before school, and tie a scarf around my head so that I would not frizz it up. She laid out my school clothes the night before, and when morning came, it was not hard to get dressed for school. Everything seemed easy as long as I didn't have to see Mama cry. I liked it when Mama and Auntee would laugh and talk. I liked it when I closed my eyes at night and would wake up to hear Mama and Daddy talking. I was happy that I had not seen Mama cry in a long time. I hoped that she would never have to cry again.

I had begun to do my own hair. I thought I was a big girl. It probably looked a mess most of the time, but it was the best I could do. Trying to comb and style my own hair was a major catastrophe. I didn't have braids or a perm. It was difficult because my hair was so soft and fine, and I couldn't keep it from springing back to the roots once I pulled it away from the scalp. I worked with it and worked with it and learned how to operate with it.

Mother would go back to bed some mornings, after she got Baby Brother and me up to get dressed for school. Daddy would be in the kitchen cooking breakfast. Some mornings Mama got up to have breakfast with us, some mornings Mother didn't feel like it. On days when Mother wasn't feeling well, she would always make sure that Baby Brother and I came by her bedroom to give her a big kiss. She made sure that she knew what we were wearing before we left home to go to school. Mama said it was good to know what your children were wearing before they left home. We would give Mama a big fat kiss before walking outside to go to school. Cisseley would be waiting outside in the driveway and the three of us walked to school together. I always escort Little Brother to his class.

Life for Little Brother was different. Not only was he Mama's baby, he was also my baby. I made sure that he got to his first-grade class safely. I made sure he arrived home safely to Mama; after all, that was her baby. Although no one did this for me, I would make sure he carried his books home from school, and I questioned every day whether or not he had homework. No one ever questioned if I had homework, or how my day at school was, except for my Grandmother. I'm sure my parents assumed I was just like them, naturally smart and intelligent. But I made sure Baby Brother got everything he needed out of the books.

At the time I didn't realize what role I was taking on. I just knew this was my Little Brother, and I had to do everything I could for him. This just came natural. Neither did I realize that Mama and Daddy paid little attention to my schooling. As long as they didn't hear anything bad coming from the teacher, they assumed everything was fine. What they did not realize is that by moving into our new home, and me going to a new school, was a bad thing. It was a bad thing because none of the teachers knew me that well. I was free from even attempting to study from that time on.

The Year of Integration

The first year of integration for me was in 1969. I am sure lots of people were happy and excited about this. I can not say how I really felt; going to an all-black school would have been just fine for me. Sooner or later, the teachers would have realized that my concentration level was off and would have begun to wonder what was wrong with me. Sooner or later, one of the teachers would have contacted my parents to have my head or body examined. Back then, that was just the way it was. Teachers took an interest in you. It was more important for you to learn than anything else. They had a reputation and a certain kind of love for you—a neighborly love that made you want to do well, that made you want to grow up and be someone proud, and to make someone proud of you.

Integrating the schools only made it easier for me to give school and homework less thought. The only worry I had before school integration was the teachers who knew my parents. If the teachers had ever written home to my parents about me, that would have been enough for me to think about books and try to start studying and focusing. Since the schools were integrated, I knew that none of the white teachers knew my parents, and probably didn't care to know my parents. Therefore, I had nothing to worry about as far as getting into any trouble.

One day in my math class, I could not focus. I was sitting at my desk and darkness seemed to overshadow me, and I began to cry. I had a lot on my mind, which was not unusual. Most times I worried all of the time. I worried about everything and anything. I worried because none of the little boys found me to be attractive. I worried about my legs being so skinny; I worried if I would have to wear a dress and show my legs and everyone would laugh at me. I wanted a boyfriend. All of the other girls had boyfriends, or some boy was always trying to walk them to their lockers or run behind them like honeybees. I resented the fact that none of the guys paid me any attention. I can't be sure if this is totally true, but it is what the little voice told me. I always had something in life to worry about. I worried so much I didn't have any room left inside of my brain to concentrate, especially in my math class. The little voice was always steps ahead of me. If ever I could learn how to figure in my head, I wouldn't have had time to worry. Something about being able to add, subtract, and divide—all of those calculations in the head—leaves very little room for worrying much about anything else. I could never understand the concept of fractions and dividing, and I sometimes got confused with adding and subtracting. "What on earth was she talking about up there?" I wondered. I was terribly confused and frustrated. All I wanted was to sit quietly in class and learn the math; instead I cried. I laid my head on my desk and began to cry as silently as I could. I cried and I cried, and I could not stop crying. The other students finally noticed I was crying and looked at me as if they wanted to know what was wrong with me, but the teacher paid me no mind. When someone brought it to her attention that I must not have been feeling well, she finally noticed. When she noticed, I was crying uncontrollably. She didn't seem to care and she didn't seem concerned. She came to my desk and asked me to leave the class and go to the principal's office. She didn't ask what was wrong. She took no interest in what could have been hurting or bothering me. Her name was Ms. Pratt. I will never forget Ms. Pratt.

She was a short white lady. She had short, stiff, white hair, which always stayed in place. It was stiff as biscuit dough. Her hair was so stiff that a strong wind could not blow it out of place, but the style fit her. She had brown, blue, gray, or green eyes; I think you call it hazel. Ms. Pratt never smiled. She talked, but not to me. She liked P. J. He often said she was a good teacher, in his opinion. But he was also a lover of math. He understood all of that figuring, and adding this number to that number to get this number. It was fun to him. I was too naïve to think she might have been prejudiced. Besides, I thought there were just good people and bad people. It never dawned on me that I might have been just a little colored girl in school who was disrupting her class. It never dawned on me that she didn't care whether I learned or didn't learn. All I know is that she wanted me out of her class.

I got up and went to the office as I was instructed. When I got to the office, I did not know what to say. I didn't know what reason to give the principal for my being in his office. I was in tears and I could not pull myself together to talk to him. He paged Ms. Pratt and requested her to come to the office. She came to the office and told the principal, Mr. Lacer, that I was disrupting the class. She said I was crying while she was trying to teach the class. He did not ask her why I was crying. No one seemed to care if I was sick or in trouble. The principal got mad at me, and I got angry with him, because like Ms. Pratt he did not question why I was crying. He told me I was expelled from school. I cried again, but this time my crying was not silent. I cried louder and louder, then cried out and told him it was fine, I didn't have to come to his school anyway! I accidentally kicked his desk when he told me this, and walked out of the office. I walked away crying furiously. I was afraid. I was afraid because I knew when I got home; Mother was going to put a *whupping* on me out of this world. But I kept right on walking. I tried to reason between the tears and the fears of my mother and the thought of this man telling me something crazy like not being able to come back to school ever again. I could not make any sense of it. It was the middle of the school day, and I knew I could not go home right now. I could not begin to imagine what Mama would have thought, had I walked into our house before the end of a school day. I kept walking, but I did not go home. I could not let Mama know I had been expelled from school. I knew she would skin me alive. That is what the old folk called a good spanking back in the day. I walked across the street headed toward my aunt's house, which was only a few feet from the school. I knocked on the door, and my first cousin Dottie let me in. I could tell from the look on her face that she was concerned about me. I could tell by the look in her eyes she was baffled and wondered why I had come home from school early with tears in my eyes. I was tired of crying by now, and I was beginning to rationalize things; I felt like I had been mistreated. Dottie must have felt my pain. She had really changed a lot. It was funny how Dottie was standing in my defense today. She used to baby-sit Baby Brother and me when we were smaller. I used to dread going to Aunt Claudia's house because of Dottie. She was so mean. She used to spank me all of the time. She would spank me for getting off of the sofa to stand on the floor. I did not understand what was so bad about getting off of the sofa and standing on the floor, and walking into the kitchen. I did not know what was so wrong with getting off of the sofa and walking to the front door to look outside. When Baby Brother and I would ask her why did we have to sit for so long, she would say, "because, I said so." "Dottie used to be so mean," I thought to myself. That wasn't the only thing that she used to do. When she cooked, she made us eat. The one thing that I hated the most was the one thing she cooked every day it seemed. It was rice. I disliked rice so much. I didn't like the way it looked. I didn't like the way it tasted, and I didn't even like the way it smelled. I hated it. It wasn't until I got married, went across the water, and sampled some Chinese rice that I realized it could look and smell, and taste differently. I was still not too fond of it. But I liked the way it smelled. I liked the smell of onions, and peppers, and gravy or sauce mixed up in it. I wasn't sure what to call it at that time gravy or sauce but it accented it so much. It didn't taste anything like the rice I had tried to swallow when I was a kid. But Dottie tried hard to make me like it. I would sit at the table and stare at the hot rice steaming on my plate, trying to figure out how to get rid of it without eating it. Dottie would sometimes sit directly across from me to make sure I ate every bite. Baby Brother wasn't any better than I, when it came to eating and liking rice. Because what ever I liked he liked, and what ever I didn't like, my Baby Brother didn't like. He got away with not eating his rice most times, because he was the baby. I am sure Dottie didn't want to spank Mama's little baby too often. But I on the other hand, had it rough. I would put the rice on my fork, put it into my mouth, and hold it for as long as I could. Sometimes, I would gag. Sometimes I would wait until Dottie left the kitchen, and then I would spit the rice out of my mouth into my hand, and to the garbage can I would run. I would run to the garbage can as quickly as I could before she got back. Once she entered the kitchen, she would look on my plate and instinctively know what I had done. She wouldn't say a word; instead she would walk out of the kitchen and into the living room. She would get the skinny black belt, which hung across the backside of the sofa and whup me. She would whup me across my legs as I sat at the table. She would then spank me when I got up to leave the table. I guess she enjoyed spanking me. But today I was a big girl. I was really too big to be getting spanked by anyone, even Mama.

I explained to Dottie, who had graduated years earlier. I told her what I had just experienced. She was shocked and furious. She did not feel I had been treated fairly either. She walked straight to the telephone to phone Mama. I begged her not to tell Mama, and she immediately hung up the phone. I knew Mama would find out, and I wanted to be the one to tell her. Dottie promised she would not mention it to her. I stayed at my Aunt Claudia's house until three o'clock in the afternoon. It was time for school to get out, and I ran outside and waited for my friends, Naomi and Cisseley, to get out of school so we could walk home together just as we always did. When they got closer to my aunt's house, I ran and met them and we walked home together. By now they had heard the news of what had happened to me in school. I am sure they were wondering what I was going to do. I could not elaborate much on what I was going to do. I was still afraid of what Mama was going to do to me. They were afraid for me. We journeyed on home together.

By the time I got home from school, I had almost scared myself out of the fear. I walked into the house and I was surprised, because I was not scared anymore. I went into the kitchen where Mama was, and I began to tell her what had happened to me in school. She listened, and I knew she heard the whole story, but the part that stood out in her head the most, was the fact that I had been expelled from school. Mama was upset. She was not hearing it, and she was not going to stand for it. No, she was not hearing that anyone was kicking her child out of school for crying. Mama asked, "Were you fighting?"

"No, ma'am"

"Were you fussing?"

"No, ma'am."

"Bad wording or anything like that?" She asked. I told her no to all of the questions, and I told her the truth. "Were you goofing off to keep from doing your work?"

"No, ma'am" I knew in my heart I had done no wrong. I knew in my heart that the fear I felt before I arrived home from school that day dissolved because I had done no wrong. I had not done anything bad enough to deserve the kind of punishment the principal was inflicting upon me. I explained to Mama. I told her why I was crying. Mama was still upset. She was upset by the reaction of the teacher. She did not understand why the teacher acted in the manner in which she did. Mama said, "Okay, don't worry about it, baby, we will take care of this tomorrow. I will find out more about what happened, so you can run along," she said.

I was relieved. I was so happy that my Mama did not spank me. I was so happy and shocked that she did not scold me. This was unusual for Mama. Normally, if an adult told Mama I had been bad or misbehaved in any way, Mama would take their word, and I would get spanked. It was useless for me to try and explain my side of the story. She would make me go out front and get a nice switch from one of our two plum trees, and she would skin me alive. I could not believe Mama was not going to beat me. She waited for Daddy to come home from work, and she talked it over with him; Daddy, being the quiet man that he was, listened. He apparently thought it was a good thing that Mama was going to take care of this the next day.

The next day when Mama had gotten me up to get dressed for school, she got dressed for school also. Since Daddy had to go to work, Mama asked Daddy to take us over to Aunt Claudia's house while we waited for eight o'clock to come for school to open. When eight o'clock came around, Mama and I were at school in the principal's office. I do not know what Mama said to the principal, and I do not know what he said to Mama. All I know is that Mama shook his hand and walked out of the office, and my homeroom teacher walked to the office to escort me back down the hall and back into my homeroom. I was in school and in class the same day. Ms. Pratt never picked on me again or singled me out.

The Lost Years

I guess you can say I was lucky, whatever that means. If escaping your homework assignments and passing through your most important stages of life, without ever realizing or knowing that it would one-day come to haunt you, then I was lucky. Sometimes I can't believe that I graduated from high school. It is even more amazing to believe that I would later graduate from college. God is good. Had it not been for God on my side, where would I be?

I never remember taking books home from school to study. I never remember being able to focus long enough to concentrate on what I was supposed to be studying for. All I remember doing was daydreaming. I daydreamed a lot because it was the only way to relax my mind. Whenever I was not daydreaming, I listened to music. I loved music. I chose sitting in my room listening to music and writing poetry over going out with my friends at times. I chose to sit in my room, listen to music, and dream about the beautiful life that I would one day have. I did not concentrate on school and studies any. I didn't know how to concentrate, and I didn't know how to study. The ones who cared enough about me, making sure I studied, were no longer around. After moving and leaving D.A.Smith High School. I felt like I was on my own.

<u>Jokes about a Spanking</u>

Sometimes my friends would kid me about getting a whupping. Cisseley and Valeria never got whupping. I never saw their moms whip either one of them. They never told me about any whuppings that they ever got either. They also kidded me about being able to hear my mother's little bitty voice whenever she called me. It amazed them that a lady with a little bitty voice like Mama's could whup me so hard. They used to wonder how she could even fuss. They kidded me about always being able to hear her call my name when it was time for me to come inside. No one around me could hear her, but I knew my mother's call. I knew that little bitty voice anywhere. Her voice was so little that her nieces, nephews, sisters, and brothers all called her Parrot, the nickname was given to her by her parents for speaking so softly. Sometimes they would put a handle on it and say, "Aunt Parrot;" sometimes they would just call her Parrot.

Another School Experience

It seemed I was becoming more and more disconnected with school, disconnected with learning, and really confused. The things that I did may have been a silent plea for help, or maybe a plea for special attention. Honestly, I don't really know what was going on with me. I won't make any excuses, but looking back, I think I needed some of Grandma's love. Maybe I was just becoming bad. Like I said, I really don't know. On this particular day, I have to assume I was miserable. This is just how life is supposed to be, miserable. People mistreat you if you don't look a certain way, people mistreat if you don't talk a certain way, and with all of that in mind, I treated myself the worst. I unconsciously longed for attention, so maybe attention is what I needed on this particular day.

This was the first year of integration. I still was not studying. I was still not focusing. No one had noticed my poor studying habits, and no one had noticed how poorly I continued to do in school. Basically, I went through the day going through the motions. This was not the first day of class, but it was the day the teacher decided to test us on our knowledge. She gave us a test, and of course, I had not studied. I have to assume that she had given us chapters to read and maybe even an outline to study by. Since studying was not my thing, I had no idea what the test was about. I had no idea what the answers were to any of the questions. I felt dumb.

I felt stupid. I felt ignorant. "What am I supposed to do with this test?" I thought. "Why is she testing us anyway so soon? Is she doing this just to make me look bad or what?" I didn't have answers to any questions, hers or mine. I studied the paper she had just handed out. I looked down at it, not knowing where to begin. I looked at each question, not knowing the answer to any of the questions, and then an idea came to my head. I was getting scared because time was running out, and I knew I needed to get started with the test. I looked around the classroom, and everyone seemed to be answering the questions to the test. Me, I did not know where to begin. I felt so left out. I felt like I must have been the only dummy in the classroom. I had to do something, and I had to do it quickly because class was only going to last for one hour. I put my name on the test paper and began answering all of the questions. I looked around the classroom again, and I began to fill in the blanks with the names of every one of my classmates. If the question was "What is the name of the sea that crosses over ___?" I put the name "Melanie" in the blank. I went down each row and put everyone's name that would fit into the blanks to answer all of the questions. Then I was done. I was ready to turn in my test paper. I tried to wait until almost everyone in the classroom had turned in their test, then I turned in mine. I could only imagine what Ms. Jane would do when she got to my test. I could only imagine what was going to go through her mind. The thoughts of what her reactions might be scared me more and more. I wished I had some other way of dealing with this situation. I wanted to go home. I wanted to cry. I wanted to disappear. But we still had a few more minutes left in class before the bell rang, so all I could do was wait. I had hoped that by the time I turned in my test, the class would be dismissed and Ms. Jane would not get the chance to see me in class after she read over my test. I was afraid because I didn't know what would happen to me if she went over my test while I was still in her classroom. I didn't know if she would find it funny, or if she

167

would think I was insane, or if she would spank me. It never crossed my mind that she would call my mother, because I didn't think she really knew that much about me or my parents. But the truth is, she did know them, and she knew them better than I thought she did. I didn't know if she would think I was being a smart aleck or a big dummy. She sat at her desk and began reviewing some of the papers, checking to see who had studied and who had not. I watched her as she went through each test, one after the other. My heart had started to race, and fear must have been all over my face. I knew that whenever she reached my paper, I would be able to tell without the shadow of a doubt by the expression that would show on her face. I knew she would do something out of the ordinary; the problem was I didn't know what she might do.

When she got to my paper, I knew it was mine. "Oh my God, what am I going to do?" I thought. She stopped and stared at the paper and held it in front of her much longer than she had any of the others. I began to shake in my boots. I was even breathing louder and harder. I wanted to get up and run out of her classroom, but I knew better than to do that. I would have gotten myself into some serious trouble had I done that. When she finished reading over my test, she looked up at me and said, "McKenzie Lee." I didn't answer her. She held the paper in front of her and began reading it aloud to the class. Some of the students laughed out, and some had a funny look on their face. All of us were afraid of Ms. Bettye Jane. Like me, they were so afraid of Ms. Bettye Jane, the students did not know if they were supposed to laugh or cry for me. When Ms. Bettye Jane finished reading my answers aloud, she called me to her desk and asked me to sit in the chair right beside her desk. She asked me two questions: "Do you want it in your hands or across your lap?" I held out my hands, but I could not stand the pain, the stinging, and the hurt she was inflicting on me. It was hurting really, really bad. Every time she would reach up and come down with that black rubber strap, I would jerk back my hands and cry. Since this didn't seem to be working, she reached down and spanked me across my legs. I tried to hold back the tears and the loud cries, but the beating was too painful to hide. I hated to admit it, but her paddling felt worst than Mama's did. Ms. Jane never used a regular paddle, like most teachers. She spanked her students with the black rubber from a car tire. It was thick, long black rubber that stung more with each hit. It hurt so badly that when I cried out, my classmates didn't laugh. What I thought would turn out to be funny turned out to be disastrous. Then I was sent to the office, and this time I knew I had done something wrong. I was kicked out of her class for three days and made to sit outside on the breezeway as punishment. No one ever told my Mama about the incident as far as I knew, because I would have been in hot water and beaten again and again. Mama didn't play when it came to discipline.

I hated the thought of Mama's spankings. Mama's spanking sometimes felt just as bad as Ms. Bettye Jane's did. She always made me go out in the front yard to get my own switch from the plum tree, which grew directly in front of hers and Daddy's bedroom window. A few times I would go and pick the littlest switch I could find, but I quickly learned that was not the thing to do; that only made Mama angrier, and she would go outside and pick one of her own. She always picked the biggest and strongest switch to spank me. It seemed as if she whupped me until she got tired. Sometimes she would spank me so long, I would finally reach up and grab the switch and break it, but oh Lardy, I even stopped doing that. Whenever I did that, Mama would go outside, get another switch, and start whupping me all over again. There were no escaping Mama's whuppings. I didn't want to experience Mama's old-fashioned spanking anytime.

When we moved to our new home, we didn't have big plum trees at first. It took a long time for those little trees to grow, but Mama had a substitute. She whupped Baby Brother and me with Daddy's belt. One day she whupped me so hard, I cried to the top of my lungs. Actually, this wasn't one of the times that it hurt the most. It was one of those times I didn't feel like I deserved to be whupped. I screamed so loud that Granny, the next-door neighbor, came down to our house, knocked on the door, and asked Mama if everything was all right. My prayer had been answered. Mama had to stop whupping me to entertain Granny for the short time she visited. A few minutes later they were out front in the flower garden, looking at flowers. "Thank you, Jesus," I said to myself.

Apparently, it never dawned on the teacher that I might have needed special attention; by this time teachers didn't seem to care about kids in the same manner. I cannot say that Ms. Bettye Jane did not care. She beat me long and hard enough, she cared about something. I never answered questions to her test again. When I did not know the answers, I left the questions blank. I knowingly had done something wrong this time. I knew I had been bad. I was never going to tell Mama about this incidence, even after Mrs. Bettye Jane beat me so hard. I had marks on my legs days after the beating, but I hid them from Mama.

Taking the School Away from Us

Somewhere in the course of my school days, integration took place and we no longer had our own school. They took it away from us and changed the name. The name changed from D. A. Smith High School, which was named after the late and great Mr. D. A. Smith. He had been the black principal of our school for many years. Somehow in the course of integration the school's name changed from D. A. Smith High School to Ozark Junior High. It was no longer a school for all grade levels; only the seventh-, eighth-, and ninth-grade students attended. This was not a good thing. A part of history had been taken away from us without any consideration in my opinion. It happened so fast that if you blinked, you would have missed what had just happened. We had to get our piece of heritage back.

My brother Joshua Jr. and others fought hard to regain our school's original name, and thank God, the name was changed back. I don't recall the names of all the others that participated in getting our school's name back, but thank God for all of you who stood up. I never really knew the details of how the transition took place; however it happened and I am glad it did.

Meeting the Gang

I had my friends back home and I didn't think I would ever need any more friends. There were eight of us. Initially there were five. We included the other three friends over a period of time after they began to hang out with us. The original five were the five of us who lived in the same vicinity. Cisseley and Valeria, they were my next-door neighbors. Naomi was my best friend. She lived about a mile away from me. Ebony was my best friend prior to her going to another school and meeting Valeria. I used to accuse Valeria of taking my best friend away from me. And then there was me. We were the group.

Precious, (Chocolate Doll) was my best friend also. She was my twin, my first cousin, and my best friend. She never became an official member of the group. She preferred to be a loner. Chocolate Doll did not live close to any of us. When we moved away from Smith Homes, they moved also. Uncle Toot and Aunt Mae Lee bought a nice house in the country. Actually, she lived about ten miles away. Chocolate Doll did not know Naomi, and Naomi did not know Chocolate Doll. But they knew of each other. We did not become the three best friends until we went to college, and Chocolate Doll met my new best friend. She was not pleased with this at all. Chocolate Doll had heard of Naomi, and she knew we were friends. She knew we went to the same school, but she did not know that Naomi and I had become best friends also. It shocked her to find out that Naomi knew as much about me as she did. She could not believe that I had shared all my secrets with her. She knew all about my dream boyfriends. She knew every guy I had a crush on. She knew if the guy didn't feel the same way about me, and how bad it made me feel. She knew my parents. If I was in a bind, Naomi would do whatever she could to help me out of the bind. If Naomi was in a bind, I would do whatever I could to help her out of the bind. We were true friends. We were such close friends that anyone who was my friend and not a friend of Naomi wouldn't dare say anything negative about her to me, and if anyone said something negative about me to her, I would definitely hear about it. I don't think anyone would have taken a chance of gossiping to me about her, and vice versa. It would have been like someone talking to Gail about Oprah. "Look! You don't talk about my friend," we would say. That is the way good old friends used to be. There was nothing like a best friend. Everyone needs someone they can share their joys and their sorrows with. Everyone does not rejoice in your joy, and certainly everyone does not feel your pain. If you have one friend today, consider yourself truly blessed. A true friend is hard to find; each year they become harder and harder to find because the world is changing. All of us were very good friends. We all knew each other's life stories. If I picked up the phone now and started talking to either one of them, there wouldn't be anything going on in my life that would be too embarrassing for me to share with any one of them. I can call Valeria, Ebony, Cisseley, or Naomi and not be too embarrassed to share with them the way my life is going. They would probably be disappointed. There was no doubt that if anyone out of the gang would succeed, it would be me. Especially with Cisseley, somehow I think she believed in me. She believed I could do anything. She never understood why I wasn't as successful as I should have been.

Even though we were all very close, we still had our closest friend out of the group when the group split. Naomi and I were best friends. Ebony and Valeria were best friends. Cisseley and Renee were close friends. Cisseley and I had a special kind of friendship because we were next-door neighbors. I was also her best friend. She was my ace in the hole. Since Cisseley and I did not define ourselves as best friends, we became cousins. One day we overheard our parents talking about how they thought we might have been related in some way, and that was enough for us; following that conversation Cisseley, Valeria, and I were no longer friends but cousins.

No one knew how lonely I felt on the inside, so having a best friend and the rest of the gang was all I felt like I had. Cisseley had other friends; sometimes she would hang tight with Renee, our other next-door neighbor, and because they played softball together, they had more in common. It was just a matter of fact that the girls who played sports got the guys. I didn't play sports and I had no guy. I tried a couple of times to play with them in Renee's backyard, but I could never hit the ball. I could never catch the ball, and I slung my bat when I swung at the ball. Everyone would get so mad at me for slinging my bat. If I ever hit the ball, it would go out in the field but only a little ways, and my bat would go swinging way behind me. It made the teammates so mad because they would all have to run way back to keep from getting hit by me with the bat. After a few laughs about me not being able to hit and me feeling like my legs were too skinny to wear shorts, I gave up. I was so caught up in the fact that my legs were too skinny and the boys were not going to pay much attention to me that I stayed inside while they played softball. Sometimes I would go outside and watch the game, but when the boys came around, I began to feel left out and I would go home and watch them through the window. But as soon as the game was over and the crowd fizzled, it would be Cisseley and me sitting outside in the driveway of our house laughing and talking.

I liked Renee, but I thought she was even stranger than I was. As much as we laughed and talked, Rene never seemed to let me inside her world. She never talked about the guys that liked her so much, she never talked about what she wanted to do when she grew up, and she never shared a lot of anything about herself. I know about as much about her today as I knew then, and it wasn't very much. She was very pretty, and the old folk used to say she was shaped like a Coca-Cola bottle. All the guys liked her. All of my cousins were crazy about her, and my big brothers, too. Whenever my cousins or guys talked to me, it was always about her. They wanted to know how to get her phone number, or they wanted to know if I could call her on the phone and ask her to come outside so they could get the chance to say hello to her. I didn't know any better, so I would get on the phone or walk down the street to her house and ask her if she could come outside to play. Sometimes they would get mad at me if I told them her phone was busy, or if her mom decided not to let her come outside. It was always the same ole thing, everyone wanting me to help them to get together with Renee or another one of my friends. I must have looked like a matchmaker to them. To this day, I still find myself in that same predicament, playing the hook-up queen. I suppose no one ever gave it much thought that maybe they should have been hooking me up with someone. It was fun and it was all a part of growing up. But when we grew older and it was time for us to go out on the town and get dressed to go to the club, it was all good!

It was during this time that Jeneen and McKendra Lou started to hang out with us. We knew each other from school. Jeneen was cool. She went with the flow, but McKendra was a mess! She was loud very loud. She always wanted to be the center of attention. It did not matter how far she had to go with her unfunny jokes it seemed, as long as all eyes and ears were on her. She loved embarrassing people. If we met someone new, especially a guy; she always had something bad to say about either of us. If she was not badmouthing me, she was badmouthing Naomi. She was a trip. She tried many times to embarrass Cisseley but it did not work. She would stand up to her, and they would go at it in front of the stranger. Naomi and I tried to be cool and sophisticated. We would wait until we were alone with her and question her, trying to understand why she did the things she did. It was always important for her to stress that she was Kenzie number one, and I was kenzie number two, because our names were so similar. But I knew who number one was. She was still the new kid on the block. Out of the presence of others, she was cool. She was so cool that I would forget how quickly she would change on us. The name-calling and ugly comments never stopped. Finally, Naomi cut her off and stopped speaking to her for several years.

My First Night at the Club

It was a long time before I got the nerves to go to the club. If my cousin Katie had not been persistent in persuading me to go, I might have missed out on a lot of fun. She told me how nice it was. She told me how much fun it would be if I went, and she even bet me that someone would ask me to dance. I was too afraid to go at first. Katie was a seamstress. She was always making beautiful outfits to wear. I remember when she made herself a pair of plaid elephant ears pants with a plaid jacket to match it. I thought the outfit was bad! I wanted her to make me one just like it. I promised her if she would sew me an outfit together like that, I would go to the club. In a few weeks I had myself a pair of plaid elephant ears and a plaid jacket to go with it. I hate to brag, but no one could tell me that I was not looking good in my new plaid, just-made outfit. I had confidence when I put on that outfit. The pants were very tight across the butt and thighs and extra-extra big down the legs. I didn't appear to be so skinny in the outfit. I thought it made me look fine. It certainly made me feel fine. I would look in the mirror and say to myself, "I am not as skinny as they say." I built up my nerves and off to the club I went that night with my plaid jacket and elephant ears pants. I knew I looked good!

I went to the club that night, and I will never forget the great fun I had. I danced, sang, popped my fingers, and had the fun of a lifetime. I even got some play! Yes, I did. I got eyes from the guys and dances, too. I let go of my fears for a minute and started having myself a good time until I started to get the feeling that everyone was watching me. I began thinking that they were probably saying to themselves that I couldn't dance well, or talking about how stiff I moved. I was afraid to move and

176

get down, but the main thing was I got asked to dance and I was on the dance floor sliding from left to right and right to left. I had lots of fun. But it was funny and kind of strange, that as close as I was to my friends; I didn't talk much to them about my feelings. Whenever I mentioned such to Naomi, she would say something like "Oh girl, stop tripping." She didn't take this concern of mine very seriously. But I thought about it all the time. I never felt like they thought I was strange. I never felt like they gave me much thought at all. But that wasn't true; Cisseley must have felt my pain. This did not sit well with me at first, because I thought I had learned to deal with my feelings until one day she chose to challenge me.

A Challenging Moment for Me

One day Cisseley took it upon herself to challenge me. She was my close friend, but I believe I was her best friend. I felt like I was always there for her. Sometimes I became very impatient with Cisseley because she was so reserved. I didn't know it was reserved then; I thought she was slow. But now I see she was observing. She spent most of her time with me. Besides, we were neighbors; we saw each other everyday. But I did not think she would challenge me. She was more reserved than I was, but very sociable. She played softball and ran track. She was into her sports. She knew lots of people, and she didn't allow anyone to get very close to her. She always acted older, even though we were the same age. I don't know if it was wisdom or instinct that made her challenge me.

I got the chance to ask her several months ago. "Cisseley, why do you appear to be quiet whenever you meet someone for the first time, and me on the other hand meet someone for the first time and start talking to them like I've known them for a long time?"

Cisseley looked at me and said, "Kenzie, I sit back and see what kind of person they are, and where they are coming from before I start flapping off at the mouth."

"So where did you get that? Did someone teach you to be that way?" I asked.

"No," she said. "I have always been that way." She was right about that. She had always been that way. She was a step ahead of the game, in my opinion. But I thought she had a lot of nerves challenging me, the so-called leader of the group. Yes, she called me out!

One day while we were sitting outside in the driveway, where we sat while our parents sat on the porch talking, she asked me a question that I had never thought about. "Kenzie," she spoke, all seriously. "Why do you try so hard to make people laugh?"

"Make people laugh?" I thought to myself.

"Why do you try so hard to be funny?" I could not believe she was asking me such a question. Why would someone dare tap in on my brain in that way? I thought long and hard to myself before I could speak a word. I didn't realize I tried so hard to make people laugh. I didn't know I tried so hard to be funny either. I could not believe she was asking me this. I asked her to repeat herself because I wanted to be sure I understood the question. I looked at her. I could not answer. She continued to question me. "Is it because you want people to like you? Are you afraid that if you do not keep people laughing all the time, they will not like you?"

"Where did this come from?" I asked myself. I could not believe she was asking me all of these questions. Even though we did not keep secrets from each other in our circle of friends, I could not answer the question. I did not know how to answer the question. Was she in some way feeling my pain? Was she prying deep inside trying to understand me? Did she sense my insecurity? Did she know that as much as I wanted to be in the crowd, I always stepped away from the crowd because I was afraid? Did she know that I feared letting others know who I was, because I feared they might not like me? How did she know so much about my inner feelings? For the first time in my life, I was speechless around one of my friends.

Taking the Challenge a Step Further

This wasn't the only time Cisseley challenged me. One time during the summer, I had gotten a job. I worked at the employment office. This was a prestigious job. I worked at the front desk, greeting people as they walked in, answering the phones, and pulling and filing files. If the customer was not a first-time employment seeker, I would pull their existing application, which was on file, and put it in the basket for an interviewer to review. If the customer was a first-time job seeker, I would give them an application, and ask them to fill it out, and then ask them to have a seat while I reviewed it for completion. I liked the job. I felt nervous and scared at times, but after all, I was a child, a young teenager. I thought I played my fear and anxiety off really well until the day Cisseley came to the employment office. She came to the office one day looking for a job. Being the reserved and slow person I thought she was, she observed me. She observed the fear in my face. She observed how much time it took me to give her the application to fill out, she observed the tension. Actually, she observed everything. I am sure she observed how nice and professionally I treated everyone, but she could not understand my tension and my fears. She could not understand how the big mouth of the group could be so afraid when it came down to performing. I thought

I was bright. Underneath all of my fears and doubts, I still felt like I was a smart kid. I challenged anything and anybody. Whatever I believed in or felt right about, I stood up for it. Despite my fears, I was never afraid to speak up and speak out. Even my friends gave me this much credit. But why was she questioning *me and my ability?* I knew it was because I was expected to do well. I knew it was because I was expected to be sharp and smart. I knew when she observed the fear and the anxiety in me; it did not register properly in her head. It was moments like these that made my life so difficult. It was moments like these that confused me and challenged me into becoming the bright and intelligent person I was born to be. I didn't know how to explain these feelings or express these feelings with anyone. I didn't know what they were. But it still interests me to this day that Cisseley had the nerves to ask. She wanted to know why I acted so nervous. She wanted to know why I seemed so afraid. She asked me things that no one else ever asked. It turned out that she was the wisest and smartest out of the group. I visited her a few months ago and tried to express what a great impact she had on my life. We never got the chance to finish the conversation, because I knew that one day soon I would be writing about her, and I wanted her to see just how much she impacted my life and what she meant to me as a friend. I never got the chance to speak with her again.

Hanging Out but Being Alone

Hanging out with my group of friends were some of my fondest memories. I never felt insecure. I never felt embarrassed. I never felt left out. If there was any such thing as a group leader, I considered myself that leader. I did not request to be the leader; all of the gang just kinda went with the flow. They knew who they were, so it did not matter if they stood out or not. We shared our deepest thoughts, feelings, and concerns with each other. We were all so close. It wasn't until we went our separate way that I realized how unique I really was. Yes, I was really unique. I did not socialize with anyone outside of the gang. I tried to socialize, but it didn't feel right. I always felt like I was supposed to act a certain way. My mind was constantly telling me I was not cool enough to hang with others. Sometimes it would tell me that I was not pretty enough, and because of that, people automatically disliked you. I was afraid that people wouldn't like me once they spent time around me. There was nothing wrong with me, but the little voice told me there was. I was paranoid. I was paranoid that if I didn't look happy and smile all the time, I was strange. I didn't know how people were really supposed to act, but I thought I was supposed to be liked by everyone. If someone didn't like me for whatever reason, I thought I had done something wrong and it saddened me deeply. Many times Naomi told me as we got older that I was arrogant. She told me I judged others too harshly. She said it was me. She said I was picky. She said I chose to deal only with certain people, the people I considered elite. She told me I classified people too much and if they did not act a certain way, I didn't accept them. She said I never took the time to get know a person before I called them out. I thought about these things being said to me, and a small part of me agreed with her, but I didn't dare admit it. It turned out that all of the negative things I thought about myself, I thought about others. I didn't like myself and I didn't like others. But the ironic thing about my negative feelings is that I thought I knew how to treat others. I knew I was supposed to treat people with kindness, respect, and love. This is what I was taught, and this was the only way I knew how to be. The desire to say negative things about others or make fun of them was never something that I did or thought about doing. The negative feelings I had were always about me. I needed to love me. I needed to ease up on myself.

At school Valeria, Naomi, Mattie, Doris, and Linda all had friends that they socialized with, and I only had two friends. My two friends were Alicia and Donna. Cisseley, hung with us most of the time. She knew lots of folk, but she didn't fit in well either. But when it came to her sports and the guys, she fit in well. But my other friends socialized with everybody. They could fit in with the crowd. They could laugh out loud, talk out loud, and just mingle with everybody. Hanging with my two friends was about as sociable as I got. I liked them, but they were oh-so-boring. It was interesting because everyone knew of me and I knew of everyone, I'm not sure if anyone ever noticed I was not a part of the crowd. Only I knew. Everyone liked me. Everyone knew I was intelligent. It didn't matter what grades were on my report card. I was naturally smart. I was born to be that way, and no one, not even the little voice, could take this away from me. But the little voice never stopped challenging me. As left out as I felt no one seemed to have noticed, and no one ever called me out of my name. And no one ever laughed at me because I had skinny legs. It was all in my mind.

The little voice was a powerful thing. At times it seemed to have had more control over me than I had over myself. Some times I felt so left out I wanted to be left all alone. There were many times I wanted to stray away from my only two friends. They were boring with very few exciting things to talk about. When the three of us were together at break, none of us knew what was going on around school. We didn't know what the others were talking about because we were out of the clique. I am not sure if Alicia and Donna felt the same way or not. Maybe they felt left out as much as I did and never talked about it. Cisseley would be with us on days she didn't have to go to the other school to take cosmetology classes. Sometimes I hung with Sonya and Brenda. They were boring too. I don't believe any of us had boyfriends, but at least they got looks from the guys. Guys flirted with Sonya. She was tall and skinny like me, but she was not as skinny as I was. Besides she had long hair, and she was light-skinned, and pretty. Donna swore she was pretty and that all of the guys liked her a lot. She had long pretty hair. She was not as tall as Sonya and I, but she was yellow and thought she was pretty. It just so happened that the one guy that I liked, she liked too. He was short, dark, and handsome. I was certain that he liked me, but she swore he liked her.

I liked him before the party, but after the birthday party, I liked him even more. He danced with me. He smiled at me as if I was attractive. It might have been because he asked me to dance at Lynn's birthday party that I fell in love with him. Yes, I went to the party. I did not want to go, I had to go. I had to attend the event because Mother would have thought something was wrong with me and discovered that I was a sad child. Not only that, the party was within walking distance, and I could easily slip away and go home without anyone missing me. The other reason I didn't have a problem going to the party is because the party was outdoors in the front yard. This was good for me, because if no one asked me to dance, no one else would notice. But someone did ask me and it was Thomas. He danced with me more than once, and when it was time for me to go home, he walked me to the door and tried to kiss me goodnight. From that day forward, I liked him. I wanted to be his girl. I don't know what happened between Donna and him, but when school opened back up in the fall, she was head over heels about him too. This made me so angry with her. I tried to tell her that I liked him, and I believed he liked me also, but it didn't seem to matter much with her. If she was so popular and well liked, why was she hanging with the boring group?

Admiring My Hometown

I can remember admiring downtown Ozark when I was a small child. It was a small town and everyone knew each other. If a person did not know you personally, someone they knew, knew you, and it made you feel like you knew the person, too.

Downtown was a square, and the tallest building downtown was the courthouse, which stood in the center of the square. Through a child's eyes, it also looked big. It was an old, big two-story white building. It might have been only one story, but it looked like a two-story building to me and in my head it was two-story. In the courthouse yard were big, tall, huge trees; tall, beautiful green trees all around the yard. Besides being big and beautiful, they provided excellent shade that kept us cool in the summertime. Most folk would go downtown and sit under the big huge trees on the weekend. Some of the folk sat around and talked, while others sat around and watched. The weekend was the only time that some of the folk got out. People came from the country where my parents grew up. They would come to town to visit other family members or sit and enjoy the downtown scenery, and some would shop. The weekend was just a time for everyone to come together. The country was only about ten miles from Ozark. The name of the country is Skipperville, Al. This is where Mama and Daddy grew up. Sizzie and Sarah Jean were born in the country. I used to kid them about being country babies and I was a city baby. I used to get a kick out of this.

We attended church in the country. We hardly got the chance to visit the city churches. Therefore, when I got older, I realized a lot of folk didn't know my parents or me as well as I thought they did, especially the younger generation. Then I realized that I didn't know as many people as I thought I knew. If I didn't go to school with their children and vice versa, it turned out we really didn't know a lot of people after all.

Daddy was never the pastor for the city churches. All of his churches were in the country just outside of Ozark. He pastored churches in Clayton, Al and Eufaula, Al then Clopton, Al; just to name a few. People knew of us, and most thought well of us. There wasn't any reason for anyone to think any other way. But I learned that everyone will not like you no matter whom or what you are. People in my hometown didn't seem to know at first that Daddy was an energetic man who had a wife that stuck by him religiously. Most of them had never heard Daddy preach or pray. Many of the people from Ozark had not even heard my mother speak. She was known for her great speaking skills, apart from being a Sunday school teacher, the president of the Women's Usher Board, a class leader, and later an ordained AME minister. She was a beautiful person in every way: in mind, soul, body, and spirit. But when Daddy retired from being a full-time pastor, he and Mama joined the city church in Ozark, an AME Church, and we became well known again in our hometown. I guess it is true, like the ole cliché goes, out-of-sight, out-of-mind. It seemed we were forgotten about until my parents reunited with the city church. When Mother became ordained, my sisters and I changed our membership from being a Baptist to an AME member just like Daddy and Joshua Jr.

I didn't know much about the history of downtown Ozark and the people. The most I knew was I was born there and it was my hometown. But Sizzie said when she was growing up; there was a colored side and a white side for people who sat around the courtyard. She said the colored sat on the backside, and the whites sat on the front. Some of the colored sat on top of their parked cars around the square, and some of us even sat on the curb. Since we had a car, most times we would sit on top of our car; that is when we weren't walking or running up and down the sidewalk. It was just fun in the sun. Some times we did our window-shopping and some times we even shopped for our Sunday wear.

My parents didn't share a lot with me or any of the children, as far as I know, about the racism that they experienced when I was growing up. What little I knew of their experiences, I heard when I was a full-grown adult. It's almost impossible for folk to believe how ignorant I was about racism, but I believe that my ignorance of racism must have been predestined by God to spare my life. When I was growing up, I felt like I was picked on enough by my own race and my own family and relatives, and that was more than enough. I'm not sure if I would have been able to humbly accept any further abuse. My head was loaded with negative thoughts, and the older I got, the less loved I felt. I'm not sure if my response to such reactions from mankind of a different race would have been well received. It's foolish to me. It's all foolish to me to believe that people blessed with a brain, and some commonsense, two-legged, two-handed, creatures could possibly be so different from each other. We all laugh. We all cry. We all hurt and we all feel good every once in a while. I'm not sure if I would have been able to keep my mouth shut when I was told to.

I didn't know that being colored meant we were supposed to act a certain way, think a certain way, and believe that we were less than human beings. For all I knew there were good folk and bad folk. Sometimes I got the good and the bad folk mixed up, like the times when we would go to the icehouse to get ice.

186

Trips to the Icehouse

Whenever we needed ice for some special occasion, we would go to the icehouse. Sometimes we stopped at the icehouse before going to church, and sometimes we would stop by the icehouse on our way home from church. If the pastor was coming to our house after church for Sunday dinner or for dinner after revival service, we always stopped. I found it amazing that whenever Daddy would pull up in front of the icehouse, a man would come out to greet him. Daddy would get out of the car and walk up the steps, and the man would rush outside and ask Daddy how much ice he needed. Daddy would tell the man exactly how much ice we needed, and he would cut the ice with a sharp pick and bag the ice up for him. I remember thinking how cool this was. I never asked Daddy why the man always came out to greet him. I thought he was being nice and helpful, and I was glad that we were getting quick service before Daddy even made it to the top of the steps. Sometimes I saw people sitting down on the inside eating. I never asked my parents why we never went inside to eat; I assumed we didn't have the money to eat out. I knew they were eating well because I could smell the fried fish, the crispy shrimps, the good ole hushpuppies and French fries because you could smell it the minute you hit the driveway. Besides, sometimes we even ordered fish from the icehouse, and then stopped by after church to pick it up. It was umm so good. I was happy we didn't go inside to eat ours, because many times Mama would have to pull the fish off the bones for us and mash it really well so that we wouldn't get choked on a fishbone. I was also glad we were not on the inside so that I could eat my food as quickly as I wanted too. I didn't eat very fast then like I do now; otherwise, I would need Mama to still pick the bones out of my fish for me. I have to personally thank God for fish fillet today. This way I get the chance to eat fish as often and as fast as I want to without worrying or thinking about a bone. Whenever we ate food from the icehouse, we always called ahead, and when we arrived, most of the time the food was hot and ready. If we didn't call in advance, it was okay because that nice man would be rushing outside to make sure he got our order and got our food out to us in a timely fashion. I liked the icehouse and I liked the way they always came outside to greet Daddy. It felt good being treated so well. Whether I felt good on the inside or not, it was good to know that there were good people in the world, especially at the icehouse.

One day Daddy pulled up in front of the icehouse and no one came running outside to meet him. We waited and waited and waited, but the friendly man did not come outside to meet us. I didn't know what was wrong. I asked Daddy why wouldn't he get out of the car and go inside to see what was wrong. Maybe the place was closed, perhaps no one saw us drive up. It never crossed my mind that maybe they were ignoring us. But Daddy patiently waited. Daddy didn't answer me; he just waited. It must have been okay with Mama because she didn't say anything either. We kept waiting for what seemed like a very long wait. It may have been only ten minutes, or it might have been longer. Whatever amount of time it took, it was a much longer wait than usual. I kept insisting on Daddy getting out of the car and kept begging him to go inside and make sure everyone and everything was all right. Daddy just seemed to ignore me. I could not understand for peace sake why Daddy didn't even acknowledge me speaking. I kept asking, and Daddy kept ignoring me. He didn't seem to care that this was aggravating me. After a while I suppose Daddy had also become aggravated. "Ahh, hush up Kenzie!" He said. I suppose Daddy became curious also about why no one had come outside to greet us, so he finally got out of the car. I could not understand why he hadn't gotten out of the car to go inside and get our food sooner. I couldn't understand why the nice man that always came outside to meet and greet Daddy had not come out to meet him yet. "Daddy, get out!" I hollered. "Daddy, go and see what is wrong!"

He finally looked in the backseat and told me to "be quiet, child, be quiet." He said in a demanding tone. He didn't raise his voice. One thing about Daddy—he didn't raise his voice often. It never dawned on me at the time that Daddy probably hadn't said anything to me sooner is because he really hadn't heard me. He was probably concentrating. He was probably trying to decide what he should do: "Should I sit here and wait, or should I drive away, or should I listen to my child? Should I get out of the car, walk up the steps, knock on the door, and wait for the nice gentlemen to come outside?" Daddy made up his mind and decided to get out of the car. Daddy walked up the steps like he always did, and just before he reached the top step, the man hurried outside to greet Daddy. I was happy that the nice man had finally come to greet Daddy, and he even brought our food to the door for us just like always.

It would be many years later that I learned that we were not being greeted. I learned we were being stopped because we were not welcome to come inside. Needless to say, we were not welcome to go inside of the icehouse; what a rude awakening, even as an adult. And if we were welcome, we were given no clue. Thank God for his love and favor. It is what kept Daddy and the family safe. I had no idea I may have been putting his life, our lives, in jeopardy because of hate, because of racism, and because of prejudice. It hurts me deeply. I cried silently for a very long time. I didn't want to ever go back to the icehouse. Even though the food was excellent, I had to be strong willed not to go back. It was sad to discover that we weren't getting any special treatment. The realization of that made me furious. I regretted the fact that we stopped there so many times to get ice. I regret the fact that we ate their good food knowing that we were not allowed to go inside. If we were allowed inside, we certainly did not know it. If we were allowed inside we certainly were not welcome. The strange thing about me is I spent so much time worrying about being accepted, worrying about living and dying, that I slipped in time and so much passed me by. I spent far too much time worrying about people liking me. I spent so much time daydreaming that I never knew what was really happening around me. I never knew what was happening in the world. It really frightens me when I talk to Little Brother and he tells me how he remembers signs being on doors, one for the colored and one for the whites. It frightens me because I was four years older than he was, and I should have noticed these things. It frightens me when I think back on my ignorance of not knowing. Naomi was different from me, somehow she knew. I am not sure how she knew; perhaps she saw a lot of things on television. I didn't watch television. Because I couldn't focus, I found it even difficult to follow the story line. Sometimes I would get so aggravated at Chocolate Doll and her siblings for watching television and enjoying what was going on, until I didn't know what to do. I became frustrated because I wanted to go outside and play, or I wanted to laugh and talk. Sitting still looking at that television screen required too much attention, attention that I did not have to give. I knew how much Naomi loved watching television. She loved all kinds of movies. She loved old movies. She loved new movies. She loved soap operas and action flicks too. I don't know for certain where her awareness of people came from. Perhaps it was because her mother was a businesswoman, self-employed and very successful. She was professional, articulate, and austere. She meant what she said, and she said what she meant. Perhaps Naomi's family shared with her things about other people, like those people who weren't too nice. Perhaps it was because of her father's experiences, serving time in the U.S. Army. I'm sure he shared stories with his wife and family about his experiences. He was such a great man. He was short, dark complexion, and like Naomi. He had lots of personality. I even learned a few things from him. He shared some of his military experiences with me. Of course it was years after graduating from high school.

Little things that I took for granted and thought funny, Naomi would get upset over. I remember how she would get so mad and angry with us whenever we went to one of our high school football games, and the band would play their theme song. "*I wish I was in Dixie, hooray hooray*, and I, along with the others would stand up, bop my head, clap and sing along. I didn't see anything wrong with the song. I didn't know the meaning, or the lyrics. It didn't have a bad beat so why in the world was she getting so angry with everyone? I would get upset with her for frowning at me and asking me to sit down. I couldn't understand why the song with the good beat that made you bop your head, could make her become so upset. Did she know something that I didn't know? Yes, apparently she did. How did she know that this was not a good song for us? (No, not for my people). How could I be so blind I ask myself? But when you are trying to live, and your mind is so bombarded with so many things, and your only worry is to stop worrying, and your only desire is to be happy, it can indeed happen. You can miss the flowers, the rainbows that promise hope and a future, the green grass and tress. You can miss it all!

Did she know then that this was a song that mocked slavery? Did she know the story and its entirety? I discovered many years later that the song was about Negroes. Yes, it was a song about Negroes who had been freed from slavery supposedly longing to go back into slavery, to be with their slave master. This is what I later came to understand and interpret. It went deeper and much deeper than that. They would perform shows on stage laughing and mocking our ancestors. How sad I felt to have been so ignorant. They had performers who would paint their faces black, dress in rags, and portray slaves longing to go back to their master. Did she know about all of this already, or did she just feel it inside that this was not something good? Did she know about the Blackface Minstrel, which is what it was called? Did she know who they were and what they represented? Did she know that the song was considered the Southern National Anthem for them? How could she have known all of this? Was this taught in class and I missed it also? I knew I had missed a lot in class by being a worrier but I couldn't believe all the things I had missed, when I learned that I had been suffering from depression for most of my entire life. Did she really know what the song was really about? I kept asking myself, as I grew older. She never told me the history. All I knew is she just got angry. The moral of this experience is parents communicate with your kids, friends communicate with your friends. I learned it is not wise to take for granted that just because you know something, others know also.

What in the World Happened?

What happened on this day frightened me more than any of my fears. Fear was looking me in the eye, and I could not understand why. Had I done something wrong, or had the monsters caught up with me? I never feared white people. When I was growing up, I thought whites had a lot of respect for us. I thought they were afraid of us, especially our men. Our men were strong. They were tall, black, and strong. I knew we looked different, but that was all I knew. I can remember not being afraid to wear my shorts downtown. I didn't think the white people knew how skinny my legs were, so I didn't feel skinny when I was around them. I am sure Mama knew they were different. She worked for them. Growing up in the time in which I did, I should have been well aware of racism, but little did I know. It might sound strange, but when people ask me if I remember the colored having a water fountain and the whites having a water fountain, it amazes them when I tell them no. The only thing I remember is the day I went inside of the courthouse to use the bathroom.

I went inside of the courthouse because I had to use the bathroom really bad. Mama and Daddy must have thought I was old enough to go inside of the courthouse and use the bathroom alone, and they must have thought I was big enough to read. But I guess I was not big enough to do either. I wasn't trying to do much of anything but work my way through the crowd and find my way to the restroom. Back in the day, the restroom was not called restroom. At home and away from home it was called the bathroom, at least that is what we used to say back home. I walked up the steps towards the courthouse. I had managed to get around all of the people standing around and sitting down under the big oak tress.

I made it to the top step. I was happy. I walked through the big, old, wooden open doors and went inside. I began looking for the restroom right away. It was Saturday, all of the people were downtown, and I suppose it was a pretty common thing, having to use the bathroom after being downtown all day. Since it was Saturday, the doors were wide open because people were constantly going in and out. I entered the courthouse. I walked in a hurry down the hallway in the direction I thought the bathroom might have been. The hallway was wide and dark; the floors were black and shiny-looking. Even though they looked dirty, they were clean. Then on the other hand, the floors may have been plank made of wood with a few cracks here and there in the floor. My mind doesn't tell me exactly how the floors really looked; maybe I was too young to remember. The courthouse looked spooky, old, and raggedy at times. Even though it was fairly dark on the inside, you could see inside because of the sunlight and the open doors. It didn't give a lot of light, but it surely helped out. As I walked down the wide hallway, there was an old, dark brown, dried-out wooden door on the left side of the hallway. I glanced at the door through the corner of my eye and continued walking. That might have been the entrance to the storage room. I didn't know. I didn't give much thought to where the entrance would lead me; I barely noticed it. It didn't look quite right, so I kept right on walking past the door. I didn't look long or hard at anything, and I certainly did not look up to read any signs. I didn't know I was supposed to be looking for signs. All I was looking for was the bathroom. I had to use it terribly bad, and I was focusing only on making my way to the toilet. I walked passed the ugly dark-brown door and walked around the corner. To my left was a door that looked like it might be the ladies room. I went inside. Yes! This was it. I had finally made my way to the bathroom. When I walked inside, I felt relieved. I finally made it. I looked at myself in the mirrors that hung just above the sinks. The mirrors were so clean. They looked crystal clear. I looked at the two white sinks because they looked clean also. None of this seemed to be in sync with the rest of the old-looking building. It was clean inside the bathroom. Everything looked the way it did at home. I was happy to discover that the people kept the bathroom so clean in the old, raggedy-looking building. I walked over to the stalls to use the toilet, and both doors were closed and locked. I walked back over to the sink and waited. I waited until one of the ladies came out of the stall so that I could go inside. The first lady walked out. She was white, but that didn't startle me. What startled me was that look she had on her face. She looked at me with one of the strangest looks I had ever seen in my life. It frightened me. I didn't know why she was looking at me this way. All I knew is that I wanted her to hurry up so that I could use

194

the toilet and get out of there. I began to take baby steps toward the stall she had just walked out of when another white lady walked out of the other stall. She had that same strange look on her face. I walked on past her and went into the stall to use the toilet. "Why in the world are they looking at me so strange?" I wondered. I didn't know what in the world had happened. Before I closed the door, I looked back at the two ladies, and they were still watching me. I was scared. They were still looking at me very strange. I felt like I must have done something terribly wrong. I felt like I had sassed them without saying a word or disrespected them in some way. I hurried up to use the toilet. It felt good to finally be able to relieve my bladder, but I was terrified once I finished using the toilet; the thought of the look on the faces of the women unnerved me. I was afraid to come out of the stall once I used the toilet. I was afraid and I wanted my mother. I knew Mother would not have allowed those women to look at me so strange. I had not done anything to them for them to treat me like I was something out of this world. I stood in the stall waiting to see what their next move might be. "Mama, please come and get me!" I thought. I flushed the toilet and waited and waited until I felt like they were no longer out to get me; then I finally heard the door squeak and then close. I felt great relieve when I heard the door close. I assumed they were gone. But I was still afraid to come out. I could not understand why they looked at me in the way in which they did. I flushed the toilet again and hurried out of the stall. They were gone. I was so happy. I did not stop by the sink to wash my hands or look at myself in the crystal clean mirror or anything. I ran out of the bathroom so fast and rushed outside to find my mama. I never told her what happened. I did not want to get spanked. I felt as though I had done something wrong, I just didn't know what in the world had happened.

The Credit Card Company

One day I answered the phone, and it was Larissa. She always made me crack up laughing whenever she called. She was always funny, loud, and full of cheers. I don't think I've ever seen her sad. She joked about everything. She made jokes about me not being at work. She joked about me always being in and out of a job. I laughed. She had a way of making bad situations not seem so bad. Everyday she would call me and talk for what I considered a long time to be at work. Then one day she asked, "Kenzie, when are you going to go back to work?" We both laughed. Neither one of us knew what was so funny, but we were cracking up.

"As soon as I find a job," I replied.

She said with excitement and enthusiasm, "I can get you a job here."

"You can? You can?!" I asked. She explained to me what the job was and gave me a quick rundown of the job description. I assured her I would be able to do the job. Guess what? She got me the job. The job was with the credit card company. I hoped that I would be reviewing customers' credit reports, determining if they were eligible to get a certain line of credit. Instead, I was a help desk technician; just liked she had told me. I had to fix the credit card machines when the stores were having problems with them. It turned out to be challenging but interesting, just like everything else I had experienced so far. I went through training one day at a time.

Training was just like I thought it would be. I listened closely everyday the best I could. I had not completed a full week of training before the little voice started to bother me. It grew and grew much louder and much stronger each day. Some days the louder the teacher talked, the louder the ugly little voice inside of my head would talk. It would not let me comprehend what I needed to learn in order to do the job. It told me how difficult the job was going to be. It questioned whether I thought I could really do the job. It reminded me of how I was fired from the finance company: "You were fired because you did not look happy." So I tried to look happy and more interested than most of the others in training. It reminded me of Varney and how he didn't choose me for the job. It was because he didn't think that I was good enough. It told me I would not last very long. It told me how everyone in the class thought I was supposed to be the smartest and the brightest; instead, it turned out I was the slowest and felt like the dumbest. I knew it was because the ugly little voice inside of my head was not letting me do things quickly. Trying to force my mind to subside from its negative thinking was more than a task. It was impossible. It was difficult, and the old folk would have said, "It was just plain on hard-headed, having a mind with control of its own." It just wouldn't shut up; no matter how hard I tried to yell at it, change my thoughts to something more pleasant, the little voice would not be quiet. When lunchtime came around, I didn't want to go to lunch with the others. I wanted to go to my car and rest. I had already had a full day. And I had missed all of the training.

I had begun to wish that there were another way in life to succeed. I had begun to feel like I was not going to make it in the world of work. I had begun to do something that I had never done before and that was worry about my financial obligations. I had always tried to be responsible for taking care of all my debt. This is something I got from my Mama. I did not want anyone knocking on my door, ringing my phone, saying this was some friendly reminder that you have not paid your bill. I worried about my future. I wondered how I was going to survive. "God, what am I going to do if I cannot work?" I worried. There were times when I

197

felt like shouting out! I wanted to just shout it out. I wanted to scream to the top of my voice so that everyone would know how terrible I felt deep down inside. I felt if I could do one thing, just one thing out of the ordinary, it would relieve me from all of the stress, the fear, the anxiety, and everything that was so balled up in me on the inside. But I knew that I could not do this. Not only would I have been considered insane, I would have been fired on the spot again. Lord have mercy!

Because of the LORD's great love we are not consumed, for his compassions never fail. They are new every morning; great is your faithfulness. I say to myself, The LORD is my portion; therefore I will wait for him.

Lamentations 3:22–24.

Even though Larissa had gotten me the job, she had no idea how weird and strange I felt at work. If she had known how I really felt inside about being at work, she would not believe that I was the same person. I worked in fear everyday at the credit card company. This was nothing new for me, except I was getting tired of the feeling. It was like sitting on a time bomb. I felt like my nerves or mind would explode any minute. I tried over and over again to relax and work, but I was never able to force myself to relax. I didn't know how to relax. I spent my training time trying so hard to remember everything that I forgot everything. It was the fear of believing that everyone else in the class was catching on much faster than I was. It was the fear that I did not want to look like the dummy. It all turned out to be true because I could never clear the thoughts in my head about how fast I was learning and comprehending, that it was difficult to learn anything fast. It was difficult to learn anything, period. I had to go in and out of training several times. I was very professional, however—the only way I knew how to be. Several of the not-so-professional-acting people wanted to be on my team until they discovered I was not catching on quickly enough.

One time one of the girls in the training class got the nerves to crack on me out loud; that made me feel good, actually. I preferred people to talk about me to me, rather than gossip about me behind my back. One day we were doing a practice on one of the machines we would be working with, and the time came for me to demonstrate what I had learned. I was able to disassemble and reassemble all the parts and pieces. Of course, it took me longer to complete my task than any of the others in the class. Somehow I was able to grab hold of my composure and get it reassembled. The class clapped, except for one girl in the class. She began to sing an old familiar song: "They said I wouldn't make it. They said I'll never amount to anything." She did not have to sing another verse; everyone in the class knew, and definitely I knew, the next lines of the song. The chorus of the song says, "I'm still holding on." They all laughed together, even me, because I was definitely still holding on.

I got transferred to another area, my new team leader, Leonard, was determined not to let me fail. Leonard was a short, thick guy who had lots of personality. The bosses seemed to like him and the employees did, too. He wore his hair big. He wore a big gray and white fro, but he wore it well. He always kept his hair cut neat and trimmed. He was swift. He moved around the office fast. He would move from one row to another row very quickly, assisting the reps and the supervisors wherever and whenever he was needed. He was a nice man and a great trainer also.

He taught the second part of the training. Leonard, who was sometimes, called Lenny would be standing up in the call center in front of his chair when I came through the door each morning. He would

199

watch me until I got to my desk and signed on. He wanted to make sure that I was not a second late; time was crucial. I worked on the phone, and every minute counted. Once I made it through the door, I had to run, really run, to my desk, trying hard to beat the clock by one minute, and sometimes by thirty seconds. Being on time was always a challenge for me. The more I desired to be on time, the harder the challenge became. My mind always assured me that I could make it in the exact time I had allowed myself. My mind was always wrong. It caused me to be late every time and for everything. Sometimes I would be a minute or two minutes late, and sometimes even five minutes late. It never failed.

<u>Running to be on Time</u>

When I was working at the insurance company, the boss accepted my being late. God had mercy on me and softened the boss's heart and made her realize how hard I tried. She must have come to the conclusion that I had issues. I had been warned not to be late anymore the rest of the week. I promised her I wouldn't. The following day I woke up bright and early. I did not want to wake up any earlier than usual, because the more time I had, the more time I took. However, I left home earlier, which was a good thing. I got to the parking lot on time. I had exactly five minutes to park my car, jump out of my car, run upstairs, run to my department, get to my desk, and sit down. I didn't have time to huff and puff once I sat down, because I wanted everyone to think I had been at my station, logged in, with a few extra minutes to exhale before starting to work. I was exhausted by the time I made it through the front door; I felt as though I would pass out. But I didn't stop there. I had almost made it, and I was determined to be on time. I was determined to show my boss and my coworkers that I could do it. Yes, I can do it! I can be on time!!

When I finally got to my department, not only was I exhausted, I was stunned. Everyone on my team was standing up clapping. I could not believe it. They had just moved away from the window where they had been watching me. They saw my every move. They saw me drive into the parking lot. They knew where I had parked, and they witnessed me jumping out of the car and running up the steps, trying to be on time. At first, I did not know what was going on when I stepped foot in my department until the whole team started chanting, "She is here! She is here!" I was so embarrassed. I started laughing and crying at the same time. I didn't know if I should laugh or cry, so I did both. I cried tears of joy and pain. I felt joyful because I had made it to work on time and pain because it was something that I wanted to do everyday, but I was not sure how I was going to do it. That day my life changed and my boss changed. I was blessed and was given a flex schedule. This schedule worked well for me. Thank God, my boss was a boss who worked with her employees. It was not just me she worked with; she worked with us all. She began focusing more on my work than she did my being on time. She observed that if I was a few minutes late, I worked several minutes after my scheduled clock-out time. I was never in a hurry to leave work. One of my weaknesses was that I wanted to finish what I had started. When I was late, she didn't seem to concern herself with that or bother to confront me. Besides, I made it to work on time more times than I was late. And besides, my schedule was flex. This was a great accomplishment for me. But the people at the credit card company were not that understanding. They demanded that you be on time with no flexibility. They also had a very high turnover rate. It didn't seem to matter that traffic in the city was ferocious. It didn't seem to matter that I was traveling in the direction of traffic. I had been fortunate and blessed that most times I traveled to work in the opposite direction of the traffic.

God had mercy on me because he knew me. This is almost impossible to do today because traffic is everywhere in the city and is in every direction. You would be in big trouble if an accident occurred on I-285, and you would be in more trouble if it rained and you were trying to make it to work. It was tough, very tough. You had to make a decision, whether you should fight the traffic and arrive late or whether you should turn around and go back home. It was a tough decision. It was tough because at the credit card company being tardy was worse than being absent.

Leonard was my greatest fan at the credit card company. One day he was monitoring me and after I hung up with my customer, he became very angry with me. He was really upset. He had been monitoring my phone calls, just like those quality assurance people. He was so angry after listening to me on the phone he almost frightened me. He was not an intimidating person, and he was not the person I reported directly to, so I was not as afraid of him as I was of my direct boss. I didn't understand why he was so upset until he pulled me off the phone and explained to me how I didn't appear to be confident in what I was doing. He took me into the office and looked directly into my eyes without a blink and told me he knew I could do better. He expressed to me how he had faith in me, and how I needed faith in myself. He took me off the phone and into the conference room along with one of the credit card machines and made me point out every part of the machine and name its functions. He told me I was going to do this job while I was there, and I was going to do it well. When I finished that one-on-one training session with him, you can best believe that I was doing it right. I knew that machine so well in a few days that I could instruct customers how to fix and reprogram their machine with one eye closed. The only problem with this is the department that used to repair these machines had combined with another department. Had I started working here long before now, I could have lasted for a very long time on this job before having to learn all about all of the other machines we had to help fix.

I was thankful for Leonard. From that day forward, I knew how to fix that machine and I knew how to walk the customers through fixing it. I even knew when it could not be fixed and when it was time to ship them another one. I was on a roll. I managed to work there for two years before the little ugly voices got the best of me. It was there on this job that I felt like running down the aisle screaming and shouting. I had become fed up with the negative talk. If my mind would not say so many bad things about me to me, I would be awesome, just the way God planned for me to be. After all, this job was supposed to have been different. I was supposed to excel on this job, and Leonard was not the one who was supposed to help me excel here. It was my dear friend and former roommate from college, Sherita.

My Friend Sherita, the Boss

The ironic thing about being on this job was that my friend Sherita from college was my supervisor. Larissa had gotten her a job here also. Sherita excelled quickly. After six months she was promoted to supervisor. I have to give it to Sherita; one thing about her, she was skilled. She had a way with people and she knew how to play the game, as they say. She played the game so well that no one would have ever guessed that we knew each other. No one would have ever known we were roommates from college. I had to wonder if she was the same person or an impersonator at times. At times she acted like she didn't know Larissa or me. At times, she seemed to have forgotten it was because of Larissa that she had the job. At times you would have thought she had forgotten all about the talks we had before I accepted the job.

Before I accepted the job, I talked to Sherita. I talked with her about some of the things I had been dealing with. I told her how I wanted some stability in the workplace, and it was my goal to grow with the company. She was also familiar with job-hopping. She also frequently changed jobs. Was it a new generation from my parents, my siblings? It seemed with my generation things had begun to change. It seemed that staying on the same job for all of your life was becoming a thing of the past. All of us had experienced it. I wasn't exactly sure what their problem was. I wasn't sure if it was them giving up on the job, or the job giving up on them. I only knew that something inside of me, my mind, was constantly telling me I was a failure.

We all seemed to experience working here and working there before landing on the perfect job. But some of our classmates had chosen those careers where they had the opportunity to work and retire young, like the military. After twenty years they could retire. That was about how long I had been looking for a job. The military may not have been a bad choice for me, but I am glad that I did not make that choice, although the thought had crossed my mind. I can't imagine what it would have been like for me, but perhaps it would have taught me how to be on time.

I wanted to take advantage of this great opportunity at the credit card company. I knew my boss, and this was a perfect opportunity to shine. I wanted to shine brightly so that I would get some positive recognition in the workplace. She had agreed to help me. She was going to help me get over the fears. The plan was to assign me all special projects. I believed if I worked on special projects and got special attention, maybe I would impress everyone, and it would make me a better person. But more than anything, it was my hope that the negative thoughts would disappear from my head. If I could learn how to excel or do well in any one position, I might feel good about myself. Sherita knew me. She didn't know about all of the negativity that was going on inside of my head. She had no idea how I struggled and struggled to keep the little voice silent so that I would be able to survive, primarily in the work world. But she knew enough about me; we went a long way back. She knew I was a little shy at times, but she also knew the side of me that was strong and persistent. I was still a leader, a leader at heart.

She knew the challenge she would face whenever we would go out, or whenever we had to make decisions about things. Sherita and I bumped heads every time because both of us wanted to be the in-charge person. We constantly bumped heads when we were all hanging out together. There was a group of us, all from Alabama. All of us had attended the same school with the exception of Sherita's best friend, Lela. She was from Sherita's hometown. She was an alumna of Tennessee State. We had one more friend who became a friend to all of us. Her name was Sankia. She was Larissa's best friend. They had met in school before Larissa transferred to TSU. All of us got along well. I did not consider any of them to be new friends; it was more like an extended family. Being from Alabama, we all seemed to click. We all seemed to have a mutual understanding, and great friends we had all become. The greatest conflict seemed to have been between Sherita and me. We both wanted to be in control of things. We both wanted to be the boss. It seems crazy when I look back, but I guess that was all about growing up. She was definitely in charge now, and she was definitely my boss. That was a good thing for me, I thought. I had no problem giving her the respect she deserved, just like any other supervisor. But I had a different challenge.

It was another fear now that she was the boss. I wondered if I would become afraid of her. The person who I had gone to school with, had been roommates with for an abbreviated time, would I become afraid of her as the boss? Would I no longer see her as a friend, and now see her as the big boss? It was frighten to think about.

I never became fearful of Sherita like I did my previous bosses. I wanted to impress her more because she knew me and she knew I was smart. She knew I was bright and smart, but I had never worked under her supervision. I had to be the great person I knew I was for my home girl. Unfortunately, things did not work out the way I had hoped. Apparently, Sherita did not feel like I was capable of doing any of the things we had agreed upon. My fears sneaked up on me like a shadow. I could not get my faith and confidence up to par. She always found someone else to do the tasks. Never once—oh yes, once and only once—did she consider me. I did a good job, and she told me I did well. This did not help me to feel much better about myself. It made me feel like crying. Crying not only because she asked me only once to do a special project, but also because I feared if she had asked me on other occasions, I would not have been able to do what she needed to be done to perfection. I knew that the negative voice inside my head would prevent me from doing anything that would make me feel great about myself. There were days when I felt so miserable I wished I did not have to work. There must be another way to succeed in life other than working a nine-to-five. "Lord, have mercy! Please, have mercy! I wish it didn't hurt so much," I thought. "I wished I had whatever it took to find a job, do a good job, and keep the job." What hurt even more is my desire to work. I wanted to work, I wanted to be successful, and I wanted to have a future. I knew this would have made my parents proud, but apart from making others happy, I wanted to be happy. I knew having a job and some stability in life was half the way of being successful and happy in life. It was more than hurting and painful. It was embarrassing. Whenever new people would come out of training, the team leaders would sit the new hires beside another person who was new. It was as though they didn't realize I had been on the job for almost a year now. Because of this, the new hires didn't recognize my skills and ability either. That didn't help, and that did not say a lot about my ability to do a good job. It made me feel like crap. It made me feel and look more stupid. I wanted to quit every time this happened. I could not believe something like this was happening to me. Not me. I wasn't dumb. I wasn't stupid and I wasn't crazy. I knew I was bright, I knew I was intelligent, but something had a hold of me. Outside of the workplace the people I knew thought I was intelligent also, just the person that I am, just the person that I wanted to convince myself that I was. I tried to stay up-to-date on current events. I enjoyed being in the know; I wanted to know what was going on in the world and around the world. I asked myself a thousand times: Why such a contrast. Why was being in the work environment so complex and complicated for me? I worked for the credit card company for two years. It seemed that my lucky number three was changing into lucky two. Even though I didn't feel as bad leaving this job as I had felt before on my earlier jobs, it hurt, and it hurt badly. But the pain of losing jobs and feeling incompetent, and the embarrassment that came along with it, was not going to get me down and keep me down. I was slowly beginning to accept the fact that this is just how it is going to be.

I knew God had something special planned for me. The problem was trying to discover what it was. Even though I had learned many different skills by going from job to job, I had not mastered any. I wanted to know my purpose. I was losing patience. I was losing faith. I felt like God had let me down again. I felt even he didn't love me anymore. "What am I supposed to do, Dear God?" I asked. **What is it that you want me to do?**

For I know the plans I have for you declared the Lord, plans to prosper you and not to harm you, plans to give you hope, hope and a future.

Jeremiah 29:11

Yes, that is exactly what I needed. I needed hope and a future. Staying on one job for many years like most folk would have been prosperous enough for me, I thought. But I was learning that joy, happiness, and peace were most important. I still had faith and a bit of hope. I'd had four other jobs since the telephone company, including the job at the credit card company where I did troubleshooting as a help desk technician. I was happy, but I was confused. Then I worked for the payroll company. I enjoyed this job. I enjoyed my coworkers, and the boss was cool. There were times I was able to relax and talk to him. There were a few times I could go to him and ask questions. I felt good about this, because it had always been extremely difficult to communicate with the boss. Then I worked at the pest control company; this was a different kind of experience. The people there were unlike any of my past experiences. Last but not least I worked at the credit background company. This job was the job that was worth all of the trials and tribulations I had gone through.

Discovering the Problem

The day I left work from the telephone company and went to the doctor, he didn't tell me what my problem might have been. He just prescribed me some medication. I took the medication for a few days and nothing happened. Not knowing why or what I was taking the medication for didn't sit well with me. I am not prone to taking medication easily anyway, so I didn't take it for long. It was years later that I found out what the doctor was treating me for. He was treating me for anxiety disorder. I would have taken the medication every day and every night had I known what it was. I would have taken almost anything at the time if I thought it would help me to keep my job and to feel better about myself. But Dr. Welch was seeing me and not explaining to me what was going on; besides, most of the time I saw his nurse practitioner. He might as well have said to me, "Take several of these and call me back in a month." Even if he had said that, I might have questioned him more. What I understood is my blood pressure was elevated, and it had never been that way before. I told him all I knew to tell him, and that was that I was stressed out! Yes, doctor, I am stressed. I didn't know how to go into detail with him about the way I was feeling inside. I thought I was losing it. I didn't know how to say to him, "Doc, I think I am crazily going insane." I didn't tell him how I would feel my blood rushing to my head at work. I did not tell him how my chest knotted up. I did not tell him how my shoulders ached and how my head hurt. I didn't tell him how the bosses intimidated me. Most of all, I did not tell him about that little voice inside of my head having a hold on me, never letting me go.

I didn't know how to talk to the doctor. I feared him. I expressed to him that I was afraid and that he had to forgive me for shaking like I was. Every time I went to the doctor, I was either scared frozen or I shook like a puppet on a string. If I wasn't shaking, I was stiff as a wall. I would be so afraid of going to the doctor, I would tremble. I was so afraid that if I went to him for one thing, he would discover that something else was wrong with me. I was always afraid he was going to tell me I had some terminal illness and I would only have a few months to live and I would immediately drop dead, or even worse, die slowly knowing that there was no cure for my condition and knowing that no one physically could help me. If I was going to die in a little while, the last thing I wanted to do was worry about it. I certainly did not want to hear anything else negative. My mind had piles of worries stacked almost thigh high. I had worries in storage. I used to tell people it was not necessary for them to worry, because I worried enough for everybody.

Dr. Welch listened to me when I shared with him feelings of being afraid of doctors. He seemed to understand that. He made me feel much better. He made me feel as though I was not the only person afraid of going to the doctor. I felt better; maybe this was a natural feeling for me to feel this way. If I had not been feeling so uptight that day at work, I would not have been standing in his office on this day. I am glad that I was working, because had I been feeling this way at home, I would have been too afraid to go to the doctor.

I was asked to lie down on a table while the nurse connected little wires to my toes, fingers, and chest. I wasn't sure what was happening, but I was not feeling as scared. When the nurse disconnected me, she printed the results and gave it to the doctor to read. I was so thankful to God when the doctor told me I was not having a heart attack. Thank you, God. It was in his office that I found out I wasn't having a heart attack but an anxiety attack. If you've ever experienced one, no one has to tell you how much it hurts and how it frightens you.

The Turning Point

I didn't believe I could carry this burden much longer. I needed someone to talk to who really understood. I read many books. I listened to TV commercials and heard some of the people describe their pain and hurt in the same way in which I hurt. This was the first time I didn't feel like I was all alone. This was the first time I thought that someone other than me might be struggling. It didn't give me a lot of relief, because I didn't know for sure what was wrong with me. What I knew was I needed some help. My mind had finally begun to talk sensibly to me. I took classes on building your self-esteem. I rented tapes, but nothing seemed to be helping me deal with me. I knew it was not something that was in my mind. I knew it was real. I had to reach out to someone. I had to let someone who I felt really knew me know that I was on the verge. I reached out to blood.

Turning to Family

Reaching out to family was something I had never done before. I was sinking and I needed someone to talk to. It seemed my friends were getting tired of hearing the same old stories. I lost my job, my chest is hurting, and I feel like I am having a heart attack. My head hurt and my ears had begun to constantly sound like blowing wind from a cracked car window that would not go away. But the unusual thing about the blowing in my ear is that it seemed to beat the same beat as my heart. It was as if my heartbeat was now beating inside of my head through my ears. I finally went to the doctor and was diagnosed with tinnitus. It seemed like one thing after the other was happening to me.

One of my close friends whom I told about losing my job became so frustrated with me that she refused to talk to me anymore. "Why can't you stay on a job long enough to retire like regular folk?" she said. She had only called me once since I lost my last job. In other words, she said, "I just don't want to hear it." Had she been able to get away with it, I am sure she would have told me to "grow up!" But that would have ended our friendship once and for all. This was not about growing up. I was already grown. I had to speak to someone other than my friends. I needed someone else. I decided to discuss it with Daddy. I didn't go into a whole lot of details.

"Daddy, I lost my job today." I said.

"Humm, umm, Kenzie," he said.

"You ain't lost your job, have you?"

"Yes sir," I replied.

"Lord, you need your job Kenzie, you ain't never gon be able to retire if you keep changing jobs."

"No Daddy, I sure won't. I really loved that job and I desire to go back to work."

"Can you just pray for me?" I asked.

Daddy assured me that he would pray. Daddy also made me feel better because he didn't say," You keep on losing jobs, what is wrong with you?" He made me feel as if I had some control over the matter. He said, "You keep changing jobs." Yes, I keep changing jobs, but now it's not by choice." I thought to myself.

I expressed to Sizzie, my oldest sister and best friend, how terrible I felt. I told her how life had dealt me a heck of a hand. I told her my life was a mess, and I was not sure how I was going to deal with it. I was drowning in misery. I felt lonely and empty. Apart from feeling worthless and like a failure, I was beginning to truly feel like I could not go on. She did not realize how sincere I was, because I laughed. Even when I was crying, I laughed. I never wanted anyone to know, not even my family, how I hurt. Even though she spent more time with me than anyone, she never recognized the pain and suffering I endured. I was told that I was always happy, always full of life and fun, and most of all, the life of the party. It was ironic how I longed for happiness. I wanted to feel peace within myself for once. I wanted that joy that my father had promised in his words, "Peace I leave with you." I longed and prayed for the joy my Mama talked about, the joy that the world could not take away. I longed to feel that joy deep down in my soul. I continued to share my feelings with (Sissy) my oldest sister and best friend. She finally began to take me seriously. I was reluctant to open up to my other sister, Sarah Jean; surely she did not think life had dealt me this heck of a hand. To her, and to most of my family and friends, you keep swinging back is what I am sure they thought. That is what they think. But inside this thing was growing. It was becoming bigger than I.

I never felt like Sarah Jean cared that much about me anyway. In her eyes I was the baby girl of the family and nothing more than a spoiled little brat. I felt certain that my life was no disappointment to her. I knew I would regret sharing my story with her. But I had to let someone know. I was no longer sure of myself. I was not sure of my possibilities.

I shared with Sarah Jean the feelings I had at work. I began to notice that these funny feelings were not only haunting me at work, they had begun to haunt me in public places. I was afraid to talk around acquaintances and friends. It was as if my brain was no longer registering words fast enough for me to respond. I didn't desire to be around folk much, because I knew I would appear slow. I knew I wouldn't be able to make them laugh any longer. I could not find words to contribute to any of the conversations, and trying to initiate conversation was something I couldn't ignite any longer.

What was happening to me? Whenever I was put on the spot or in a situation where I had to talk, I had begun to stutter. Something was going on and I didn't like it, but I didn't know what to do anymore. Yes, I had to share this with someone who I thought just might be able to help me. My thought pattern was slowing down. No longer were words dropping out of the sky and into my mouth. My body and all my mannerisms were tightening up on me, and I couldn't relax enough to engage in small talk. I was feeling more and more uncomfortable around others. I worried if they could see the paranoia I was feeling on the inside. I worried if they thought I was cool for not talking, or did they feel I was crazy and ignorant?

Naomi caught me off guard one day at a party that we were invited to. Out of the blue, she said to me, "Why don't you open up your mouth and talk, Kenzie?" I jumped because she startled me. I could not believe she of all people would be telling me to open up my mouth and talk. As long as she had known me, I was always the talker. No one who ever knew me would imagine me being afraid to talk. I don't remember my response to her question that almost scared me into being myself again, but I am sure it caught her off guard that I did not respond like my usual perky self. This bothered me. This incident was eye opening for me. I had to find out who I was before I became a person I did not long to be.

I told my sister Sarah Jean how I always experienced feelings of choking and tightness in my chest, and how all the blood in my body seemed to rest in my head. I told her how my heart ran marathons more times than I could count. I tried to describe the voices that I heard constantly, and how they fed me all negative and bad things about me. But I did not want to confuse her into thinking that I literally heard someone speaking to me; no, that wasn't the case. Thank God. I knew it was my mind. I told her how I felt like running down the aisle screaming and shouting at work so many times to release the tension. I told her I believed it would do my heart good if I had the courage to do such. I would never fear anything ever again. I believed it would somehow liberate me. I believed it would make me brave and take away the fears. I believed it would make me feel better. I would be alive and free. I could be free to fly like a bird, and run around in the backyard like squirrels playing, running up and down the trees without a care or worry in the world. I would be free to let the world know that I have no more stress, I have no more weight on my shoulders, no more racing heartbeats running faster than I could imagine ever moving.

She was looking at me and I could read her thoughts from the expression on her face. "I'm not sure that is what you really want to do, Kenzie," she said. When I finished expressing myself, she disagreed that running down the aisle to relieve myself would be a good thing. She said in a laughing and joking manner that it probably would not give me the freedom I desired. I agreed it wouldn't be a good thing to do after all. Good! We were already in agreement with one thing. Maybe talking to her wasn't a bad idea after all.

She listened intently as I shared with her all that I had been feeling, and all that I had been going through, and she seemed to understand. I was astounded. She was taking me very seriously. She acted like she didn't know I was catching so much hell in life, but I believed she did. She did not speak until I was finished. Then I asked her, "What do you think about all of this, Sis? What in the world is wrong with me?" I asked. She didn't have to think. From what I said, she already knew. She did not ask me to come into her office for a check up. She must have known that I needed to see someone right away. She suggested that I see another doctor.

"I am going to refer you to a psychiatrist," she said. She referred me to Dr. Shannon. I bet she was surprised at my reaction when she suggested I see a psych. This didn't offend me. She was my sister, and even if she didn't love me the way I thought she should, I knew she wanted the best help for me. Besides, before today she probably thought like everyone else that I was just arrogant, spoiled, and cocky. I wanted help, and wherever I could find it would be a blessing for me. I took the information she gave me and put it into use immediately.

I scheduled an appointment with Dr. Shannon as soon as possible. I noticed immediately something different. Normally when you call a doctor's office, the receptionist asks what seems to be the problem. She did not ask any questions regarding what the condition was. I gave her my name, address, and date of birth, and she gave me a date and time to meet with Dr. Shannon.

Visiting Dr. Shannon's Office

I visited Dr. Shannon on my scheduled date and time. I had not rehearsed what I was going to say. All I knew is I wanted some relief. I needed some answers to why my life was so messed up. I wanted to know why I was spending so much time worrying and very little time living. I did not know how to live. I worried about everything. I worried about living, I worried about not living. I worried about my parents living, and I worried about my parents dying.

I worried so much about my parents dying that one day I asked Jeanette what she would do if her mother passed away. She and her mother talked on the phone every day. I admired their relationship. They seemed to be very close. I would go by her office some days, and she would be on the phone laughing and talking to her mother like I did with my sister and my other friends. I observed their closeness. She answered me without hesitation. She answered and said, "I will go on." She said, "I would be hurt, it would hurt me deeply, but I will have to go on with my life." I thought she was insane, because I on the other hand, felt like I would be unable to live if God took away one of my parents from me.

I worried about becoming sick. I worried about staying well. I worried about becoming old. I worried who would take care of me when I got old. I worried if I would live to become old. I worried about what I said to someone in the course of the day. I worried about what people thought of me, I worried if people did not think of me. The worrying was out of control. These worries were not your ordinary concerns or thoughts. The worries run deep, deep down into the soul. These thoughts were relentless.

I worried so much I could not sleep. I could not turn off the voice inside my head that talked about everything negative. It was as if a war was being fought inside of my head and the enemy was winning the battle. It was as if something inside of me hated me. It did not want me to be happy. It did not want me to feel at peace; whatever I tried to tell myself in a positive way, that other part of my brain always defeated me. It was destined not to let me find joy and peace in my life. I appeared fine on the outside, but my mind was out of control. I was tired of it. I needed help. I needed someone to help me!

At times, I felt like I wanted to lose my mind. I believed that if I lost my mind, I would not have to feel the pain. I would not realize how badly I was hurting or how I had failed in life. I would not be responsible for the way I felt and the way I thought. I looked at people strange whenever they would say, "It's a blessing to be here." They must not have been catching hell in the way in which I was, I would say to myself. I looked at people strange when they said, "I am happy to be here. Life is rough and tough but I am alive." I on the other hand, often wondered if, since life here was so miserable everyday, maybe I would find peace in dying. I thought they were crazy for thinking the way they thought. All I could think of was relief. I needed relief!

Meeting the Doctor

When I walked into Dr. Shannon's office, I was impressed. The office was only a few minutes from where I lived. It was beautiful. The paint on the walls was soft and calming. It was not a bright, sunny yellow or hot pink that stood out and looked at you, to remind you to look out, I'm here! I am here because something is wrong with me. The truth is something is wrong with all of us. But I didn't need to be reminded.

The walls were painted in a cool lavender color. The paintings on the wall were beautiful. I think the color on the wall helped to accent the pictures. I admire art, all kinds of art. The plants were big; they were big and green and refreshing. I felt very comfortable. I was beginning to feel a sense of relief just thinking that someone or something could possibly help me. Lord knows, I needed it. I was smothering myself to death in fear, shame, doubt, guilt, and pain. Thinking about help being on the way gave me great comfort and some relief.

The office was very quiet, and I was the only patient sitting there. There was no receptionist face to greet you when you walked in. I sat down in the single chair against the wall and waited for someone to slide open the glass windows that you could not see through. I sat there for what seemed to have been about ten minutes. I'm sure I did not sit that long in an unfamiliar place before knocking on some door or window or ringing some bell to let someone know I was there and waiting. But the wait seemed long.

After waiting for a few more minutes and no one came coming out front, I went to the sliding windows and knocked on the glass, and to my surprise no one responded. Here it was now 10:15 and my appointment was scheduled at 10:00. I did sit here this long after all, I realized. I was beginning to get a little nervous. Of course, a psych's office is not the kind of place I would choose to be. I walked back over to my chair, picked up a magazine, and attempted to read it, but my concentration was off. I was becoming impatient. I was about to get bad vibes about the place. That is when a little, short lady walked out front with a big smile on her face, and walked over towards where I was sitting, and reached out to shake my hand. "You must be McKenzie," she asked.

"Yes, ma'am" I replied, "and I am here to see Dr. Shannon."

She looked up at me with a friendly face and a happy smile, and said, "I am Dr. Shannon."

I could not believe she was the doctor. She looked like a college student or a high school senior. She seemed very nice. She was very pretty and approachable. She stood about five feet tall, her long black hair hung on her shoulders, her complexion was a suntan yellow, and she was very friendly. She said, "I was watching the clock and wondering what had happened to you when I decided to walk out front to see if you were here." She asked if I had seen the sign out front. The sign instructed patients to press the button beside the name of the doctor they were scheduled to see. I had not noticed the sign on the wall next to the receptionist window; perhaps I was looking too hard. I apologized that I had been remiss in not seeing the sign. Doctor Shannon invited me to come with her and I did.

I followed Dr. Shannon through the door and down the hall. As I passed one of the offices, I looked inside. I noticed this room because I saw a bright red, yellow, and blue table with a little blue chair slid under the table. I saw what appeared to be toys. I saw a baby doll lying on the table. She was not a regular baby doll. She was stuffed with cotton and sewn together. It was one of those dolls that you always see on TV when a little child is being questioned, usually regarding a molestation case. I felt sad just to think that innocent little children have to suffer psychological pain, any kind of pain. It was bad enough that I had to be here. Imagining a child going through a tenth of what my mind was putting me through sent chills down my spine.

I walked into the office; I noticed a picture on the wall. I do not remember the exact painting. I think it was of trees and a lake and a walkway, with someone who seemed to be either relaxing or sad. It could have been someone sitting on a bench in front of the lake enjoying nature. It could have been a picture of serenity in my mind. I was mesmerized, caught in the moment. Maybe it was just pleasant thoughts running through my head.

Dr. Shannon asked me to have a seat. I sat on the light cranberry sofa with the tan flowery leaf print that was very comfortable. I was tired. I could have fallen asleep already. She asked, "How are you today, McKenzie?"

"I am okay," I replied. I realized I had lied. I was not okay. If I were okay, I would not be here today. Dr. Shannon sat across from me, handed me some papers, and asked if I could fill them out. After I finished the paperwork, I handed it back to her and she scanned over each sheet quickly and carefully. She read through it quickly as if to recognize me as a familiar patient. She looked up at me. She looked directly in my eyes. I became unnerved. One of the things I feared the most was looking inside someone else's eyes. I was afraid. I was afraid that it would reveal the fear and frustration I felt inside. Even though I wanted her to see my pain, to feel my pain, but most of all help me to get over my pain, I was still afraid to look into her eyes. I began to pray. God, I hope she will not require me to look into her eyes so she can read me. I wanted her to help me, but I didn't think I could look into her eyes. I'm sure she didn't know I was sad and hurting this badly. I felt like I looked normal. Most times I was always smiling. I knew it was my nature to always smile. It was my personality. I did not want to look sad but I did not want my smile to confuse the doctor into thinking I was happy. I did not want to confuse the doctor by looking so happy that she would tell me that everything was all right. I knew better. I caught myself at times trying to look directly at her and into her eyes. There was no doubt that she noticed how difficult it was for me when I had to look directly at her. There was no doubt that she noticed how I swung my crossed leg when I had to look at her. I noticed these things, and certainly she did.

It has never been uncommon for me to drift and wonder. It did not matter if I was talking to someone or listening to someone. I could always drift off. Many times I didn't realize that I had drifted. Sometimes when I would come back, I would be able to pick up where the person who was talking to me had left off, and other times I would miss the entire point. I had no problem with my friends. They would ask, "Kenzie, were you listening?" I would say to them, "I heard most of it. Go ahead and repeat it." I ran into trouble whenever I was not able to look at some people who did not know me that well. Whenever I would look up at them, their heads would be rotating from left to right and up and down trying to make eye contact with me.

One time I was working a part-time job as a cashier. I would smile and greet the customer as he or she approached my counter. I would scan all of their goodies, each one of them one at a time. Whenever it was time to take the money and give them their receipt, I became very nervous. I would count the customers' money in their hand and give them their receipt without ever looking up at them. One day I had counted the customer's money, and something made me look up. When I looked up at the customer, I could not believe the expression I saw on her face. She was looking at me as if I had some kind of problem. She was looking at me as if she wanted to ask me if I knew whether or not I was giving the money to the correct person or not. I could not speak. I was thankful for that day when I looked up and saw her face. I smiled at her and she smiled back. "It is about time you looked up at me, Ms. Lady," I imagined her saying. I tried from that day forward to at least force myself to look up at the customers. Each time it hurt me more and more. I began to shake and feel the muscles on my face tighten up like dried soap on my skin.

Oftentimes I would sit at the breakfast or dinner table with my sister and talk. We would talk about what kind of day we had at work. It had become funny, but embarrassing to me not looking into the person's eyes that I was talking to. It was Sizzie who made me well aware of it the first time. When she shared with me her day's experience, I would listen. I would listen as well as I could without drifting off. If she thought I was drifting, she would ask, "You with me now?"

I would laugh and say, "Yeah, girl. Of course, I am listening." When she was finished sharing her day with me, I would begin to share with her my day. I would look directly at the TV but talk to her. I was so used to doing this that I never thought about it, I never realized it, and I never paid it any attention. Sometimes I would look toward the window. I never stopped talking. I would continue sharing with her my day at work. It frightened me when I finally looked at my sister; she was turning her head this way and that way, trying hard as she could to follow my eyes. Oh my God, I thought to myself, I must really be crazy. Even my sister is having a hard time listening to me because I would not even look into her eyes. I looked at her and began to laugh. "You are trying to follow me with your eyes, aren't you?"

"Yes," she said. "You are talking to me, aren't you?" Boy, I laughed and laughed. I promised my sister I would get better. I promised her I would not put her through all of that again. I promised her that from now on I would look at her whenever I am talking and would look at everyone else.

When I discovered that this was a problem for me, I began to analyze it and question myself about why was I doing it? I knew the answer right away. I did it because I could focus better. I could hear and comprehend things better if I did not have to look at you when I was talking or listening. If I did not look at you, I did not have to worry about you seeing my fears and self-doubt. If I was looking away from you, the only thing I had to concentrate on was what you were saying, and if I was the one talking, the same method applied. It seemed to have worked for most of my life. If my sister and my coworkers had not been making it so obvious by trying to follow my eyes so that they could make contact with me, it would still be working for me. If I had not felt the stare and puzzlement of the lady whose money I was counting back to her that day, I would probably still be looking away from everybody. But not anymore; I felt certain that after I left Dr. Shannon's office, she would help me to take care of that too.

Mama's Day at Work

It was a beautiful morning. Mama got up bright and early. She cooked breakfast for Daddy, Baby Brother, and me. She made sure we ate before she left home for work. Then she did her light cleaning; yes, all of this before going to work. When I think about this to myself, oh boy I say, how time has changed. It's a hassle for me just having to get up early and get myself dressed for work. I cannot imagine how she did all of this before going to her job.

Good housekeeping was essential for Mama. She believed in being clean and keeping a good clean house. I guess I got lucky being born years later. The older kids were always talking about how Mama taught them so well how to clean. They learned early on how to cook and clean. They learned how to mop and wax floors, and clean the refrigerator as well. It was no joke, even though folk kidded and joked about how clean our house was, and how our floors were always black and shiny. It was the truth. We had one of the shiniest floors in the projects.

Daddy was a spray man, and he didn't like roaches. None of us liked roaches. But it seemed to me that some folk had a higher tolerance for the bugs than we did. Mama was neat and clean. She made sure the roaches had nothing in our home to feast off. Daddy would kid me about bringing other folk's roaches into our house. Whenever I went to spend the night with others, it never failed that somehow a roach would crawl into my sleepover bag, and into the house with me he would go, multiplying by the dozens. It was good that Daddy was a spray man. It turned out to be a good thing for me, when I started working for the pest control company. If no one understood the zero tolerance for bugs, I did. I understood when the customers called upset because they had seen one bug. "One bug, is that what you're calling about?" someone in the office would say, and someone else would laugh. I laughed but commented, "I bet there is another one from where he came from," and we would all laugh.

Mama finished cleaning and got dressed for work. She was feeling great. Today was no different from any other day. At least the morning started out in its usual way, but it ended quite contrary.

Mama walked to work every morning, through downtown. It wasn't to take the scenic route, but it was the only way to get to work from our house. It only took her about fifteen minutes to get to work. There was something about walking. I believe it did her heart good. I imagine she loved breathing in and out, the freshness of the morning air. It was oh so refreshing; there's nothing as revitalizing as the freshness of the morning air. Mama enjoyed looking through the windows at the beautiful clothes in the showcases as she walked past the local stores. I imagine her saying to herself; this is the reason why I walk to work everyday, so that I can shop for my children, my husband, and even myself. Mother loved flowers, all kinds of beautiful flowers, and I am sure they brought her much joy, as she walked down the shady street called Broad St.

Just past all the stores downtown were very big houses. These were the houses that the big shots lived in; that is what Daddy used to say. They were the houses where most of the people who owned the stores downtown lived, at least that was what I was told. They called it Broad Street. I think every small town has a Broad Street. So you can imagine how big and beautiful the houses were. The trees were so big and beautiful that they hung over the sidewalk. Sometimes the trees would grow moss so long that whenever we walked on the sidewalk, we would pull it off the trees and wrap it around our heads and pretend that the moss was long white hair—just a bit of fun being a child. As we grew older and walked down Broad Street from high school, CHS where I graduated, the moss would aggravate us. We hardly gave playing with the moss a second thought. It would land on your head and into your hair without you wanting it to touch you.

Everyday Mother traveled this route. Being the person that she was and living the life that she lived, I am sure she always saw the beauty in the mornings and the art of God's great work. Mama enjoyed working, but even more, she enjoyed working for the people that she worked for. They were very nice; at least that is what Mother thought, until today. It's hard to believe that people can change from warm to cold so quickly and so suddenly. Today Mother saw a different side of her boss. There was a change in her attitude, a change in her personality.

Mama reached work about six forty-five. She knocked on the door before entering the house and walked inside. The door was never locked, but Mom always knocked to give them forewarning that she was about to enter their home. She walked inside, but she didn't see anybody. Normally, she was greeted with a smile and a warm welcome. But today the boss was out of sight. Mama glance down the hall but didn't see her. She looked to the left in the huge living room where no one ever sat, and she wasn't there. Then she looked to her right in the big dining room, where people sat only when a gathering or big dinner party was being held, and she was not there either. Mama didn't give this a lot of thought at first, but it was obvious that something was wrong. "Where is the boss today," she thought. When the boss finally came out of her bedroom, she didn't seem very happy. She didn't greet and smile at Mama like she did most mornings. "What a way to start the morning?" Mama thought. Mama was confused. She wasn't sure what to think. She didn't want to come right out and ask any questions. I am sure she thought her boss wasn't feeling well. "Hopefully, she will start talking soon," Mama hoped.

Mother had been working there for almost six years now, and never once had she seen her boss act this way. Perhaps she was off to a slow start. Maybe her mind was bombarded with much. Everybody has a few bad days sometimes. Maybe she and her husband had a disagreement. All kinds of thoughts were running through Mama's head, but she didn't feel comfortable asking her any questions. After awhile Mama could no longer deal with the unusual quietness, so she built up the nerves to ask her boss if she was okay. She nodded her head to imply that she was doing fine.

Mama started her day. She walked towards the storage closet and set out the cleaning supplies that she needed. She wanted to get started with her day, hoping that she would be finished before her usual time.

"Perhaps today, I can get started right away and hurry up and get out of here," she thought. She tried to ignore the unusual behavior, but it was impossible. Her boss was still acting very strange. She still had not spoken another word to Mama since she said "Good morning. Mama walked down the hall and began her regular routine. She took the dirty sheets off of the beds. She walked from room to room. She still had no idea what was wrong. Neither did she have any idea that she was about to find out what was wrong. When Mama walked back into the kitchen, the boss was sipping on a cup of coffee. By this time she was ready to talk. She looked up at Mama and called her by her first name.

"Yes ma'am," Mama answered.

"Gracie Lee I won't be needin' you here anymore."

"Ma'am?"

Her boss repeated, "I won't be needin' you anymore." I am sure Mother thought she misunderstood what she heard.

Ma'am? Mother, repeated.

"I won't be needin' you 'round here anymore." She repeated.

, "Now, "Lord ha'm mercy. What in the world?" Mama asked herself. She stood there looking at her, speechless. She had no idea why her boss was saying this to her, "won't be needin' me anymore?" She asked.

"Did you say you won't be needin' me here any more?"

"Yes, that's right. I really don't think you need this job," she said with a smirk on her white face. Mama stood there waiting for her to tell her why she felt like she no longer needed her job. "Had she found someone else to replace me?" she wondered. "Is she no longer satisfied with the work I'm doing around here?" But no, it wasn't any of these things. Actually, she was well pleased with Mama and the work that she did for them. But something was wrong, and Mama waited patiently to hear what it was. Then she said. "The word is you have a daughter away in college. I hear she is at one of those big, ole colored schools over in

228

Atlanta, Georgia." She said. Sizzie had gone to Spelman College. Not only was it a colored school, it was a colored private school. "If you and Homer can afford to send a child to college, then you don't need to be working here, do you?" she asked. I am sure she didn't want a true answer from Mama. Mama couldn't believe the words she was hearing coming from such a nice lady.

"After all I have been working for you for six long years, and now you're telling me you no longer need me because my child is in school. "My God, well then if you feel that way, you're right! I don't need to be working for you." Mama said. I can imagine Mama wanting to say a lot more than those few words, but she knew she'd better accept the fact, that she was no longer needed and walk away in peace.

Mama was hurt, and disappointed. She needed her job. She needed to help Daddy with the bills. She needed to buy clothes for her little ones. "The reasons I've worked so hard is so that I could send my children to school," Mama said. She stood still, waiting for her boss to respond. Tears filled up in Mama's eyes. For a few seconds she was so choked up that she could not move. Then she realized she'd better gather her things. She gathered her belongings, and walked out the door. "If I have to lose my job to save my child's education, then losing my job it will be," she thought. Mama picked up her purse, opened the door nice and slowly, walked out the door, and started her walk back home. There wasn't anything Daddy or anyone could do to help Mama get her job back. I didn't see my Mama cry this day, so I felt safe.

Mama Looking for another Job

It didn't take Mother a long time to find another job. She was fortunate and truly blessed to have found a job so soon. She was a hard worker. I didn't have to go to work with Mama to know that she was a hard worker; I knew this by being her child. I was spoiled in many ways having a mom like Mama. Even when I had left home to go away to school, Mama was still Mama. Before I could unpack my suitcase and carry my dirty laundry to the washroom, Mama would have gone through my luggage, gathered all my dirty laundry, and washed clothes for me before I could return from my friends' house to say hello and let them know that I had come home for the weekend. I guess if I had a little sister back home who was as spoiled as I was, perhaps I would have been jealous of her, too. Perhaps I would have thought life for her was on the up and up. What I learned about being spoiled, as they call me, is when you leave home trying to find someone to treat you like Mama and Daddy did at home it is going to be a rude awakening. It's like cold water being thrown in your face. The real world is no joke. It can be cold and lonely. Yes, I had it made and I didn't realize it until I was on my own. I didn't realize it until I was faced with all of the challenges.

She found this job, hoping that things would be different. Things were different, but things weren't a whole lot better. This time it wasn't the fact that my parents had children in school that caused her to lose her job. It would be something even more challenging. This time it was the name._

Mama's New Job

Mommy had found another job and for several months, close to a year, things were going well. The family was nice. Mother cleaned and ironed clothes for the family, just as she had done on her previous job. The family didn't live on the main street, but a very nice home in the suburb. It was farther out, so Mama couldn't walk to work. Her boss arranged a way for her to get to work and back home each day. They were very nice people to know and to work for, it seemed.

It wasn't until the day Mama called Daddy's name that the family's attitude changed. It never ceases to amaze me the things that we endure and the things that bother us. How can you like a person so strongly and dislike them so deeply? It's a part of life, I am told. It's another part of life that I don't understand.

Something had come up and the boss was unable to drive Mama home from work this particular day. It wasn't a problem for Mama or even an inconvenience, because Daddy could pick her up. Daddy's name was not a secret. Daddy was Daddy, and all we knew is he was a hard-working man who tried to live a good life, a good and humble life. And as far as we knew he was perfect, at least perfect for us. But apart from being quiet at times, easygoing, and tight (stingy) Daddy was perfect to me. Whenever Daddy finished his meal and his stomach was full, he was ready to tell us a joke. Daddy's jokes were always funny. His jokes were much like his love for his family. He would tell the same joke over and over again, and it didn't matter if the same folk heard it, they all laughed like it was the first time they had heard it. Everyone called Daddy by his middle name. It wasn't until Daddy started preaching that he begun using his initials, J. H.

Daddy's name did not come up a lot in the workplace. I guess there wasn't a lot of interest in our family; why would there be? We were just a colored family like everyone else, trying to make a living. But this particular day Mama told her boss that Daddy would be coming to pick her up. This didn't seem to sit well with the boss when she heard Mama called Daddy's name. Her eyes bucked and her ears perked up like a dog's; that is what I remember Mama saying the day she came home and told us her story. Mommy didn't pay much attention to her boss' reactions at first until she asked Mother to repeat exactly who would be giving her a ride home. Mother told her it would be her husband. "Yes, I heard that part, but what is his name?" Mommy repeated his name. She immediately noticed the expression on her boss' face.

"Is something wrong," she asked? Immediately Mother recognized that something was wrong.

The family that Mother worked for who were so nice and caring changed in a split second. The day they discovered my dad's name was not a good day. Unbelievable, I thought. She refused to accept my father's name, and this is what caused Mommy to lose her job. The boss did not like the fact that Daddy had the same name as a white man in town. Even though Daddy's first name is Joshua, he always went by his middle name. This is the name Daddy has always gone by. This is the name his parents gave him. This was Daddy. The family that Mama was working for must not have known much about us before Mama took on the job; if so, they would have known his name.

They were remiss in not knowing much about us. We were poor, so maybe we didn't stand out much. This may have been the reason they didn't know Daddy's name already. Even though we were poor, we were blessed. We were rich in spirit and rich in heart. We did a lot. Even when Mama lost her job again, we still survived. Now that I am all grown up, I can look back at all of the things God allowed us to accomplish. We were some rich, ole colored folk. Having a name like my daddy's must have implied more to being rich than we knew. Mama's employer thought so.

Daddy had the same name as a well-known white man, who owned the white folk funeral home. I didn't know him, but from what I had heard he was rich. I was aware of the funeral home because as far as I knew, we only had two: one for the colored and one for the whites. I also knew it because it was named after Daddy. I should have been excited or glad that someone had named their business after Daddy. After all I knew Daddy before I had even heard of the establishment. But I didn't give it a whole lot of thought being a kid. But it was difficult for Mama's boss lady to understand why Daddy had to have the same name as the white man.

She requested an explanation for Daddy's name. Mama gave her the only explanation she knew. "I don't know why he was given the name, but when I met him that was his name and I never questioned my husband about his name. This is the name given him by his parents, and that is all I know." Apparently the woman was displeased with the answer Mama gave her, and asked her not to come back to work for her anymore.

It was sad being let go, but life had to go on. I believe it was these experiences that led Mama to open her own business. Mama opened a daycare at home. She loved children, and this turned out to be one of the jobs Mama seemed to enjoy the most. Mama kept lots of children. She kept foster kids, family friends, and relatives.

Being Poor

Being a kid I wondered how my family was going to make it many times. Why do people have to be so poor? We were poorer than most of our relatives and neighbors. I don't think any of them realized how poor we were. I couldn't wait until I graduated from college. I was going to buy my parents a bigger house, so they could chase behind each other. Thank God Daddy had good friends who always had money, and they would loan Daddy money. They loaned Daddy money all of the time. He borrowed so much money from them that he had established credit. They trusted Daddy because they knew he would pay them back. Sometimes Daddy had to borrow money from another friend in order to pay back the original friend.

Daddy didn't only have good friends, Daddy knew important people, like the mayor of our hometown and he gave Daddy good advice on what he thought was best for Daddy. He would also loan Daddy money when he was in great need. The mayor was a good man to most of the colored. I can remember hearing the adults talking amongst themselves about how good the mayor was to the colored. He was such a good man that every time he would run for mayor, he won; I was told.

One time when one of my girlfriends was awarded some money, Daddy borrowed money from her. It seemed every weekend when he paid her back the money he owed, he had to re-borrow the money to pay on another bill. Daddy borrowed money from her so often she would often kid me by saying, "Kenzie, um gon put this to the side for Rev. Joshua. I know he gon be asking me if he can borrow some money, saying, 'Valeria, you got twenty-five dollars I can borrow 'til Friday?'" We would just laugh. I was not embarrassed because she was my friend. I knew she would do whatever she could to help my family or me if we were in need.

I believe God gave her the heart to help us and made her available so Daddy could continue the welfare of our household. It didn't make me feel bad. By now I was a big girl. I was about fifteen or sixteen years old. She was two years older than I was. It no longer embarrassed me, because Valeria was my friend and her generosity helped to keep the furniture truck out of our yard.

The furniture store people were always coming to our house threatening to take away our furniture; and once they threatened to take our brand-new carpet away from us. They were always trying to do something obvious to embarrass us. One time my Auntee told Momma to let them have the carpet. I bet this would have made them very happy. They threatened to take away our brand-new sofa Mama had just bought. One time they threatened to take away her brand-new dining room set. It was something all of the time. Mama loved nice things, and she always bought the things she felt necessary or the things that would beautify our home. She always kept things nice. She was always clean and orderly. Mama did not like to fuss. This is one of the reasons she never talked about people; instead, she addressed the issue. I kinda took that from Mama. It's hard for me to stand back and not say anything if someone I love is in a bad situation. I felt obligated to express my feelings. It's hard for me to stand back and not speak out when something is wrong, and everyone around agrees that it is wrong, and no one says a word. It is not the Christian thing to do.

I was beginning to wonder if the truth was best. Yes, I still believe in the truth and I still believe in love. It is true that loved ones and friends don't always enjoy hearing the truth. They don't always understand that it is meant for their good. It can be difficult at sometimes, but the truth is, if I didn't love you so much, it probably wouldn't matter as much. I am struggling with that because it isn't the godly way for me to become. I know I should speak the truth, and I am aware that the truth hurts. It hurts whenever I'm addressed. But Mama never stopped speaking her mind and her heart. If there was something in her heart that was bothering her, she told you about it. Sometimes after Mama spoke her heart and expressed how she felt, the person or persons she spoke to didn't always receive it very well. Yes, I was a lot like my Mama. She didn't hold grudges and she didn't want to speak bad things about a person to another person, so she spoke to the person. Mother wasn't any different when it came down to the furniture men coming to our house threatening to take away our goods. Mama would have to tell them to leave our house and stop with all of the nonsense. "As soon I get the money, I will bring it to you, just like I promised." They knew Mother was serious when she spoke, and off they would go.

Discovering Why We Were So Poor

Daddy was not a rich man, but in many ways he was. I asked Daddy one day without any knowledge of his income if he knew why we were so poor. I didn't get an answer right away, but I eventually got an answer. I suppose Daddy felt it worthwhile to explain to his little one why we were poor. He started to tell me about his jobs. "Ahh, Kenzie," Daddy said, when I first started working for the city, I used to make about twenty dollars a week" I believe that's the figure he gave me. I'll give and take on that figure. He said it went up to thirty dollars a week, and by the time I graduated from high school, Daddy was making almost six thousand dollars a year. I am not exactly sure of that figure either. I don't remember the exact amount; I didn't know how to calculate the funds. It was hard for me to understand, and I wasn't sure if Daddy was going to keep on answering my questions anyway.

At first he seemed hesitant to answer the question. Daddy just looked at me. He looked at me as if I had asked him something that he could not answer or didn't want to answer or didn't know how to answer. In a few minutes, he finally answered my question. I think he may have been surprised. I'm sure he must have wondered why I questioned him. I also thought Daddy was tight, like stingy. I'm sure he wondered why Baby Brother and I thought he was so stingy. Daddy was so stingy it was unreal. Little Brother and I would beg and cry for hours before Daddy would reach into his pocket to give me a dime to go to the store to buy a honey bun. Mama would get tired of us crying. She would finally say with her little soft voice, "Honey, if you got it, please give it to the children." Daddy would finally give in, dig deep into his pocket and pull out his wallet, and slowly hand us the dime to go to the store to get a honey bun.

Baby Brother and I would immediately stopped crying, dry our eyes and I would run across the street to the store. My mouth would be watery from the thought of the taste of the honey bun on my tongue. I could hardly wait to run back across the street to open it. Honey buns to this day are still so good, especially when I think about how long and hard I had to cry just to get one of them bad boys down my throat. But I still wanted to know why Daddy was so tight. When Daddy realized I was no longer joking or kidding, he began to explain things to me.

Telling the Story

First, Daddy said, "Kenzie, you see we always had a place to live, your mom and me and the children. When your Mom and I got married, we had room to take a lot of our relatives in. I took my sisters in and my brothers in, too. We always had a home. Baby, I have always had a car," he said. This is something I later realized that a lot of other people who lived where we lived didn't have: transportation. Daddy said, "I even had a T-Model at one time."

I listened. "Daddy, I can't remember that far back. But I can remember that old green car we had," I said. It must have been a 1959 Ford, definitely a site for young eyes.

Daddy went on to say, "I've had a car ever since your mom and I first got married." Mama and Daddy had been married for fifty-five years before she passed away. As I listened to this story, I began to feel better; better about being poor, better about crying for the honey bun, and better about going to the neighbor's house around dinnertime.

I was that child who knew how to plan my playtime with my friends around their dinnertime. It worked with most families, but there was an exception. One family, no matter how long I hung around during dinnertime, they never offered me any of their food. I would sit in the living room listening to their silverware hit their plates and ice rattling in their glasses and do all I could to fight back my stomach growls and my watery mouth. Most times I never knew what they were having for dinner. When their mother called all seven of them to come to the table, they went. It would be years later that I understood why the mother never invited me to the table to eat, with seven little growing mouths to feed; I probably wouldn't offer anyone any food either. I'm sure it took all they had to feed all of their kids. Even though I felt bad about never getting the chance to eat the crumbs from their table, I made up for it at my other friends' house.

Daddy Continued

Daddy didn't stop there. He went on to say, "When you were growing up, Kenzie, I had just sent your oldest sister, Sizzie, to school. Two years later, I sent your other sister to school, Sarah Jean." I asked Daddy if the government hadn't paid for them to go to school. I was shocked at his answer. Daddy said, "Nore..!! Your mom and I had to send them to school out of what little money we had."

"What money did you have?" I asked Daddy.

Daddy went on to tell me the story. "I didn't have a lot of money of my own," he said, "I had heard about a place down in Mobile, Alabama, where you could borrow money. "I called down to the place and inquired about getting money to send Sizzie to school. They agreed to give me a loan, and that is how she got to school." I asked Daddy why he and Mama wanted the kids to go to school so badly. "Besides your Mama and I wanting y'all to go to school and get your education, this is something your sisters and your brother wanted badly and I didn't want to deprive them from the education they wanted and needed. We believed in school and we believed in education. We believed it was the key to bigger and better things. We believed it was the key to great opportunities. So we did the best we could, with the best we had, to get them the best education they could get." Daddy went on to explain to me about the loan.

Daddy said, "When they approved the loan, they gave me twelve months to pay it off." He accepted the loan and agreed to pay it off in the twelve months allotted to him. Daddy said the twelfth month had come, and it was time for him to make his final payment. He did not have the total amount due. He was nervous. He panicked. He didn't know what he was going to do. I can imagine him calling on the Lord and asking him, "Lord, what am I going to do? Please *ham mercy!*"

Daddy was working at the sawmill, he said. He had gotten off work, and nighttime had fallen upon him. He still did not know how he was going to come up with the final payment to pay off the loan. He went to bed and tried to sleep but could not rest. He tossed and turned, wondering how was he going to come up with the money. He wondered if it would affect Sizzie in school if he didn't pay off that last payment. He couldn't sleep. That is when he got out of bed, just before daylight. He grabbed his work pants, put them on, walked outside to the car, and went to his boss man's house and knocked on the door. I am sure his boss must have wondered who on earth was knocking on his door this time of the morning? Daddy stood nervously at the door, wondering if anyone was going to answer.

I can imagine Daddy in my mind standing there, tall, dark, thin, and handsome. It seemed the older he got, the more handsome he became. It was certain the older he got, the younger he looked. I can only imagine what must have been going through his boss man's mind when he opened the door and saw him standing at his door looking helpless. "Mr. Joe, Um sorry to bother you so early in duh morning, but I need some help." I am sure Mr. Joe had to adjust his eyes and compose himself before asking Daddy what kind of help he needed.

"What is the problem?" he asked. Daddy said he explained to Mr. Joe about the loan.

"I owe some money back on a loan I got from down dare in Mobile, Alabama, to help send my daughter off to college." Daddy has always talked fast.

"Slow down," Mr. Joe said. I am sure he was talking faster than usual.

"Dae want me to pay dis money back in twenty-foe hours and I just don't have it. Um wondering if you can loan me duh money so I can pay dem off," Daddy said.

"Calm down," Mr. Joe said. "Now how much money are you talkin' 'bout borrowing?"

"I need 'bout five-hundred dollars to clear the debt. I'll be sho and pay you back, as soon as I git duh money to pay ya back." Without hesitation, Daddy said, Mr. Joe went to the back room of his house, came back with a check, and gave the money to him. He could not believe it. God had made another way. *"Jesus is a way maker;* Certainly, Jesus had made a way for Mama and Daddy. He could pay back the loan. Sizzie could stay in school. He could breathe again. He did not know it would be this easy. He thought his boss man might have him sign some paper, agreeing to pay him back. He thought that maybe his boss man might need some time to think about it. But God had already worked it out for him.

He left his boss man's house happy as he could be. I can imagine him running to his car like a little kid in the first grade. Daddy walked fast, also; Daddy walked about as fast as he talked. Talking about energy, Daddy has lots of it. Actually, at eighty-six years old, he has about as much energy today as he did way back then. I am sure he was walking faster than usual to get into his car so that he could shout and scream: "Thank God! Thank chu, Jesus!" I bet he had a smile out of this world on his face. The thought of his oldest daughter not having to drop out of college because he did not have the money to pay off the loan could only make him and Mama the happiest people in the world. *Cooter was going to be able to stay in school.* Mama was one of the most God-fearing and praying women that I have ever known. Where would I be if she had not prayed for me?

Mama's Prayers

Not to take anything away from Daddy and his faith, but I can assure you, that Mama had already been praying before Daddy got up to go and ask his boss man for the money. The power of prayer was awesome. The power of my mother's prayer is what kept what little food we had on our table. The power of my mother's prayer is what has brought my family this far. It is the power of prayer that will carry us on. I watched my mother as a little girl, and I observed her faith. I never saw my mother get up out of bed and leave her bedroom before bowing down on her knees to pray. I never saw her go to bed at night before bowing down on her knees to pray again. This is as long as I can remember. Even when Mother got to what she called old, she was still bowing down on the side of her bed to pray. I thank God for her. I am not as consistent as Mama. I pray daily. Sometimes I sit in bed and pray, but most times I bow down on my knees beside my bed just like Mother.

Mother studied and read the Bible daily. There wasn't a night that I can remember that she didn't pick up that Bible and read. Daddy would sit in one chair and read the Bible and Mother in the other. Sometimes I would hear them discussing the Bible and trying to interpret what they had just read. On the first Saturday of each month, our pastor would come to our house and spend the night because he had to travel long distances to get to the church on the first Sunday. When I came inside from playing, the three of them would be sitting in the living room studying the Bible. I find it kind of strange that Mother never insisted on Baby Brother and me coming in the living room with them to read the Bible. It didn't seem to matter much to either of them at the time whether I studied the Bible or not, but when Sunday came, I had to be in church. The lesson I learned from this is that children don't always do what they are told, but they do what they see their parents do. If you are not practicing what you are teaching, don't expect the child to do as you say; it is evident they are going to do what you do.

A Nice Change with the Guys

The job with the payroll company was the best job I had had. Things were getting better. I had no qualms about the job. It was a stress-free environment until I was around the supervisor or until he was around me. He was a nice supervisor. He was cool and easygoing most of the time. Everyone seemed to get along well with him. I did, too, as long as I didn't have to question him about how to do something or inform him of an error I had just made while batching my accounts. Even when I had to go to him for assistance, he was still cool and calm, but it didn't stop me from feeling weak and afraid.

I reviewed payroll for errors. This was a part-time job. I enjoyed it a lot. I was unable to convince the boss, Brad, into hiring me full time and permanent. I tried. My coworkers, who were mainly guys, tried also. They tried very hard to convince him to hire me. He never would. Could it have been that when I was in his presence my chest tightened? My blood seemed to rush straight to my head. The muscles in my face seemed to tighten. This happened every time. I could not control the fear. I fought, I prayed, I tried to smile and laugh it away. But this kind of fear was a stubborn fear. It said, "I ain't going anywhere!" with big, black, bold letters written across my face.

The atmosphere in which we worked was nice and laid back, and working with the guys was a nice change. Whenever you screwed up, they would just explain how to fix it. The guys, even the boss, never seemed to get upset. Even when we all screwed up big time, the excitement and chaos did not uproar the department. Men just seem to handle things differently. When things upset them, they didn't go berserk. Even though we knew the guys were upset, it was just different. They handled things calmly. The atmosphere was ideal for me. "Yes, this is the place I wanted to be," I thought. "Yes, this is the place I will enjoy working until I get old and gray." I didn't pay it any mind that I was a temp, and a part-time temp at that. I had high hopes that I would become a full-time permanent employee. Not only was the department that I worked in cool, the people in other departments seemed very cool, too. You can tell a great company by the faces of their employees. Everyone you met in passing had a smile on his or her face. That kind of expression only made me want more and more to become permanent. I had high hopes and I knew there was a chance that I might not become permanent. I tried not to allow myself to get caught up on false hope, so on my free time I would look for a full-time job.

I worked for the payroll company only twice a week ten hours a day. I was blessed to have found another job very close to the same location, working the other three days of the week. Both of the companies I worked for were great companies. I worked the two jobs for several months. I kept inquiring about becoming full-time, and Brad kept telling me that he only needed someone to do my job two days out of the week. He stated these were the busiest days, and his regular staff didn't have enough time in the day to do what I did on Mondays and Tuesdays.

I started out batching and grouping accounts together, then transferring them to the final payroll department to be processed. Because of my eagerness to stay on with the company and get more hours, I cross-trained and learned how to identify payroll with errors and how to correct the errors. I did this in hopes that an opportunity would soon present itself to me. After several more months of doing my job and the new job, nothing had become available. I found a full-time permanent job. I hated to leave these jobs, but I needed something permanent. I needed benefits. But in hindsight, I should have kept the two part-time jobs, had I known what I was about to launch out into.

The Diagnosis

It wasn't until after my visit to Dr. Shannon's office that I began to feel better and act better on the job. By nature I was a pleasant person, and I suppose this may have confused even the doctor. I had a sense of pride. The time had come for me to lay my pride and my ego to the side. I wanted the doctor to see me. Maybe she could figure out who *me* was. At first she looked me over as if to question my being there. Perhaps I was misreading her, or the little voice inside my head was playing tricks on me again. The voice was trying to convince me that she was not going to help me, and that she was probably wondering why a sane person like me was coming to see a doctor like her. Then on the other hand, sometimes it is the people who seem level, calm, and happy who are experiencing the most pain. Sometimes you never know.

Dr. Shannon asked, "How are you doing?"

"Okay, I guess."

"What seems to be bothering you, McKenzie?" I could hardly wait to tell her what I had been going through. I spilled my guts out to Dr.

Shannon without giving the question a thought. I told her how worthless I felt. I told her how hopeless I felt. I told her how most of my life I had felt like nothing more than a complete failure. I told her how I never felt happy. I told her I could count the days I experienced being happy or feeling joyful. I told her how I was afraid to die; I told her that many times I was afraid to keep living. I told her how the little voice inside my head would never stop talking to me. I told her it talked to me so often I could hardly think. I told her how I could not reason. I told her how everything it said to me was negative. I told her how my family mistreated me. I told her how none of them ever had a kind or positive word ever to say about me or to me. This is when I wanted to cry.

I stopped talking for a minute. That is when she asked, "Why do you think you feel this way, McKenzie?"

"I don't know, except I haven't been able to keep a steady job. People in high positions on the job do not like me. I don't know what I am doing wrong to make them judge me. It seems to happen all the time and on every job." She sat there listening without saying a word. I paused for a second.

Dr. Shannon looked at me and asked the question I had been waiting for. "McKenzie, have you ever been molested?" I wondered what molestation had to do with my feelings, but I knew it was a common question and all shrinks ask that question.

"No, ma'am" I replied. She waited and looked at me to see if I had anything more to say. She must have realized I was exhausted from venting and releasing my feelings. She wanted to know how I heard about her. I told her that my sister was a doctor and that she thought it might be great for me to come and see her. I told her how I had expressed to my sister the way I was feeling. I told her how tired I was of feeling this way. "To tell you the truth, I do not think I can go on in this state much longer," I said. "I am so tired, so tired of being tired, and so tired of feeling this way." Sleep and lethargy had the best of me.

As soon as I finished talking, Dr. Shannon said, "McKenzie, I think you are suffering from depression."

Depression? "What do you mean depression?" I asked her. I was not feeling sad because of the loss of someone. I had been struggling with the loss of my eighteen-year-old nephew. I loved him so much. He was the brightest, most humorous and loving child anyone could have asked for. I believe God sent him here just for me, and now God had taken him away. I missed him so much. And six months after his death, my niece passed away mysteriously. I loved her so much. She was the daughter of my adopted brother, but she spent a lot of time around me. She and her mother had moved to the big city. She would spend many of her weekends with us. We never knew the cause of her unexpected and untimely death. She was only a few years older than my nephew. I couldn't understand why God allowed them to leave us so soon. I suffered from their loss and was on a slow recovery from each of their deaths. So why was she telling me I was depressed? And besides what is depression? If it doesn't mean you are sad because something unexpected had happened to you, then what was she talking about? I soon found out it was more than that. Yes, it was much more than that. There were many reasons for depression and some that the doctors have not yet discovered. It was much more than feeling sad. It was something big. It was something that affected your concentration, something that affected your ability to reason and make decisions in a timely manner. It was something that made you feel insecure. It makes you feel out of touch with others. It made me feel inferior. It made me feel paranoid. It made me feel worthless, left out, and like a failure. It made me tired. It made me unhappy, very unhappy. It hurt. It made my shoulders hurt. It made my head hurt. Sometimes

247

it even made my stomach hurt. It made me worry. I worried constantly, nonstop, and I had no idea that these feelings, these horrible feelings, had a name.

In other words, I thought depression meant you had to be feeling sad because your man walked out on you or because a loved one died. To me depression was when you felt bad and disappointed about something for a period of time. As for me, as far as I could think back, life had always been cloudy for me. I had always been in a world of confusion and depression; most of the time I never had energy. I hardly desired to put on clothes during the day, any day. I would walk around the house all day in my pajamas because I had no energy to take a shower and no energy to put on clothes. I had nothing to do, so why should I put on clothes. Why should I shower? And why should I comb my hair, when I have nothing absolutely nothing to do? I asked these questions of myself. I dared to say these things aloud. I knew there was much to be done around the house, but I had no energy, no desire, and no interest to do that. Mother would say to me, "It is four o'clock, almost time for your dad to come home from work, and you haven't gotten dressed yet. He might need you to ride with him to the store or go somewhere for him." "Or soon Cisseley and Naomi will be coming to visit you, and you still will not have put on any clothes." None of that mattered to me. If Mama had allowed me, I would have gone back to bed and slept all day.

Once I put on clothes and went outside, it would be evening. Besides, this was my favorite time of the day. This was the part of the day that I lived for. It was cool, the sky was blue, and peace seemed to embrace me a little before dark. Cisseley and I would sit outside in the driveway, which was slightly inclined. It was far enough away from the street for us to feel safe sitting there. At least at the time it felt safe. Our parents were constantly telling us to move down farther from the street. People sometimes drove fast. We would sit there talking until the stars came out. We talked about nothing and everything. We would watch the sky, looking up at the stars arguing about which was the Big Dipper, Little Dipper, and North Star. We talked about boys and everything else under the moon. We were trying to be grownups like our parents.

The Pest Control Company

I decided to give up the part-time jobs and accepted a full-time job with the pest control company. Working at the pest control company, I was an administrative assistant. This was one of the not-so-good jobs. It paid me the lowest pay. I had not worked for such little money since one of my first jobs here in Atlanta. I give my goddaughter credit for me taking this job. She convinced me that I needed something full time, something permanent, and that I needed some benefits. All of that was true, and I agreed with her totally. She gave me pep talks on how and what to say in the interview. I couldn't believe how the tables had turned; the shoe was on the other foot. It used to be me encouraging her. It used to be me giving her the best advice I knew how, and here she was convincing me that I needed a full-time job. I talked to her about my interest in the job. I knew that I needed something full time and permanent. I knew I deserved much more money than they were willing to pay me. I was back to settling. I felt like school, my education, and all my credentials were never going to get me anywhere. I expressed to her that the pay was very little. I even told her how I had spoken with the manager and asked him if he could at least match the lowest hourly rate of one of the part-time jobs I was working. I should have known immediately from his answer that this was not the place for me to be working. He said to me, "*I don't have a job paying that amount.*" And that was all he had to say about me making more money. He left no room for negotiating. Everybody leaves room for negotiating.

I went back to my goddaughter and asked Rudy if she felt like I should accept the offer even if he insisted on paying me the little money. She said, "Yes, Kenz." We laughed and kidded about this, and she asked me to shake his hand and say, "Thank you sir, I'll accept it." At first I thought she was jiving about me accepting the job. "At least you will have great benefits and a job," she reminded me again. That was true, and I accepted the job.

Once I accepted the job, I could not believe the mentality of the people. They were so backwards. I don't know how I managed to stay there for two years. The people were strange. This was one of the most racist companies I had ever worked for. There were exceptions; two of the people in the office were nice, Mr. Jackson and Kaitlyn. They were the only two people who seemed to have kept the same personality everyday. Everyone else acted like they hated to be there. Even the technicians who worked in the field, when they entered the office they acted like it was the last place they wanted to be. I could not believe this. First, the office space was very small. I worked in this small office space with three other women. Our desks were lined up side by side. It was awful that we had to sit so close together and look at each other's side view all day long, and sit so close to each other and deal with the different attitudes all day long. After all, no one seemed happy. I had been fortunate that I had not worked in a lot of places where everyone seemed so unhappy. "What's up with these folk in here?" I used to ask myself all of the time. We had no jeans day on Friday, no dress-down day at any time of the year. We had to work constantly, nonstop, until our lunch break. We had to come back from lunch and work all day until time to get off. When I inquired about my two fifteen-minute breaks, the supervisor, Sharon, asked me, "What breaks?" We did not get two fifteen-minute breaks like all of my other jobs. This was a big adjustment. She always had an attitude, and this was a big adjustment as well. Had she not been married, I would have sworn she needed a man in her life. I never ever adjusted well with her attitude. I smiled a lot and tried to make her laugh a lot; but she was a challenge.

The second year I transferred to another division. It was much better than the first year. But after the second year, I was fired. I felt the agony of the loss. But this was probably the best thing that could have happened to me. I don't think I would have ever quit. I gave the job my all, and they still found reason to fire me. How does one retire, if they keep getting fired? I asked. How will I ever be able to earn enough money to save? It's crazy, all crazy. I thought. "

It was an ordinary day. I had worked for six hours. It was month-end. My supervisor and I were working very hard on month-end closing. I had input all the jobs for the month into the computer. I calculated all the hours the guys had worked. I did everything I was required to do. "Yes!" I thought. We were almost done with month-end, and I was feeling really good about it.

My supervisor and I had finally gotten everything entered and posted into the computer and were ready to run our report. Everything looked fine. I was ready to sit back, relax a minute, and exhale from all the stress of the day. This time of the month was always a stressful time. You had to gather everything together that had been done for the entire month and somehow bring it all together and hit the penny on the nickel. We had done it all, thank God.

251

It was getting close to quitting time. We only had about two hours left to work. The branch manager and the field managers had gone for the day. Alberta and I were the only two people left in the office. I didn't notice anything strange about her and I being the only two people left in the office at first. This happened often, but normally not at month-end. Usually, we were so stressed out trying to get month-end closed that by the time we finished, we were too tired to leave the office, and the managers would stick around to make sure that we had everything in order before they would make a move. Today was strange. Everybody was gone and this was the end of the month for us. I could not believe this. "The nerve of them to leave so soon," I thought. "Maybe something urgent came up." Nonetheless, I was happy and relieved that we had done our part. Alberta didn't seem as excited as I was. I had never seen her so calm before. Once that button had been pushed to close out the month, we shouted and jumped. Today she acted strange. She got up and walked to the back of the office to, and then came back up front. It was obvious that she had something on her mind. She sat down at her desk, took a deep breath, then looked over at me and said, "Kenzie, I need to speak with you."

"Oh really," I said in my usual soft tone. "I hope we don't have more work to do," I said. Then I laughed. But she did not laugh back. This was strange, very strange. It made me nervous. She and I were always laughing and talking whenever we had some down time, but today she was acting unusually strange. "What's up?" I asked.

She repeated herself again, and said, "McKenzie, we need to talk."

"That's cool," I said. "What do you want to talk about?" And "Why are you acting like that?" I asked. She sounded even more serious this time than she did before. I squinted my face and looked at her, as if to ask her why was she sounding like that? It sounded serious but I did not think that it would be as serious as it turned out to be. I wasn't used

252

to her speaking to me in the tone in which she spoke. It sounded like trouble. But she and I were always cool. Because of her, I continued to stay on the job despite the mentality of the company. We worked really well together. She was my boss, but we got along well. This was great for me. For the first time in a very long time, I was able to ask her questions and not feel intimidated. I felt like God had delivered me from the anxiety, the anxiety attacks, and the little voice that always told me I wasn't good enough. I rarely had the rapid heartbeats and the feeling that all of the blood in my body had rushed to my head. I rarely suffered anxiety attacks working with her. For a while I thought that I was cured. I thought that whatever it was that kept me in bondage had decided to get up and walk out of my life. It was one of the greatest feelings in the world, being able to work, and not work in such great fear. I didn't fear her or the big boss, Stan. Stan bragged about the good job I was doing for the company. He even gave me a raise the day I started there. He spoke well of me to the guys in the field and demanded that they give me respect. He stressed how important it was for them to adhere to what I had to say. He had lots of respect for his admins. He had lots of respect for Alberta, his office manager. He was well pleased with us. We were a great team, working well together. He respected his managers in the field, but they did not have it as good as we did. They got cussed out a whole lot more than we did.

I didn't fear any of the technicians who worked in the field. Unlike next door, they rarely came in the office. Sometimes I would have to page the field and request that they stop in the office to bring in their paperwork so that I could update customers' accounts. The sales team was no different. Sometimes I would have to page them in order to get their information to record how many sales they had made for the past couple of days. I had lots of work to keep me busy, and it had turned out to be one of the best jobs I had ever had. I forgot about the little money I was making. I had peace of mind for once in my life on the job. I felt great. Life was worth living.

Actually, Alberta had been one of the coolest bosses I had ever had. We shared office space. She sat at her desk, and I sat a few feet to the side of her. It was much more refreshing being in this office than being in the office I had transferred from next door. We shared the same building, but were in different offices and a different division within the company. Our having to share space and get along was a miracle for me. I was not my usual nervous self, thank you, Jesus! Everything was working so well. I tried to stay out of her space, and she tried to stay out of mine. Whenever we had down time, we would talk, laugh, and joke. Most of our days went by really fast, because usually we had so much work to keep us busy. The job that had started out so slow was on the move. But I didn't know what she wanted to say to me that made her not laugh today. After all, we had wrapped it all up and we were done. We normally chanted like cheerleaders and then we were ready to kick back and relax a few minutes before we started the process all over again.

I was already going through the pile of papers on my desk. Already my tray was piled high with jobs that had been done by the technicians on the first and second of the new month. Job security, I thought to myself. It never ends. I realized money was not everything, having peace of mind was far more important to me. I learned how to budget myself and adjust. I rarely made enough money to do some of the other things I enjoyed doing after work, like going out to dinner or going out to the mall. I didn't worry a lot about a new outfit like I used to, and the good thing about it was the size of the office; it didn't seem like either one of us did a whole lot of shopping. Actually, it didn't seem like anyone in the office did a lot of shopping. Luckily, the guys wore uniforms. I wouldn't have minded it if we had to wear uniforms, too. Then I really wouldn't have missed going to the mall as much. But the flip side of this was whenever I did go out and buy something new, the whole office noticed. But Stan, he wore suits every day. He was a neat freak, to be a man. He was straight, too. His hair was always in place. He never had a wrinkle or spot on his shirt or tie.

The new month had not started according to the company and already, as I stated earlier, I had stacks of papers piled on my desk. We could not begin working on any of our new paperwork until month-end had completed its process. I knew my supervisor was just as excited as I was, even though at this point she still wasn't showing it. I still couldn't understand why she was not jumping up and down and running down the hall like we always did. Something was definitely wrong with her today. This was not the person I had come to know. I tried to be cool and not worry about her, but it was hard to avoid the strange feeling in the air. I sat at my desk and started making new folders for the new month. I was waiting for her to talk to me. I knew when she felt like talking, she would. I looked up at her; she looked puzzled. She looked sincere and indefinable. "Something is wrong," I thought to myself. I stopped smiling.

She looked at me and said, "I have to do something today, Kenzie that I have never done before." I wondered what in the world that was. "Is she about to offer me a raise?" I wondered. "Is she about to tell me that she is leaving the company and I will have to run the darn office by myself?" She stopped and paused for a long time. I wiped the smile off my face and looked at her with a sincere look.

"What's wrong?" I asked. She did not speak. She just looked at me. Then she got up and walked to the empty desk on the side of me where we kept our miscellaneous papers and things, and sat on top of the unoccupied desk and looked at me.

Then she said, "This is very hard for me."

"Girl, what is hard for you?" I asked. "Go ahead and talk to me," I insisted. I held my head down and looked at my watch. By now it was forty-five minutes before I was to get off work. "Can't this jus wait until tomorrow?" I was thinking. When I looked back up at her, a tear rolled down her cheek. She could not speak. I began to feel sorry for her, sorrier than I was feeling for myself. I knew what was about to happen, even though I did not want to face it. I could no longer handle the way this was going. I knew what she wanted to say, and I knew she did not know how to get the words out. I had to ask her the question. "Alberta, am I fired?" Tears began to roll heavily down her face; she nodded her head and tried to mumble the word "yes" out of her mouth. I felt chills all over my body. I couldn't believe it had happened to me again. I immediately began opening my desk drawers, pulling my things out of each drawer one by one while she watched as I packed all of my things. I knew how it went. If you knew it was coming, you got the chance to pack your own belongings. If your guards were down, you didn't get the chance to pack anything; they packed it for you. Then they would escort you to the door and out of the building. I knew the routine. I knew it oh so well! Knowing this didn't make it any easier for me. I was angry, I was disappointed. I didn't know what to feel. I didn't know how to feel. Suddenly everything was moving so fast, the time and my heart. It was racing. I could not believe I had just lost another job. What had I done wrong this time? What will their excuse be? I began to think that I must have been the greatest failure in the world. Yes, Murphy's Law, whoever Murphy was, I believe he once said whatever could go wrong will go wrong. Yes, something had gone wrong again; time and time again. She then got the courage to stand up and escort me to the door like I was a criminal. I wanted to go off! I wanted to school her about standing up to corporate America and tell her how she shouldn't let them feed her junk. I wanted to tell her if I was in her shoes, I would leave also. Even though like me, she needed her job. But I felt like if the shoe was on the other foot at that moment, I would have left the company, too. "How will corporate America ever get the message if someone doesn't take a stand?" I thought. I will leave this company, and hopefully I will not have to look back. I am so tired, so sick and tired of always being mistreated. It's the same ole bologna all of the time." I felt so helpless. Was this a reason for the little voice to come back and remind me of how I couldn't make it even when things seemed to be going well? I needed someone to talk to, but I didn't want to talk to anyone. All I could think was how long I stayed there trying to do good, trying to be good, and working for ten dollars and some odd change per hour with a college degree. I was sure that people on paper routes made more than I did, their hours were shorter, and they probably had less time to deal with the boss. This was my next mission—maybe I needed a job out in the field. "Oh my God!" I thought. "Must life be so unfair and so cruel?" I started singing an old hymn that I learned to sing in church when I was just a little girl. I had to stretch my hand to God. I didn't know anywhere else or anyone else to turn to.

Right now I didn't know where to go, and again I didn't know what to do. If God would not help me, I would never be able to help myself, I thought. I was looking to the hill from which cometh my strength. I was reaching up and reaching out to God because I couldn't understand why something that seemed so simple to many was so complicated for me. I was still feeling like a complete failure. Apparently, I had pissed someone off really bad. I had an idea, even though I wasn't absolutely certain; I felt certain it was the lady from the home office, Jeanne. She was the administrative secretary for the home office; she was the big lady. I had no doubt that she was the reason behind me losing my job.

From my understanding, she was the big boss's secretary. She was also over all of the administrative assistants for this division. Before transferring from next door, I had never seen or heard of her. We had someone else over us on the residential side of the business. It was someone we didn't see a lot. As a matter of fact, I only saw her once. She was the one we probably needed to see more of. She was Sharon's boss. I'm sure Sharon did everything she could do to keep her boss from visiting our office. I'm sure she didn't want our head lady to see much of her attitude.

Jeanne wasn't the nice person she appeared to be. She had a dress code of her own. It was certainly her own, because I don't believe anyone else could dress like her and get away with it. She probably dressed perfectly for her boss and Mr. E. also. Mr. E's real name was Edward; but sometimes we called him Ed. For some reason, Sharon shortened it even more and called him Mr. E. Ed was the branch manager for the residential side of the business, the division I had transferred from. The residential and commercial side of the business was run like two different companies. The commercial side of the business was run so differently, it seemed like two different companies. I preferred the commercial side, but right now it wasn't making much sense to me either.

I had met Jeanne on a few occasions. She seemed nice. She wore her hair short, and her skirts short too. She wore her skirts way too short for work. This wasn't the type of business for any woman to be wearing her skirts as short as she wore hers. A pair of jeans with a nice blouse would have been more conservative than the skirts she wore. For this to have caught my eye, it must have been pretty serious. I didn't notice people's clothes that much. If the person wore something nice, I complimented. I didn't get too caught up in fashions. I knew I had to wear a suit and heels every day. I had to look the part to get the job, and dress up everyday to keep the job for as long as I could. Yes, I had to dress to impress. Transferring had been a wonderful change for me. I was feeling so much better. I could care less about dressing up. I had peace of mind, and it no longer mattered how I looked to anyone. I knew my job and I knew it well, and that was just enough for me.

I had been warned by many that Jeanne was sneaky but that didn't change the fact that I thought she was a nice person. I was still naïve about corporate and the games that we needed to play. I had to learn quickly how to become a quick study, especially now since I had begun to feel better about myself, but even now it seemed too late. Jeanne had come into the office and disturbed things. It felt good having my worries and fears leave me. I was able to focus and even concentrate. I couldn't thank God enough. I had learned how to open up, relax, and talk freely with the boss and upper management. I could even engage in conversation with them without drifting off to something else. I couldn't understand why anyone would want to get rid of me now. Couldn't they see the progress I had made? The truth is they had no idea. No one had any idea what I was going through or what I had gone through.

Ed, the manager next door took it upon himself one morning to call me into his office. Calling me into his office took me by surprise. I couldn't imagine why he wanted to see me in his office. Once I got into the office and sat down, he started to talk. He wanted to tell me the story of how the company got started, and the founder's feeling about women. He told me how women were supposed to dress like ladies at all times, and I strongly agreed with him. But I still wasn't sure where he was going with this story. I had already been informed that we couldn't wear jeans. We didn't have a jeans day on Friday like most companies I had worked for. But I couldn't quite figure out where this discussion was going. I had pretty much figured out how the company felt about women when I was informed that we had no paid maternity leave. That said a lot in itself. Thank God, I was not anticipating becoming pregnant anytime soon. But he wanted to share with me, for some interesting reason, the dress code of the company after I had been with the company for almost a whole year.

I wasn't excited about hearing all of this, but apparently he felt the need to discuss this with me. I looked over my outfit before he could say anything about it, trying to judge it openly and honestly. It looked fine to me. In the past I had always tried to look professional, but it was hard trying to dress professional in such a small office. It was small and country. It gave me that good ole down home feeling of being casual and feeling at home. It only felt this way when it came to dressing. Being in the environment I didn't feel the need to dress up. It just wasn't that type of environment. I have to give it to Sharon she dressed sharp everyday. You couldn't help but notice her. After all, there were only four of us packed in this little one room together. There wasn't a day that she didn't wear her high-heeled shoes and an outfit to match. She was the boss; maybe she made enough money to keep up her image. Me, I was just happy to have a job. I got the impression that the company wanted to keep an old-fashioned image, and if that made everyone happy, this time I didn't want to be the one to try and change things. I was trying to learn how to play the game—keep a low profile and go with the flow. No need to express my opinion about things, no need to mention how wrong it was not to even offer us a break. No need to mention that every other company in the world offered a jeans day or a dress-down day. It was as if the company had no interest in what was modern. I looked at my outfit, and I thought it was just as nice as anyone else's. "Was it appropriate or inappropriate?" I asked myself. Actually, it looked fine. I had heard the story before of how the company was a small family business that grew and grew and kept growing and became a mega company. I admired the business before it was all said and done. Before I was fired, I had heard rumors of other folk in the company trying to open their own pest control business. Business was booming. Bugs were running everywhere. It was the kind of business to start. I even considered opening up one myself, being the entrepreneur that I am. There was great demand for service. The boss man always reminded us that our business was here to stay, because the bugs weren't going anywhere. "Maybe this was a good time to go back to school since I was going to be out of work again," I thought. But I realized I needed money to get into school to learn about all of the different bugs and pesticides. But I didn't even make enough money to put any to the side.

Being in training didn't teach us much about the bugs. I was the office girl, making sure that the bug man got to the businesses, making sure he killed all the pests, and sending him back out to the business if there were any problems or complaints. We were supposed to go out in the field every so often with the techs to see what being in the field was really like. We were supposed to get the chance to see what chasing behind rodents, carpenter bees, and ants was really like, not to mention all of the other critters the guys had to chase behind. It turned out to be interesting, but I wasn't the one who had the guts to chase behind them. I would have been like one of the techs who admitted he was afraid of rats. He told me that once he went out to do service and instead of him chasing the rats, the rats were chasing him. I couldn't get mad. It

261

was hilarious. When Tommy couldn't kill the rats, we would page the manager, and he would go out to make sure that the critters were caught and killed. I never told the boss how he feared them.

Ed talked to me and told me how the company expected us to look every day. I took it that he meant very professional, but I think he meant country and homely. If he meant professional, of course, I had no problem with this: dressing professionally was the only way I knew how to dress in the workplace. But I'll be the first to admit that since the little voice inside of my head was quieter, I no longer felt the need to dress as professionally as I did before. I was feeling free. I was feeling much happier these days. It didn't matter if I wore a suit and pantyhose with high heels or not. It didn't matter anymore if I wore a scarf to go around my neck to accent my outfit. For once in my life I was feeling fine being me whoever "me" was. Today of all days, Mr. E. felt the need to address me about the outfit I was wearing.

He reminded me again how the founder had required women to wear dresses only. "The rules have changed a bit since the old man died, and women are now able to wear pants," he said. I happened to be wearing pants, so what was he trying to say to me or about me. He stressed to me that the rules had changed but hadn't changed very much, and the particular outfit I was wearing was inappropriate. He said. "Things have changed around here, McKenzie." "Yes sir." I said. I was wearing a white pair of pants with a red and white blouse that covered the hips and butt. The blouse had three-quarter-length sleeves and they were floppy. It covered all of the breast and most of the chest, with enough chest out to show off the beautiful red and white necklace I was wearing. I even wore red shoes. Sandals were not permissible, and all toes had to be covered. It was summertime, and I thought this rule was another crazy rule for a company. The office was small and not many people came to the office. I could never understand what was wrong with wearing a beautiful sandal. A lot of the rules were dated, but who was I to say? I was busy trying to learn how to play the game. Things next door were not as strict. Stan did not focus on our dress code as much as he did on making sure the office was run smoothly. He wasn't as backward when it came to being comfortable and happy in the working environment. His concern was sales, getting more sales and keeping all the customers. I liked this about him.

I didn't understand why Mr. E. disliked my outfit. I didn't think I looked out of place. But since I was trying to learn the game, I wasn't about to express my true feeling. This was unusual for me. Usually, I spoke what I felt when I felt it was right. If I believed it, I spoke it. I wasn't going to become defiant and lose my cool. I kept calm. "Should I go home and change clothes?" I asked. If I was not looking presentable, I was willing to leave, try it again, and hopefully get back to work before the day ended. I didn't mention to him that I didn't have enough gas to drive all the way home, change clothes, and then drive all the way back to work and then home again. I am sure he already knew that, so he agreed that I could work throughout the day and keep on my outfit as long as I didn't wear it again. I didn't feel comfortable with myself after leaving his office. "Was I really looking out of place?" I asked myself. I wanted someone else's opinion about the outfit. I asked everyone at work, including Sharon, and even she thought it was fine. I'm sure she would have told me the truth. He blew my day for the rest of the day, before I figured out exactly what he was trying to say. It must have been the floppy sleeves that Mr. E. didn't like. I think it made me look a little too black. The floppy sleeves; must have looked too much like the seventies. When we were coming out. Shouting out loud I am black and I'm proud.

Then it hit me, this was the outfit I had worn on Saturday to the Black Art Festival at Greenbriar Mall. "Oh! I see!" I thought. I get it now."

Jeanne had come to assist me for approximately five or six days out of the entire time Alberta was out of the office on maternity leave. She must have had a change of heart for me. I thought she liked me and my work; if not she put up a nice front. I liked her. I even stopped to pick up breakfast for us a couple of mornings. I let my guards down, relaxed and did my job daily, and talked to her in the same manner I talked to Alberta. I was never disrespectful. That just wasn't how I was reared. I gave her all the respect plus more, just like I did Alberta. Since this was the first time I had experienced being comfortable with the boss, I'm not sure if I had become too comfortable. I may have laughed and talked about things I shouldn't have. I didn't know. I was so excited that I could work, talk, and not be afraid; I didn't know what to do. I didn't think she was overseeing me with a whip and planning to chop my head off until her sixth day of helping out in the office.

I didn't understand why she felt like I should have known how to run the entire front office all by myself with the few hours of training I received. There was no official training for me before Alberta left to take time off to have her baby. I was lucky to have trained with Alberta for the few hours that I did. When I learned all the things that she was doing, I was swept away. Actually, I had no idea she did so much, and actually I never learned half of the stuff she did to keep the office running as smoothly as she did. I learned the most important thing there was to learn about her job, and that was how to close out the month. Technically, it would have taken a couple of weeks to learn this, but we didn't have a lot of time to train between trying to keep up with her work and mine too. But Jeanne felt like I should have been able to do Alberta's job without a doubt. She complained to Stan about how I spent too much time working on my initial job and not enough time overlapping or multitasking. She was right about that. Again, there was my weakness surfacing again, my weakness shining bright and clear for the whole world to see. I believed I had to finish one job completely before starting on something new. This was something I was planning to work on earlier. Yes, this was my weakness. I felt like I had to complete one task totally before I began on another one. My sister use to call it overlapping. She says it's good to overlap or multitask. She says it's also good to delegate. But I had no one to delegate my workload to. I thought that was what Jeanne's job was supposed to have been. She was supposed to do all the things in the office that I didn't know how to do. I didn't know how she was going to do it all in time for month-end, because she wasn't in the office enough to assist me. What was her purpose? It took two people to run a four-man office. How in the world was I supposed to do it alone? I didn't know. So she turned me over to Stan. Alberta had mentioned something to me a couple of times about time management; time management—what was that and why was she mentioning that to me. I didn't know. I finally got the nerve to tell her that I didn't know what time management was and didn't know why she was always using that term around me. She finally told me, and I tried to do the time management thing the best way I knew how, but it didn't work out well.

Mr. Stan usually listened to my suggestions. Whenever the field was not responding like they should after several reminders, I brought it to his attention. He always listened and he always followed up. To me he was a good manager until it came to standing up for me in the presence of Jeanne. I had asked Mr. Stan about bringing in a temp to help out, but to my surprise it was too much to ask for. I thought this was absurd. He accused temps of not being dedicated if they came in to help for six weeks only. I had been a temp most of my life, and I knew I did a darn good job. Maybe Mr. Stan thought that I was able to run the office alone. If that was the case, I appreciated his faith and confidence in me, but I needed help and needed it badly. Actually this was the day I was fired, but he waited until Alberta returned back to work to drop the bomb on me.

Days at the University

Being in college was an experience that I will never forget or regret. I felt blessed even then to have the opportunity to go to college. This was something I knew would make my parents very proud, and I wanted to be proud in return. My grades weren't the best. I barely got accepted into college. This was just another time that I knew someone was praying for me. God answered my mother's prayer. It is strange to me now when I look back on how difficult it was to concentrate and study way back then, and I never realized that it might have been a problem. I was a drifter. I drifted and daydreamed most of my life. I lived, but I lived in my own world. The real world was too much for me to handle in my mind. Many times I ask myself how I made it over.

I began my studies at ASU, and transferred after my third year to TSU. I didn't know a lot about the college I attended. One thing I knew is that ASU was a predominately black school. I knew that a lot of the great teachers from my hometown had attended this university. The other thing I knew is that I was happy to be accepted. I was excited about being away from home and feeling like an adult. I enjoyed the independence. I loved the campus grounds. I loved the dormitory living. I loved the different groups and organizations. I admired the sororities and fraternities. I had heard so much about them from my big brother Joshua Jr. I already knew which sorority I wanted to pledge before I even registered for college. I loved making my own schedule. I even loved waking up to an alarm clock in the morning and sometimes in the afternoon between classes. I thought it would take me much longer to get used to getting up without Mama calling me, "Kenzie, get up!" Sometimes I could still hear her sweet, soft voice, which was only a note above a whisper, whenever I would take a nap in between classes, telling me it was time to stop snoozing and get up and get out of here and go to class.

My first two years of attending college, I didn't take very seriously. I went to class whenever I was scheduled, but that was about all I did in class—attend. I don't remember studying while in high school, and I certainly didn't know how to study being here. It would be three years later before I realized that being in college was no joke and that I had to figure out a way to get my study habits intact. It was within two years that I would come to realize that it was more than being away from home, with my own space in a secured dormitory with a measurable amount of freedom to laugh and to have fun.

It was great to be able to go when I wanted to go, and come when I wanted to come. It was even greater that I did not have overly protective parents who tried to keep me in the house with a close eye on me all of the time. It was their trust in me and the freedom that they allowed me back home that followed me when I was away from home. I didn't feel as though I had missed out on a lot in life. I didn't feel the need or urgency to go out and stay past midnight. I stuck to the same rules I had back home, and they were not hard rules to follow. So my freedom away from home did not cause me to fly very far away from what I was accustomed to. If I stayed out past midnight, so what? I knew how to wake myself up and get started for the next day. There was never a need to stay out all night. I had no relatives off campus to spend the night with, and all of my friends stayed in the dorm.

But I had concerns. My poor study habits followed me and haunted me. I needed to learn how to study and concentrate. Looking the part and acting the part was no longer satisfying my spirit. I needed more. Playing cards all day and most of the night were not teaching me enough. It taught me how to jive and kid more and to carry on in such a way that I could almost talk myself into a winning hand. After all, I was not playing with experts. I only played with my girls from home, and my roommate, Katherine. We could hardly wait for class to be out so that we could play cards. We would meet in Naomi's room; that seemed to be the meeting place for the card games. Sometimes we would get so wrapped up in playing our game that we could hardly wait for one of us to get out of class to challenge the winning hand. Sometimes we would get so wrapped up in our game that we would forget to go to class.

Having the freedom also taught me responsibilities. It was my responsibility to buckle down and accomplish the goal that I had set out to accomplish. Naomi had already begun to feel this way; after her second year at school, she transferred. I could not transfer or leave school at this time. I had to prove to myself that I could do my work and could acquire some study habits. It was my third year when I began to take school seriously. I knew I had to believe in myself before I graduated and went out into the world to help others. I wanted to be a social worker, counselor, psychologist, and I knew I needed to do more. It was time out for fun!

The other concern I had before I began to study was my graduation date, which was quickly approaching. I had taken all of the required courses that I needed to take. I felt myself becoming very fearful because I had not applied myself in the way I should have, and I did not feel like I had learned all I needed to know before I took a leap out into the real world. My greatest desire was to help others. I believed God had given me that gift. As time moved on, I was no longer sure if God had given me the gift, or if it was my strong need for help from others that made me feel like I could help others. By the time I graduated from college, I still was not sure. It would be day after day and years after years that my need to be helped would become evident—the need to be supported, the need to be encouraged, the need for self-love and the need for self-esteem in order to help others to overcome their struggles, their obstacles, and worries. I realized I needed to be cured.

I felt like I had proven a lot to myself before I decided to transfer, like Naomi, to attend another school. Transferring to a predominately white college was an altogether different story. I will not say that I regret transferring to TSU. I experienced the difference in the schools. The exposure of the grounds was different, the way they handled business and registration was different, and most of all the cafeteria food was different. We had choices. We could choose what we wanted for breakfast; believe it or not, we had choices. There was a difference in the quality of the food. Actually, for a college campus the food was pretty good. The love and the concern that the professors had for you at ASU was not there. The professors at TSU did not seem to care if I showed interest or not in my classes. Even if I showed interest, the instructors never reached out, and this was not boosting my ego one bit. At times I wanted to go back to ASU, since I knew how to study and the instructors seemed impressed by me.

A Devastating Experience at TSU

One of the most devastating things happened to me there. It happened in my tennis class. I attended the class twice a week. I went religiously, never missing a day. I knew nothing about tennis but decided to take the class in hope that it would be a learned skill and therapeutic game for the mind. But it turned out to be a fiasco. The most devastating thing that could have happened, happened. Thank God I did not incur any physical injuries, because that would have been most painful. But receiving a grade D in this class was almost as painful; even though it was not physical, it was terrible. It haunted me so badly that I had to put the memory of that in the back of mind to forget it once and for all. I was so devastated about this that I refused to challenge the instructor. I believed he did this out of his own prejudices. I was convinced he was racist. I became angry every time I thought about this dehumanizing act. It was terrible. It was devastating. It was unacceptable. How could someone get a grade D in a tennis class? If anything you got a C for showing up everyday, and a C+ for trying so hard making a fool out of yourself. That should have counted for something. Welcome to TSU!

My experience with the other professors was also interesting. There were no instructors giving me advice on how to improve. No instructor referred me to a tutor for assistance. I missed the love of the instructors from ASU. I missed the interest that they took in you, if you were trying. I missed the love. I did not miss the administrative side. I did not miss the extra long lines of standing for days trying to register. I missed many things about ASU, but I learned things by attending TSU.

The educators at both schools had quality education, but I learned that it is not how much you know, but how well you present what you know to your students. I discovered you can achieve the same quality of education from a black institution as you can from a white institution. It would be years later that I came to realize it was prejudice and racism that made America so full of hate. I was so caught up in my own world of worries and stress that I didn't realize I was being discriminated against. I simply believed that some people were good, and some were just plain on bad. This has been a hard thing for me to accept and receive.

Chasing the Little Red Car

One thing I did not do on TSU campus was let the little red car out of my sight. As cold as it was I was determined to keep up with that car. I was driving behind the cute, little red sports car, honking my horn and flashing my light. Since I had only one headlight, I wasn't sure if he would notice I was flashing it. Finally, the driver looked in his rearview mirror and noticed he was being followed. I could see from his mirror that he was curious about the car behind him, honking its horn. I got nervous, but I couldn't chicken out. Sherita and Naomi would have never let it die. I was not about to back down now. I had gotten his attention, and he slowed down. I was becoming even more afraid and nervous now that he knew we were trying to stop them. But I had to be brave. I rolled down my window and motioned for him to turn in the parking lot in front of the dorm. My heart started to beat really fast. It was very cold outside, but I was feeling warm. I looked over at Sherita and Naomi, and neither one of them said a word. I could tell by their facial expressions that they were just as excited as I was. I pulled in the parking space next to the cute, little red sports car and smiled. The guy on the passenger side looked at me. I looked back at him. He rolled his window down, and then I rolled down my window. At first I didn't know what to say, and then I remembered the old familiar line. "Oh, I'm sorry, I thought y'all were someone we knew," I said with a soft voice and innocent smile. The guy looked over at the driver, and I can only imagine what they must have been saying or thinking. "Yeah right," I'm sure they must have been thinking. Then he looked back over at me. I was lost for words. I didn't know what else to say. "Help me," I was thinking. It was time for Naomi or Sherita to say something. But I guess they must have suddenly become speechless. The guys didn't seem too surprised that we had tried to stop them. We had small talk, and as it turned out, we discovered that we had a mutual friend. The driver of the car asked if we knew any Deltas on campus. We all said, "Yes, we are Deltas!"

The driver said, "We are looking for a Delta name Carlia. Do you's know her?"

"Yes," we said in unison. I knew right away that the guys couldn't have been Southerners; instead of y'all, they were saying you's. I hated you's about as much as the Northerners hated y'all.

My sorror Sherita said, "She is my roommate. I was just about to go to my apartment. Would y'all like to follow us?" Sure," they said. I put the car in reverse. This was about the easiest part of driving a stick to me, putting the car in reverse. It was much easier than trying to shift gears with three people sitting in the front seat, but I had gotten used to it, especially on cold days like this day. I backed out of the parking lot and headed to my sorority sister's apartment.

I pulled up into the apartment complex. I parked the Bug and hurried to jump out of the car. I asked the guys to stay there as I ran inside to see if Carlia was home. When I opened the door, about six of my sorority sisters were sitting in the apartment. I ran into the apartment shouting, "Sorrors! Sorrors! I have some fine men in the car outside!" They didn't say a word. They all jumped up with excitement without asking any questions. Some started brushing their hair, and some started running to the back to put on lipstick. They quickly scattered. There is something about the words "fine men" that will make a woman move every time. I went in the back to see if Carlia was home. She was not home from class yet. I walked back to the car to tell Sherita. Sherita said it was okay to invite the guys in. They seemed like nice and decent guys, thank God.

We invited the two young men to come inside. By now all of my sorority sisters were made up and looking nice. Finally, I got a good look at each one of the guys. Neither one of them was bad looking. I was certain that neither one of them would find me interesting. I didn't pick up on any vibes from either of the guys. I didn't have a lot of self-esteem, anyway. I wasn't feeling pretty, and besides I was too skinny. "Who would want to talk to someone as skinny as I was?" I thought.

This was my second year at TSU, and so far I hadn't had much luck with the guys. I was fortunate to have gotten a dance here and there whenever we would have a sorority party or whenever the brothers would have a frat party. Other than that, there wasn't much excitement going on in my life around the campus. I observed both of the guys from the sports car. Both were tall, and both were handsome. If I had to choose one, I would have probably chosen the driver. I thought he was the cuter of the two. The one who sat on the passenger side had a darker complexion, which is what I preferred. The blacker the berry, the sweeter the juice, that is what the old folk used to say, but he seemed so cool; I didn't think he talked much. I wasn't interested in anyone who was not willing to talk a lot, like me. But he had a nice smile with pretty white teeth. *That* I noticed when he smiled back at me. He had nice hair and nice waves and a clean low-cut, with a nice grade of hair. He also had nice thick black eyebrows. I could have taken an interest in him easily, but what the heck? No man wanted a girl with all skin and bones. Besides, I had a prior engagement that evening, and I was excited about going out.

I sat on the floor of the apartment, so that everyone else could find a seat. The living room was small. We offered the sofa to the guys, and one of my sorrors sat on the sofa beside the guys. Another sorror sat in the side chair. One sister sat on the arm of the chair. We made enough room so that everyone was comfortable. We engaged in small talk. I didn't do a lot of talking; my mind was preoccupied because I had plans. I had a date. I was thinking about the time, and how I would have to get up and leave this great company. I was enjoying the conversations, but I had to cut my visit short. I got off the floor, stood up, and got my things together before saying goodbye. Even though I knew that they probably hadn't noticed me other than me being the one who was driving the car, I still wanted to be nice. I told the guys it was nice meeting them and apologized for having to leave so soon. I'm sure they could have probably cared less about my leaving; it was protocol. I had my big smile on my face as I was leaving, and I turned around to say goodbye to everyone. I had no idea I would be seeing either one of these guys ever again.

The Job of A Lifetime

It had finally happened. The place I wanted to be, and thank you, Jesus. Looking back, I could see why things had gone the way they had. It was all for me to land this one. The job I had long awaited. I didn't know I could feel so excited about going back to work. I didn't know that anyone could be as excited as I was about landing the perfect job. It made every other job in my past all worthwhile.

Several months after being fired from the pest control company, I received a call from my agency, asking if I was interested in going on an interview. "Of course," I said. The agency advised me that this job was a decent-paying job. Finally my education and all of my difficulties of trying to find a job will pay off, I thought. The agency advised me that after ninety days, I would get an increase and become a full-time employee with the company; that is, if the company liked me and I were a fit. I prayed to be a fit.

The time had come and I welcomed it. Everything was so right. The pay was great and it was an excellent company to work for. I was becoming overwhelmed with my volunteer work. I had been working voluntarily at the church. We packed boxes of food for the needy. I did this twice a week. When I was not at the church, I would baby-sit. Whenever I wasn't working at the church or baby-sitting, I slept. I had done so much sleeping, I was tired of sleeping. I was ready to try corporate once again.

I went to the interview. To me, the interview went really well. The next day the agency called me. I wasn't home because they had sent me on another assignment to work for three days as a fill-in. It felt good to be working while waiting. I didn't have to sit on the edge of my seat waiting to hear from them.

When the agency called my house, my brother answered the phone. Harvey Lee. was visiting with us for a few days. He answered the phone and recognized right away that it was the agency. He knew too well about my desire to find a permanent job. Since I had run out of friends to talk to about not having a job, I called him. So the phone call came as no surprise. Rebecca asked to speak with me; I don't know what she was thinking, calling me at home. Apparently they had forgotten I was already on an assignment. Before they could leave a complete message, my brother asked her if I had the job. "Ma'am, just tell me please does she have the job? I am her brother."

"Yes, sir, she does." Thank God he did not hang up the phone on her.

When Rebecca said "yes," he quickly told her, "I will call her right now on her cell phone and let her know! She is going to be so happy. I'll call for y'all." He didn't give her the chance to say anything else. He quickly hung up the phone. He seemed happier for me than I was for myself. He immediately hung up the phone and called me. The office phone was ringing on my desk, and my cell phone ringing in my purse. They were calling me at the same time to tell me the good news. I answered the office phone and put the caller on hold so that my cell phone wouldn't be heard ringing in the background. It was my brother; I shouted and screamed when he told me the good news. I was already familiar with the company. I knew the company was great. I knew it was a great company to work for. I couldn't talk with him long because I had the caller on hold. I went back to the caller, and it was the agency. I knew it had to be them! I knew it! I didn't tell the agency I already knew I had been chosen; I didn't tell them that my brother had beaten them to the punch. I gave Rebecca the pleasure of telling me the good news.

"McKenzie, they thought you were great, and the company would like for you to start work on Monday," she said. I was so happy. I agreed that Monday would be fine.

I just had one question: "What are you going to do about someone filling in for me on Monday?" They suggested that I tell Ken. I had to tell the man I was working for that I would not be returning to work on Monday as promised. I didn't want to tell him. I didn't want to disappoint him. I knew the agency should have handled this, but they insisted on me telling him.

I had been on this assignment for two days; Thursday and today, and was scheduled for one more day. Here I was finally getting the job of a lifetime, and I was wondering how was I going to tell Ken that I could not come back to work for him on Monday. I wanted to do the right thing; I wanted to hold to my word and the word of my agency. Even though they didn't seem concerned, why was I? It was my nature, and it was the right way to do things.

The office was a three-man office, but one person occupied it most of the time, and that person was me for the time being. Sometimes Ken would be in the office with me but most of the time he was out of the office peeking other properties and attending business meetings. The other two individuals worked throughout the building, one male and one female. They roamed the building throughout the day, making sure everything was running smoothly. I didn't mind being in the office alone, because I felt nervous whenever Ken was around, especially when I had to ask him a question. At first he seemed like a nice, likeable guy. He was tall. He was about six feet six, slender, with black hair. I don't know what color his eyes were. I never looked anyone in the eye, but I assumed they were brown. He was also very tall to be a white man and also very attractive. Where were they getting all of these tall white men from all of a sudden? On one of my other jobs all of the men in the office were tall, but they were not handsome like Ken. He was cute. He trained me for about fifteen minutes. I had it down pat. I had run the front office many times before. I had been a receptionist many times before also. He demonstrated how to operate the phone system and gave me his extension number, just in case I had questions or needed to speak with him. He showed me how I was supposed to use the walkie-talkie to page the building maintenance. I wasn't comfortable with this at first. I didn't feel cool talking on a walkie-talkie, but once I learned how to talk on that thing, it was fun. Ken specified that whenever he was in the office, I didn't have to answer his phone. I grasped everything that he taught me quickly. I was getting better, catching on quickly for a change. I was really getting over my fears and all of my anxiety. I was really able to take notes, read them, and follow them, something I had never been able to do. The only thing I couldn't seem to get a grip on was not answering his phone; it felt strange having the boss answering his own telephone. I thought that was my job. Whenever the phones rang, I answered; if it was his line, I answered it too. It took me a minute to get a grip on not answering his line. That upset him, having to keep reminding me, "McKenzie, I am in the office; you do not have to answer my telephone." This was not the way I was accustomed to doing things. Normally, whenever the phones rang, I answered. This was another thing to learn because of having so many different jobs.

I had been the front desk assistant so many times.. I knew the routine: Someone calls for the boss, you screen the call, tell the caller the truth, "He is on another line, or he is out of the office. May I take a message?" Then you would walk to his office and give him the message, although sometimes before you could take the message, he would somehow appear in the office, that is, if it was someone he wanted to talk to, or if it was his boss. But Ken did not want me to answer his line, period. I ended up apologizing several times throughout the day for mistakenly answering his line; this is when I realized he was not the nice, cute, naïve man I thought he was. Surely, he didn't become the president of the company by being nice and naïve. His looks were deceiving.

The day I started working there he gave me a walk-through. During the walk-through, I noticed the vending machines and the automatic coffee maker. It was fancy. It was very much like the one they had in the office where I did the payroll work. I was familiar with operating the machine. I may have looked naïve, but I had been exposed to many different things. I had been working so many jobs that I was finally getting used to working with and around people. I had courage around him, at least so far. Besides, I thought Ken was nice. But as nice as he seemed, he showed me differently. I was stunned when I went to work the following day. I opened the door and entered the office. He had already given me a set of keys. The office was beautiful. It had beautiful paintings on the wall. The plants were healthy and green. The huge pots they set in were colorful, big, and just as beautiful. It was also nice and peaceful. I decided to do a walk-through to make sure no one else was in the office and things were in order before I started my day. I walked through the office, making sure that all lights were turned on and all the blinds were opened, and then walked into the break room. I checked the copier and fax machine; everything was up and running. I decided that I would make a cup of coffee. I walked over to the coffeepot. I couldn't wait to grab a cup and push the button. It was better having a cup of hot coffee in the morning when the pot did everything for you, but when I looked at the machine, I could hardly believe my eyes. Did I see what I thought I saw? There was a handwritten note taped to the coffee maker.

"What could this be? Was it out of order? Oh, it couldn't be," I thought. Today I wanted a delicious hot cup of coffee. I was not a regular coffee drinker, but it was the thing to do in the mornings. I had begun to drink a cup before getting started. It was the thing to do. This is the way grown folk did it; I smiled to myself. I walked closer to the coffee machine and began reading the note: "Please do not touch," it read. I hesitated. "*This coffee is for employees only.*"

"What is this?" I thought. I was in awe. I was shocked. I was so shocked that I began laughing. "Has the man lost his mind?" I didn't know what to think, and I wasn't going to think, and I was not going to try to make any sense out of what I had just read. "This man must be insane! Did he leave this note for me? If so, I will leave it here for him until he returns," I decided. I must have been on my road to recovery because I did not trip. I did not break down into uncontrollable tears. I did not call the agency to tell them how crazy I thought this was and how it had offended me. I just laughed. I could hardly wait for the building maintenance lady to come into the office so that I could point the note out to her so that she would get the same kick out of reading it. We both got a good laugh for that day. I was not going to allow the stupidity to affect me. I thought this was one of the funniest things I had seen in a long time. The thought of knowing I was not supposed to taste the coffee made my mouth watery for the taste and smell of the fresh coffee dripping in my cup. I could not wait to push the button for the flavored coffee. "Today this cup of coffee is going to be the best cup of coffee I've had in a very long time," I thought. It smelled so good. I could not decide today if I wanted French vanilla, hazelnut, walnut, or almond. They all sounded good and tasty today. "I think today I will try all three!" I decided. I made a toast to myself.

Anyway, I built up my nerves to tell him that today would be my last day. Since he was out of the office, I called him on his cell phone. He was not happy about this. He asked if I could come back for one more day. I told him about my permanent job offer and apologized for not being able to come back. I was excited about starting my new job, but I still had my dreams, dreams of doing my own thing. I always dream of getting my own business. Since I didn't know exactly what I wanted to do in life, it seemed I wanted to do it all. The problem with wanting to do it all is you never end up doing anything. Once when I was out of work, I started my own cleaning business. I sent out fliers advertising that I would clean your house spic and span. I did just that. Shortly after I started the business, I was offered a permanent job as an operator. I got the chance to run my own business for a few days. I did not work long enough to get it off the ground. I worked on my housecleaning on Mondays and Tuesdays, which were my off days with the telephone sales company. This company was fun; it was like an online yellow pages service. I did not leave this job, and I was not asked to leave this job; the company went out of business before I was let go.

I was amazed at how many people responded to my fliers. The apartment manager of the apartment complex I was living in was one of the first to respond. She was also my first client. Then others in the complex started calling and wanting to schedule appointments. I was getting more calls than I could handle. I solicited help on my day job, but I never found anyone interested enough in housecleaning to help me with my side gig. The only person who seemed interested in doing the work had her own cleaning business on the side. She was moonlighting just like me. She tried to convince me to start working for her. She said we could combine our customers and work under the name of her company. I did not want to give up my company's name. I wanted to get my new idea off the ground. I wanted to become established doing my own thing. The idea sounded good, but I was not willing to quit the job with the telephone sales company. I did not have enough clients to combine with her anyway. Maybe I missed out on something great. My company lasted for a very short time. I had many dreams considering I never knew what I truly wanted to be. But that didn't matter now; I had been offered the job of a lifetime. But it didn't diminish my dreaming. I didn't know why all of my dreams were still entering my mind if I was so happy about the job I had been offered. I shook my head at myself.

I often dream about real estate. I love property and homes. I could spend hours looking at real estate, and if I had money, I would invest in lots of real estate, lots of homes. I would buy houses new and old. I would lease them out, and some I would sell. I would time-share them. This is my dream. I would live in as many of them as I could. I dream of opening a school for girls and boys to teach them how to become ladies and gentlemen. I had many dreams of doing business. I just didn't know how to get started. I felt overwhelmed. I felt it possible but impossible. I dreamed of becoming a singer one day. I dreamed of being an actress. I wanted to shine. I wanted to be a star. I wanted to feel free. I wanted to feel free enough to stick my neck out. I did not want to continue smothering myself underneath my shell. I wanted to be. I wanted to be somebody. I didn't want to be depressed any longer. I didn't want to feel unloved. I didn't want to be a failure. I wanted to be known for something big, something more than just plain McKenzie Lee. I wanted to own my own moving company. I dream. I dream. I dream. I dream of having a company or family business that would be mine, or ours. But lately, my dreams seem to be fading away. My hope of ever finding a stable job with corporate America has faded, especially after my last job experience.

Sitting in Dr. Shannon's Office

While sitting in Dr. Shannon's office, I began to cry. Because I did not know I was sick. I felt guilty. "You mean if I had come to you earlier, you could have diagnosed me with depression, and by now I would be healed! Cured!" I thought. All I could think of was all the years I had lost by being depressed. I thought about my mother. I wondered if she had been diagnosed with her depression sooner, would she still be alive. "What can we do about it, doctor?" I asked.

"We have medication that can treat the condition. There is medication that will make you feel a whole lot better."

"Will it make me keep a job?" I asked her.

"Yes, that is quite possible, McKenzie," she said.

"I hope it does."

"I really hope so, Doctor Shannon."

"I need to work." I reiterated.

"I want to work and I want to be able to keep a job. I want to work and not be worried every minute or every second whether or not I am being accepted. Do they like me enough to keep me? Do they think I am bright, or do they think I am just so-so? Will the boss single me out because he suspects I am afraid and insecure? Will the look of fear overshadow me?" There were so many questions. I did not wait for answers to the questions that were running through my mind. All I knew is, I wanted help and help was on the way. I hadn't told her how disappointed I had been with my schooling. It was impressive to say that I had been to college and that I had a degree. I hadn't mentioned to her yet how I felt that even my education had let me down. It had let me down just like I had let myself down and everyone else.

Making the Connection

I never thought I would see those guys again from that cute, little red car. It was funny how I left to go on a date. My date did not materialize. The guy I was going out with was on call. He was a fireman who had been sent home and released from work unless things got busy. Well, things got busy, and they needed more help, and he was called in.

It was twelve midnight when the phone rang. I didn't want to answer the phone. I rolled over and answered it anyway. Sherita was on the other line. "Kenz, wake up, girl, wake up! I got something to tell you. Are you awake?"

Trying to force the sleep out of my eyes, I said, "Yes what's up?"

"Guess what?" she said.

"What?" I asked.

"The guy."

"What guy?" I asked. She said the guy who was on the passenger side of the car. "Yes," I replied.

"Girl, he wants to talk to you."

"What? He wants to talk to me," I replied.

"Yes, girl, he left his number and asked if you could call him."

"Call him?" I asked.

"Yes, he wants you to call him as soon as possible, and he wants you to call him collect." I just listened. I rubbed my eyes, turned on my night-light, grabbed a pen, and started to jot down all the information. I was still half asleep and I hoped that I was hearing her correctly and writing the information down correctly. I didn't think I was dreaming, but it could have easily turned out that way.

"His name is Byron," she said.

"Yes, I already know that. But what I don't know is why does he want me to call him?"

"I don't know, girl, just call the man. Did you write down the number?"

"Yes, I wrote it down," I answered. I asked her to repeat it to me again so that I could make sure I had written the number down correctly. "Sherita, how do you know for sure that it is me? Girl, don't make me look crazy by calling the man and he won't even know who I am."

He was in the Air Force and was stationed in Montgomery, Alabama. He was stationed at Maxwell Air Force Base. Pretty interesting, I thought. I took all the information and laid it on my nightstand. I wasn't sure what to do. I didn't want to call right away, but the message was call anytime, and it did not matter how late. I did just that. I picked up the phone, dialed his number, and panicked. I wasn't sure what to expect or what to say. I was hesitant to speak because of fear that Sherita might have gotten the person he wanted to call him confused with me. But it was a little too late for hesitation. I had already dialed his number and he had picked up the receiver. I could tell he was asleep. Sleep was in his voice. But he had such a soft, melodious voice; if I didn't know any better, I would have thought he was singing to me or reading poetry in Paris. I said, "Hello."

"Hello," he said. I was indeed the person he was waiting to hear from. We talked many times after that. Two months later I invited him to my parents' house for Thanksgiving. He met my parents, and they were really impressed with him. He was the perfect gentleman. He was very polite. His conversation was interesting. I think I was more nervous than he was. He was an attractive man; at least, this is what the older women thought, and certainly the younger ones. All of my sorority sisters thought he was so handsome and so fine. I didn't know what to think. I was just happy that he had chosen me. I didn't know who I was, and I certainly didn't know what kind of man I wanted. This had caught me off guard. I would have smiled more, laughed and talked more, had I known he was interested in me. I did not think he was bad looking. However, at the time I did not realize just how attractive he was. He was tall, very tall. He was six feet three inches tall. He was dark chocolate. He had low-cut, short, jet-black hair, and it even had waves in it. His teeth were white like snow; I will never forget the day I pulled up next to that little red sports car. He was definitely easy on the eye. What I liked most about him was his composure and his voice. I had a thing for beautiful voices and accents. Yes, he was definitely from the East Coast. I thought he was so cool. I liked the way he dressed, and I loved the way he cooked. When he left our house from the Thanksgiving dinner, he sent Mama and Daddy a beautiful thank you card. He also sent Mama some beautiful thank you flowers. Suave he was. Six months later we were married.

He convinced me that I was beautiful. He told me how he believed he had met the girl of his dream. He told me how he needed a wife and how he thought I would make him a good wife. The only problem with that is Uncle Sam had ordered him to go abroad to Europe, and he told me he did not want to leave, leaving me behind. He wanted me to be his bride. This made me feel good, but I could not figure out what it was about me that attracted him to me. He told me one thing was my smile. He said another thing was that old line I used on them, the day we met. ("I thought y'all were someone we knew.") He kidded me often on how that was one of the oldest lines in the book. "So what?" I would say. "It worked." And we laughed about this many of days.

He told me he had a confession to make and insisted on me promising him that I would not get mad. I went along with the promise and he made his confession. He wanted me to know that the little red sports car they were riding in that day belonged to him and not his friend. "Is that the confession?" I asked him. "If that's all you have to confess to, then I promised I would not get mad." He was impressed that I knew how to drive a five-speed. I didn't play sports, but I knew how to drive a five-speed.

A few months after I started dating him, he was sent to Germany. He wrote me everyday. Before I could finish reading the Tuesday letter, Wednesday's letter was already in the box. If I didn't know any better, I would have thought it was love. He called me as often as he could. He sent me gifts in the mail, nice gifts from Germany. But the thing he sent me the most was the German wine. I had many different types of wines. He had given me specific instructions on which ones I could drink and which ones he wanted me to save so that we could drink those bottles together. He gave his mom my phone number, and she called me often. I would also call her. We talked about getting to know each other and how we looked forward to meeting each other in the near future. At this time I thought marriage to her son would be years away. Instead of years, it was only months away.

My Last Job

The last job was the best one so far. It was with the credit background company. Yes indeed it was the job of a lifetime. One day I was there, and the next day I was gone. Like a dream, I kept waiting to wake up and find that it really wasn't true. I had finally landed the job of a lifetime. My past experiences were all worthwhile when I started working for the credit background company. If this was the end result of the long-awaited job, then I was not upset about my previous experiences.

The first day at the credit company went well. We had two hours of training. It was apparent that we were expected to learn in two hours what it would ordinarily take three weeks to learn. Everyone in training expressed how upset they were with such an abbreviated training. I was fine, because I knew that once I got on the floor if I did not understand what was going on, I would not be responsible for my shortcomings. It would not be my fault. I would remind them of the two-hour training class. I understood what we were supposed to know, even though I was not sure how I was supposed to apply what I knew. It was not the simplest job, but it was not complicated. It was not complicated at all compared to my previous work history. I was used to catching on a little bit slower than most. It seemed to be the way it worked for me. I was not threatened or intimidated by the others in the group for once in my life.

The group was interesting. Never before had I been in training with so many disgruntled individuals. They complained about everything. I have to admit it was a nice change. Just to see so many people dissatisfied and complaining made me feel so at ease. It was like seeing me in a mirror with many different faces. All of the stuff they complained about was stuff I had gone through too many times on too many of my many different jobs. They complained about everything. They didn't like the hours. They thought training sucked. They thought the job was a joke and that it made very little sense. I tried to console everyone to the best of my ability. I told them it was just the beginning and things were going to get better. I told them that I was familiar with the company and stressed how great a company it was to work for. Training was over and done, and it was time to get busy.

We were out of training and on the floor by 10 a.m. We were introduced to Becky and Tim. Becky and Tim had started working there together. They were the only two people in the department where we sat. The group scattered about. Some of us sat on the opposite side of the office, but we all learned where each other sat in case we needed to talk to each other about our short training. We were instructed to direct all of our questions to Becky and Tim. Tim seemed to have taken on the role of the take-charge person. Since this was his role, most of us directed our questions to him. Becky did not seem to have a problem with that. Besides, whenever we asked her questions, she would go straight to Tim for reassurance. Tim and Becky had been with the company three weeks prior. They were pros now.

Tim was an interesting character. He was about five feet six inches tall. He was rather short for a man. But no one would acknowledge at first glance that he was short. He stuck his chest out like he was six feet tall. Tim had dark brown hair, dark brown eyes, and a thick brown mustache. Normally, I do not look into anyone's eyes, but for some reason I was able to look into Tim's eyes. He demanded it. It was his look that made you look back at him and directly into his eyes; the penetrating stare captured you and made you hold your head still and eyes straight. It was interesting. For the first time I was looking into someone's eyes, whether it was voluntarily or not, I was looking into his eyes. I didn't feel fearful, and I didn't care about the way he felt about me. I'm not sure if he was aware of himself. He intimidated a lot of us in the group, but he cracked me up. It was God's blessing upon me. I was not fearful, and I was not feeling like a failure on the job. Not only was he controlling, he was arrogant. It was obvious that he wasn't sure about the way things were supposed to be done, but he was destined to be in control. He was young, about twenty-five years old, and it was obvious that this was his first real job. Oh boy, did he want to be in control.

He controlled the files. He controlled the faxes, and he was in control of the phones. He wanted to control it all. At times I thought he was in control of who stayed and who went. Whenever he didn't like a particular person, they disappeared. Thank God, I did not let his power struggle get the best of me. Actually, I thought he was all right. It must have been the favor of God that he and I got along well. It was interesting to see someone so eager to be. I admired his desire to be in charge, as long as he was respectful. I was willing to give him all the respect I could, as long as he did the same in return.

He pointed out to us where the files were and explained to us what we were supposed to do. Each of us picked up any number of files. Some picked up five files; some of us picked up seven files; some of us were afraid and picked up only three, which I thought, was a good number. I picked up a bundle. I'm not sure how many I had. I did not want to take many to my desk, at least not more than I thought I could handle, but I did anyway. We took what we thought we could review for that day. Whenever we had questions, one by one we would take our files to Tim. One by one we would ask the same questions, and one by one we would leave his desk with different answers. This aggravated the group. It was hilarious to me. I did not allow this to upset me. For once in my life I was feeling okay. I wasn't feeling nervous or insecure. Each day I learned more and more about what the job was all about. I was beginning to understand more and more about what we were supposed to be doing. Another thing I understood is that nobody knew a lot about anything and that everybody knew a little about some things. This was perfect for me. What more could I have asked for? We were all learning together.

There were times when I would go to my coworkers for questions; there were times when my coworkers would come to me with questions. It felt good knowing that someone trusted me, and it felt better sharing my knowledge with them. I loved the work, I loved the people, and I loved the company. I even loved the boss.

I liked Jackie from the first day I saw her. She had bright red, thick, shiny hair. She was always getting compliments on how pretty her hair was. No one would have ever guessed that she was once a blonde. Jackie had big bright eyes and long eyelashes and a big laugh. Whenever she laughed, everyone in the department would laugh because her laugh was so jovial. Jackie got along well with all of us. It was not because of my red hair, which was my hair color at the time, and my big eyes that I admired her so much. She was just a great person. Jackie did not make our working environment a stressful environment, which is why I felt compelled to do a good job.

Jackie had no problem delegating work. It was great being able to utilize my skills and knowledge; I was climbing the ladder, and moving on up. I assisted the new hires after training. I was doing side-by-sides. It was important to me to be patient with everyone. I know too *well* that everyone does not catch on at the same pace. Not only did I assist the new hires, I researched files, reviewed files, distributed files, and anything my boss, Jackie, asked me to do. I did whatever I had to do to keep my job interesting, and interesting it was. Everything was going so well. I had submitted my resume to Jackie. She was obviously impressed. I had gone way past the ninety-day probationary period. I had no doubt, not the least bit of doubt, that I would become permanent with the credit background company.

We watched people come and go by the dozens. Every week we would meet and greet new faces. It got to the point where I was reluctant to meet the new people. I tried not to familiarize myself with them because I knew that in a week or so they would probably disappear like everyone else. It had become like walking on thin ice in the place: any day you might go under and just disappear. Somehow this didn't bother me. I wanted to work for the company, and I loved working for the company. My credit background and criminal background was no threat to my job or me. The company had hired the agency, from my understanding, to do the background check on all of us before sending us out to interview with the company. So as far as I knew, everything was fine.

Star, April, Angelina, Billy, and I were the only people left out of our class of thirteen. Actually, Angelina started with Becky and Tim. She sat on the other side of the wall, and I never got the chance to get to know her. She was also a lead person for the others in my class. She was assigned to answer all questions to those who sat on her side of the building. She appeared very quiet, and I misunderstood her by thinking that meant she didn't want to be bothered. But when it was all said and done, Angelina had become a friend and a part of our class because most of her class members were already gone. You can probably imagine how close we had become.

Everyday Billy would come over to my desk and asked if I had heard anything from Human Resources. Everyday I would tell him no. I was patient and encouraged him to do the same. Star, April, Angelina, and I waited *impatiently* everyday wondering when we were going to hear something. Each day we waited and longed to hear them say we were hired. Perhaps we didn't show it as much as Billy. Billy seemed to be more anxious than any of us. I believe he checked the computer status every five minutes out of the day.

One day Billy rushed over to my desk and asked me to check the status of my application. I hesitated at first, not knowing why he insisted on me pulling up my information. Did he know something that I didn't know? He often came to my desk, either to joke or chat. He was an okay guy. He kept the office spirit lifted. He clowned and whined just as much. I nicknamed him whiney. He whined because he didn't understand having a quota. He whined everyday about the traffic; he could never understand why the traffic was so bad and why it took him so long to get to work. He whined about this, and he whined about that. This was the one thing we could look forward to at lunch time. There wasn't a day that we didn't hear him cry.

I wanted to look and see what he saw but I was not about to pull up my status in front of him, without knowing what to expect. I gradually began to pull up the info, but not before asking him to turn his head away until I took a look. He honored my request. I clicked on the page and scrolled down. I could not believe what I saw. I wanted to scream. I was joyful to see the status I saw. I saw my name and beside my name I saw the word "offer." Did this mean what I thought it meant? Yes indeed, I was about to be offered the job of my lifetime. I shouted silently and held my arms slightly above my head and said "Yes! Yes! Yes! Thank you, Jesus." I turned around to look at Billy. His face was red, and his blonde hair was slightly standing on top of his head. I didn't know what to say to him at first. I felt his disappointment and his excitement for me all in one. He congratulated me for getting the job. According to what we had seen on the computer screen and the status it was showing us, I had the job. I didn't want to become excited prematurely. I looked up at Billy.

"Did you get the job?" I asked enthusiastically. He looked sad and I saw disappointment on his face. Then he told me his status was "pending." I felt sad at the thought of the four of us not being hired together. A cold chill came over me. Even though I felt excitement rushing through my body like electricity, I was not sure this was happening. I had not received an offer letter, and I had not heard back from my boss, Jackie. I tried to console Billy, assuring him that he was going to get the job. I told him if his status was pending, there was no doubt he would be getting the job also. He smiled and walked out of my cubicle and went back to his desk. I am not sure if my consolation was sufficient to make him feel better. I was anxious to go to everyone else's desk to find out if they knew their status. I could hardly wait. I gave Billy enough time to walk back over to his desk before I got up.

As soon as he walked away, I jumped up out of my cubicle, ran into Star's cubicle, and asked if she had pulled up her application and checked the status. She sat right next to me in the cubicle to the left. She stopped working, turned around and looked at me. "Why?" she asked. I explained to her what Billy had just gone over with me. She hesitated and slowly began to log on to that screen. As she began to pull up her status, she looked back at me. I turned my head around to give her the same respect I had requested from Billy. When Star checked her status, it said the same as Billy's. Neither one of us knew what to think. We both ran over to April's desk and asked her to pull up her status. When she pulled up her status, to the right of her name it said "offer." All of us were getting confused. The three of us ran over to Angelina's desk and asked her to do the same. When she pulled her status to the right of her name, it said "on hold." Since we all had a different status, we ran over to Billy's desk to let him know what status was showing for each of us. None of us knew what to think. Something was going on, but we didn't know what.

Everyday I would pull up my status to verify if everything was still the same. So far everything was looking good.

It was Thursday afternoon. The agency called me on my cell phone. It was unusual for them to be calling me at work. My heart started to beat rapidly. I could feel my muscles tighten up, and I had not even answered the phone. I finally flipped open the phone. "Hello, McKenzie, this is Miranda from WorkStaff."

"Yes ma'am," I said.

"I was just going back over your file and discovered that you have a blemish on your paperwork." I was silent. I am sure she could hear me breathing in the phone. I tried to speak, but I could not say a word for a few seconds. I couldn't imagine what could possibly be in my file. This has to be a mistake. I was thankful that I had paid all of my bills, and paid them all on time. If I got paid the creditors got paid too; that is just the way it was. So what could it be?" I thought.

"I'm sorry," I said "But I have a what?"

She stated again, "I discovered something past due on your credit report." I was quiet again. "I thought all of this had been taken care of prior to me being sent on the assignment. Otherwise, why would they have sent me here to work in the first place?" I asked myself. I started to think back, wondering what on God's earth this could be. Was it a credit card? Was it a loan? Or what was it? She informed me what was on my report. I knew this had to be a mistake. I never made enough money in my entire life to owe money like this. Even though it was not a great sum, it did not matter; I wanted to take care of it. It just happened to be on my report. The most money I had ever made on any job was twenty-eight thousand dollars a year. And this is with an education, and living in Atlanta, Georgia. I asked if she could tell me more about the debt and the amount. She gave me the balance, and I assured her that this matter would be resolved immediately.

The next morning I wrote a check for three hundred dollars. I paid off the balance and thought everything would be fine. I didn't question the debt. I just wanted the job. I was willing to do whatever was necessary to keep this job. I thought that everything would be okay.

I continued to go to work everyday, holding my breath and exhaling at the end of the day. I was happy I had made it through the entire week. The following week I was not so fortunate. The agency called me back and questioned me about the debt and wanted to know if I could prove to them that the debt they had just informed me of was not there prior to my taking on the assignment. "The question is did you all see it?" I asked. "What was I supposed to do?" To make a long story short, I had no proof of the balance not being there, and they had no proof either, because apparently they had not checked as they had promised the company. Boy did this come as a downpour of disappointment, of loss, sadness, and hurt! This time I knew I had landed on the job of my lifetime. I was feeling happier, more confident, and powerful than I had ever before. I tried to keep my confidence. I worked to keep a positive attitude. I worked to keep a positive image. Working here had put anxiety, and stress on hold once and for all, I thought. From time to time I would have to talk to the little voice, telling it to be quiet. For the first time it was obeying me. For the first time it did not have the best of me. I was on the up and up. Thank God for Dr. Shannon. Thank God for friends and family. Thank God, thank you Jesus! It was nothing like before. There were times when I did not feel too good about myself, but most days I did. There were times when the voices would tell me I was not any good, but I kept on working and telling myself that I was some good. I was feeling good. But I had to tell my job goodbye. The agency told me that I had two weeks to work before I would have to leave. They were courteous in offering to let me stay on the job for two more weeks before my final day. I thought this was nice. I thought this was very nice of them. But I had to refuse the nice and generous offer. I didn't think I would be strong enough to endure what I thought might be the longest and saddest two weeks of my life. I refused the offer. I wanted to stick around to tell all of my supporters, who had encouraged me, how much I appreciated them. I wanted to thank them for unknowingly boosting my ego by telling me that I had brought personality, understanding, laughs, and last but not least, prayer into the environment. The pain, the agony, the disappointment, and even my pride would not let me stay. I had to accept it, that the world of work had let me down once again. I had to accept that maybe, just maybe, the corporate world was not for me. "Oh my God! How could you allow this to happen to me again?" I asked. "I have worked so hard. I have been trying for so long. I loved this job, I loved the people, and I even loved the boss. How could you?"

It wasn't the negative voices inside of my head this time. The voices were minimal. They were beginning to subside. They did not completely go away. The negative thoughts and the negative thinking would still come and try to haunt me. Because I was getting stronger; I was beginning to outtalk the negativism. It helped me to help those around me. I had become much stronger on this job. I felt like a pillar of strength for my coworkers. They all seemed to be going through what I had gone through forever. I encouraged them daily. I found myself being the counselor, the social worker that I spent years in college studying to be. I never worked in the field because by the time I received my bachelor's degree, corporate was requiring a master's degree. It was a no-win situation. But I won, I had won the war and I had won the battle. I was encouraged, and I had done well because I had helped others. I realized the agony and the hurt I felt would not last for long. I went through my grieving process. I was going to live now. Corporate, depression, stress, and anxiety were not going to keep me down. I was not going to worry and nothing, not even depression, was going to keep me down. God's hand was on me. I could feel his presence. I hummed, "*Um gonna trust in the Lord. Um, gonna trust in the Lord until I die.*"

Days Afterward

After the loss of the job, there were times I still felt like giving up. I felt like really giving up this time. But how do you give up? Do you lie in bed and not get up? Do you decide that you are no longer going to work? Do you say to yourself, I am going to sit here and wait, I am going to sit here and wait until Jesus comes? Was I going to be like the Thessalonians? They had decided to stop working, put their lives on hold, and wait for Jesus to come. But the Apostle Paul encouraged them that they must work until the end. Yes, if they wanted to eat, they had to work, if they wanted to survive here in earth. He encouraged them to keep on keeping on.

For even when we were with you, this we commanded you, that if any would not work, neither should he eat .

2 Thessalonians 3:10

As strong as I was feeling, I was still afraid. I was afraid because I knew I had to work in order to live, in order to eat, drink, and be merry; therefore, giving up was not an option. I welled in tears of disappointment, tears of anxiety, tears of hurt, and tears of fear and shame. I ached. I prayed for understanding. My burdens were heavy, and I felt like my life had no purpose. I longed for my mother. I missed her more today than I did thirteen years ago when she passed away. I wondered how she would feel about me, knowing that I could not do something as simple as keep a job. Mother was a praying woman. I knew if God wouldn't hear my prayers, surely if Mother was living he would hear her prayers, and things would be different. I sought answers from my close friends. Friends tried to console me and comfort me. Everyone kept saying, "God has something bigger and better for you." "Hold on, be strong, you will find another job" or "McKenzie, you should start your own business. Maybe corporate America is not for you." I would smile, nod my head, and say to myself, "I wish I knew what it was that God had for me." Although the things they were saying were true, the words were not making me feel any better. I felt like the comforting words were nothing more than a bunch of nice clichés. I was uncertain what to do or what to think. I told myself that this was not the end, and it wasn't the end; I had been through this before. Yes, he will get me through this also, I knew. I felt weak, but I felt confident that God was going to work everything out for me.

I did not know how I was going to share this with my church family. I had asked my Sunday school class to pray for me. They had prayed. I found a job. But how was I going to tell them that job I found, I have now lost? "Why in the world was this happening to me again?" I asked God. We were a very close, praying family. We were always praying for our friends and family members. We brought other people's burdens and put them on the table and prayed that God would deliver them and lighten their burdens. We prayed that God would deliver them from whatever it was holding them back, or keeping them on a bed of affliction. We had success stories, which we called praise reports. It was great having spiritual people in my life who loved Christ. Even more, people whom God had given the wisdom to take his word and make it plain to the students. The Sunday school teachers that God had sent to teach our class were awesome!

I had become a member of the church several years earlier but I had recently joined many different organizations. Attending the *Jarena Lee Sunday school* was one of the best things I could have done. I also attended Bible study. It taught me so much. I never thought that I would be too embarrassed to go to them in time of need. I was ashamed. I had rejoiced about the joy of having a job again. I had rejoiced about having one that I really really liked. I had a great praise report. I rejoiced about the pay I was finally going to be getting. How could I even tell them I was let go? I asked myself. I was ashamed to ask them to pray for me. I needed prayer. I needed someone godly to be by my side until I felt strong again. I was ashamed because I had failed once again. It was months before I told them I had lost my job. The topic never came up and I didn't volunteer to tell anyone. I didn't feel good about this. It bothered me. I felt like I was being deceitful. I knew in my heart this wasn't right so eventually I had to let them know. I told them one by one. It was too embarrassing even to tell the church family all at once. I wasn't sure if even they would understand. It wasn't as bad as I thought it would be sharing the news with my Sunday school class about the lost of my job. They embraced me. Everyone was comforting. They assured me that everything would be all right. We prayed and ate brunch. When I really thought about it, it wasn't really that bad at all.

Being Left Out

Going to see Dr. Shannon and attending my Sunday school class had helped me tremendously. I always felt left out when it came to hanging out with others. Whenever I had to step outside of my circle of friends, I felt left out. I always wanted to feel like I was a part of the group, but I didn't know how to fit in; that was one major difference between Naomi and me. She knew how to socialize. She knew how to open up to others and share her experiences. It was just as easy for her to tell someone outside of the neighborhood gang about herself and about the crushes she had for our classmates or some GI she had met over the weekend. I, on the other hand, was considered an introvert. I didn't feel like anyone cared to hear my story, and I didn't think they would understand even if I tried to discuss things with them. I was sure they would laugh and kid with me about not being liked by the guy even if I told them of someone I liked. But even more than that, I was afraid that they might tell the person, and everyone would laugh and make fun of me. I knew I would never be able to live down such embarrassment. I only shared my thoughts, ideas, and secrets with girls in the neighborhood. But these were my friends, they were my only friends.

But the truth is, whenever others did not invite me in, I felt left out. Sometimes I still have nightmares about being left out. In the dream all of us are together on an outing, and everyone except me knows about the plans. Of course, I don't find out until the last minute. There was no doubt that they had kept this from me. Everyone is treating me like a stranger. I wake up only to find out it was a dream, and thank God it wasn't reality. It makes you feel bad being left out; I guess no one really wants to be left out. Even loners do not enjoy being alone.

Longing

I longed for the job so much that I refused to leave home for weeks after they dismissed me; I did not want to miss the phone call when the company decided to call me back. I knew the possibility of not being called back, but I did not give up hope. Each day the reality of what had happened to me was becoming more and more real. The phone call never came through, and I had to finally rest my mind. I had to let it go. I was trying very hard not to let it get me down; no, it was not going to get me down like it had so many times before.

Since my friends were tired of hearing the same thing all of the time, I had no other choice except to my call family again. I e-mailed my family members and began to share with them my experience. I told them my story. They were well aware that I changed jobs frequently, but like me they hoped that this one was for me. We are a close family. We get along well. Well it seemed we were getting alone better since my visit with Dr. Shannon. I didn't believe they disliked me as much anymore. For once in my life, I put their feelings of me to the side and reached out to them. I expressed how I longed for my job and how I longed to go back to work there. I wanted the job so badly, I could almost touch it. I asked each one of them to come together and pray. I know the power of prayer. I requested intercessory prayer. I asked family members to stop whatever they were doing at noon and pray for me to get my job back. Recently we had gone into intercessory pray and prayed that Little Brother would pass the bar exam, and he passed it with flying colors. We knew already before he got his results that God was going to allow him to pass that exam. Because God is good! God is love, and God is merciful. We did this for a couple of days. We prayed and waited. Deep down inside I knew what God had for me, was for me. If God wanted me to have my job at the credit background company, no one could keep me from it. I did not get my job back at the credit card company, but I got peace. I had peace of mind.

Keeping in Touch

I did not lose contact with my coworkers after leaving the credit background company. They were like me, stunned and shocked that I would no longer be working with them. I spoke with them often. They talked about how dead the office environment felt without my presence; they said it felt like someone had died. I was glad that I was missed, but "thank you, Jesus," I was still alive. Something in my life had changed. I was happy to be alive. I didn't have a job today and I didn't know how soon I would find another one. Thank you, God, for today! I called the manager, Jackie, and spoke with her a few times. I believe she did all she could to help me to keep the job. She was a wonderful boss to work for. She was about as shocked to hear that I would not be working there any longer as I was. She went to her boss; she begged and pleaded for them to try and work things out. When I saw her walk out of her boss' office with that look of dejection on her face, I wanted to cry. I thanked God that even she tried. Apparently the disappointment was too much for her too; she walked back to her desk, grabbed her purse and left the office. Even though it was close to quitting time; she usually hung around. It was the following day that she came to me and told me the sad news. "I don't know why I can't keep a job." I thought. This was the first time I felt strong enough to silence the little negative voice.

I would speak with April often. She had become my close friend. I had no idea that April would turn out to be the nice person she turned out to be. She was the smart one out of the bunch. Craig and I would laugh and joke because she was so smart. She caught on faster than the rest of us. I caught on faster than he. He just didn't seem to be able to get it. The job was so easy at first; after we learned what were supposed to be doing, most of us kept thinking that there must have been more to it than what we were doing. I think that was the problem with Craig and

Tommy. I finally told them that one day during lunch while they were stressing, and it was like the light came on in Tommy's head. "You are right Kenz, the job is just too easy." He said. "Kenzie, I think you hit it. I really believe that." He eased up a lot from the whining. Craig eventually gave up and resigned from the company.

It wasn't long before April was helping Tim and Becky review our work. I saw it coming. I knew she was a quick study. I had warned her that she would be the next person in charge. I'm sure she knew it also. As smart as April was, I don't think she wanted to be considered the smartest. Sometimes she would play herself down just to keep from looking so smart. I even knew the times she pretended to not understand, just to keep us from looking so dumb. She was definitely a people person. She made sure we were a close-knit group. Everyday she would walk around to everyone's desk to make sure everyone was ready to go to lunch at the same time. She made sure we took breaks together. There were times when I just wanted to go back to being the loner I was at heart, but not with a friend like April. It reminded me of working at the insurance company. We were family. She just couldn't seem to shake it, me no longer being there. Neither she nor Star could understand why I had to leave. She and Star would rotate calling me from time to time. We met often for lunch. I'd drive up and meet them, and the whole gang, those of us who were left, would come to the restaurant. Eventually, only two of the originals were left. It was Star and April.

Star and I spoke a lot about our Christian belief. There wasn't a day that we didn't mention prayer. There wasn't a day that we didn't talk about God. We needed God in the workplace. This was another sign that things in my life had changed, because work was turning out to be a power struggle. Everyone wanted to be in charge of something or somebody. It didn't bother me in the way it would have several months earlier. It didn't get me down. Star, April, and I prayed. April wasn't necessarily a Christian, but she found God interesting. She found prayer interesting, too.

She told me she was Buddhist. I didn't know much about this religion, and I didn't learn as much about it as I probably should have. She shared with me an experience of hers when she was much younger. She told me about the time she went to the temple with her mom. She said she remembered going to the temple once with her mother to pray when she was a young child. She said her father would wait outside and smoke cigarettes and chat until she and her mom came out of the temple. She expressed how she remembered wishing she could be grown like her daddy so that she could stand outside and not have to participate. In other words, she was not the praying type. It was ironic that I met April because I was always talking about praying. I prayed before I went to the job, while I was on the job, when I left the job: I was the praying type. It became not only apparent that I was the praying type but also funny. Whenever something would go wrong on the job or someone mistreated another, April would always come to me and say, "Pray, Kenzie, pray." I would pray. April never became a Christian to my knowledge, but she shared with me her experience about prayer. But she believed in God and that was all that mattered. She admitted that prayer really worked. I was not judgmental of her for not being a Christian; I still thought she was a great person. It didn't seem to bother her that I was a Christian. I thought it was kind of funny how she described me as praying all the time.

Once she invited me and the gang to come to her house for dinner, which she and her husband had prepared. She set the table and put all the good food on the table. It looked delicious, and of course, we were all ready to dive into it and couldn't wait to get started. But before we started serving ourselves and passing the food, I looked over at April. She laughed and looked at her husband and said, "Honey, I think they need to do their little blessing thing before we get started." We laughed. Then I was given the honor to say the grace. When I was young, it was a tradition to say grace, giving thanks to God for the food, but now it was a part of me. It has always been important for me to give thanks for the food and to ask God's blessing to be on it before eating. I'm not sure if she understood why we did this. But I appreciated her acknowledging this is what we do. It's not difficult to see how April could become anyone's friend; she had that kind of humor and that kind of personality.

One day April called to see how I was doing. She wanted to know how my job search was coming along. She didn't realize that I was not feeling whole and healed at the time of her call, and looking for another job so soon was not my priority. In the back of my mind I was literally hoping to hear from someone in the Human Resources Department letting me know that they had made a big mistake in letting me go. Of course, that never happened. Maybe April was feeling a need for me to open up my prayer line, since it had worked so many times before and she had even witnessed the results of some of my prayers. She mentioned prayer to me on the phone when she called. She suggested that I call all of my family members to come together in prayer. She suggested that we pray together on one accord. I was touched. I was moved. Did I hear what I thought I heard? This type of suggestion from a nonbeliever! Once again, I recognized the power of God. If *he* could put that thought into her heart, *he* could do anything and all things; this is not to take anything away from her, because she no doubt believed in God. Whether I got my job back or not, I knew that God was real once again, and one other thing I knew for certain is that as a Christian believer:

All things work together for good to them that love the Lord, to them that are called according to his purpose.

Romans 8:28

I learned that just because it seemed unfair and unkind that God had allowed such loss to sneak upon me, all things still work together for good for those of us who love the Lord, and I love the Lord.

The Engagement

One day Byron wrote me a letter, just like he had many times before. But this particular letter was different from all of the other letters. We had talked about getting married that wasn't anything new. I didn't really take him serious. I thought we were only talking about it. Then one day, I received a letter from Byron that literally knocked me out. When I opened the letter, I found two rings taped to the last page of the letter. I was shocked. I was breathless. But I went on to read the letter and this is when it knocked me out. In the letter he wrote-by the time you get this letter, I should be knocking on your door. "Man you are a million miles away from me," I thought. "How in the world are you going to be here knocking on my door?" I asked myself. I stood in my tracks for what seemed like five minutes. I thought about it. Anything is possible, I thought. Then I begin to get nervous. My heart started beating fast; question after question was popping inside my head. What if he is serious? What if he knocks on my door right now? I asked myself. Oh my God! I fainted before I could read any further. I did not know it was this serious. When I woke up, I ran to the telephone and dialed the international code to Germany, I begged to speak with him, but I was too late. "Yes, may I speak with Sgt Johnson?" I asked. The voice on the other end of the line told me that Sgt Johnson was gone to the states, my mouth dropped. Apparently, the voice on the other end thought I had disappeared.

"Ma'am Ma'am, are you there?" "Hello, hello." I waited a second,

"Yes Ma'am "I am here." I said.

"Sgt Johnson is gone to the states to get married." She went on to say,

I felt like she was volunteering some important information, only she didn't know that I was the future bride. "Thank you." I said and hung up the phone. Twenty minutes later Sgt Johnson was knocking on my door, five days later we were married.

The good thing about being married; he insisted that I did not work for the first year of our marriage. He told me that my brain needed a break. "You have been in school for such a long time, five years to be exact, and now you need to take a break." That sounded good! Maybe it was true I needed a break but Jesus Christ! I didn't need a whole year. What would I do for a whole year of having nothing to do with myself? I took a break, but in a short while I was bored to death. I found a job at a plastic factory and only God knows why I chose that job. I had met friends who were married to Air Force men and they told me how great the job was and how it paid such good money. I asked them why weren't any of them working there, only to find out they had all worked there and had all been fired. It was an experience. I tried it. It was slavery. I thought it would be easier being in Germany and being in a factory. The first day I was given a walk through. I was introduced to all the friendly people, and then introduced to all of the machines. The first day I stayed all day. Once I started my official day on the job, I had to work my way up to eight hours a day. I never made it pass six hours. The first day was great I had to stay for only one hour. The second day was great I had to stay for only two hours, the third day wasn't bad; but when it got to the sixth hour, I stayed on six hours for as many days as I could before someone noticed I had not reached a full day. It was killing me. The plastic was hot! The knife I had to use to cut the plastic was sharp. On the third day I accidentally stabbed myself in the thigh. When I showed it to everyone, they said it's no big deal; we've all been stabbed and more than once. Shortly afterwards I started teaching at the pre-k school on base. I liked this much better.

Treatment

Before I left Dr. Shannon's office, she wrote me out a prescription. The medicine was expensive; it was more than I could afford. I had no insurance. She offered me some samples and asked me to try the medication for a few days to see if I experienced any of the side effects. I wasn't sure what the side effects were. Perhaps she told me and I was so excited about my road to recovery that I did not remember. I could not wait to get outside and into my car so that I could swallow that pill. I took the medicine until it was finished. I did not feel any different. I called her back a few days later to let her know I felt fine. I couldn't wait to get enough money up to get my prescription filled. If I was experiencing any side effects, I didn't know it.

I went to the pharmacy once I finished using all of the samples to get the prescription filled. I got the prescription and read the advisory. I wanted to be well aware of any side effects now that I was taking something that I might need for a long period of time. I was instructed to take one pill a day every morning for thirty days. Every morning I would wake up, and I couldn't wait to take the pill. I was waiting to feel better. I wanted to feel fresh, alert, awake, and alive. I wanted to feel free from worrying. I wanted to feel free from the little voice that never stopped talking. I wanted the little voice to die. I wanted it to stop telling me I was no good and not capable of doing anything. I wanted freedom! A week passed and I was still feeling the same way. Another week passed and I was still feeling the same. I was so anxious to feel better or normal, not realizing that it takes time.

Approximately six weeks had passed, and I had begun to fell better. It may not have taken that long, but it was six weeks before I realized that I had begun to feel much better. I continued to take my medication just like the doctor ordered. Then things started happening. The first thing I noticed was before going to sleep at night that little voice was turned off. Yes, it was turned off. I was not replaying every single thing that had happened throughout the day inside my head. The record player, the recorder, and the repeat button had been shut off! I have to repeat myself: that little voice for the first time in my life was turned off! Unbelievable! Amazing Grace. It was amazing, so amazing that I didn't realize it at first. I was going to bed and going to sleep not worrying about what my day had been like. I was not worrying about being sick. I was not worrying about what people might have thought of me throughout the day. I wanted to scream and shout when I experienced this. I could not remember once in my life ever going to bed without worrying about something. I had never lain down without fear of something: The fear that I might lay down and wake up to find that a love one had passed on. The fear of going to the hospital and being told I had a terminal illness and had only six months to live. The fear of losing my job. The fear that

I was not as smart and bright as everyone else was on the job. The fear of my heart pounding so loud and fast that people around me would hear it and say I was strange. All of this was gone in just a matter of weeks. God is Good! God is Great! Yes, he is real.

Signs of Healing

It seemed the medication was doing its job. Something indeed was working for me. I went to bed night after night without hearing the negative voice talking to me. I was so unused to this that I felt light. I was already beginning to feel like life was worth living. I was not worrying about whose feelings I had hurt. I was not worrying about who had hurt my feelings. I was not giving my life of confusion and disappointment a whole lot of thought. I was already beginning to feel happy. Feeling happy was the one thing I always hoped for. Feeling happy was more important to me than working. Feeling happy was more important to me than being successful. You see, I believed that if I could feel happy every once in a while, that everything else would come.

It was interesting that Sizzy, my sister and best friend, first noticed the change in me. She noticed the changes in me before I did. It was the little things but most important things that began to change. One day while Sissy and I were sitting at a traffic light, patiently waiting for the light to change, she looked over at me and smiled. I looked at her and smiled back, giving it no thought. I did not know why she was looking at me at first. When I noticed she kept looking away, then turning back to smile at me again, I wondered if she was okay. When I asked her if everything was okay, she said yes. "I can not believe it." She said. I didn't know what she was referring to. She kept smiling and looking at me strange then she said, "I thought by now you would be pitching a fit because this light has

311

not changed." I laughed. "I have never seen you so calm Kenzie," She said, with a sly grin on her face as she continued to laugh and talk. I knew what she must have been thinking. Is this my sister sitting here all calm without screaming and hollering and asking me to turn right, then left, to avoid waiting for this long light? I felt foolish, but I felt good. I could not believe that I was sitting there without going insane. Normally, I would have become so frustrated that I would turn around and go in the other direction so that I would not have to wait so long for the light to change. My nerves could not stand the waiting. Patience was something that I did not have. If I was not driving but sitting at the traffic light as a passenger, I would be fidgety. I would have been about ready to run that light and I wasn't the one driving. The treatment must have been working.

She noticed how my reactions to other things had changed. If I had misplaced my belongings, I would become so agitated. It annoyed me, it upset me, and I would feel so aggravated. I would become angry. I had very little control over the way I reacted to things. I assumed someone had taken my belongings, but even more I was prone to accusing someone of stealing my belongings. I was learning. The one thing I learned is in many situations, it is not the situations that are so devastating, it is the way you allow the situations to affect you. I changed. I was no longer letting the little things get the best of me. Whatever the situation is, and no matter how bad it appears, I look for the least of the good in the situation. There is something good in every bad situation. I believe there is a lesson in every blessing. Now when things are misplaced I say God must be trying to tell me something, Or God is trying to show me something. I believe that maybe it was just put out of my presence for a reason, a good reason at that. I rationalize now by believing that perhaps for whatever the reason, God put it out of sight for a good reason. It does not worry me much if things are misplaced, because sooner or later things will definitely surface.

I had another challenge; that challenge was giving one the freedom to exercise their opinion. If your view on things was different from mine, I judged you and thought something was terribly wrong with you. I thought my way was right, and if you did not agree with me, I thought something definitely had to be wrong with you. I would spend the rest of the evening or night wondering how could it be. How could it be possible that the person or persons I was engaged in the conversation or debate with could not be open-minded enough to see things my way. It bothered me. It made me question others' ability to comprehend. I did not realize at the time that everyone has the right to his or her own opinion. I believed I had the greatest insight on things. I still believe that my point of view on things in general is pretty rational and a good way to see things. However, it is okay if you do not see things my way. It is okay for us to differ. It takes all kind of people to make the world as it is. The medication and the therapy were working in my favor. I began to experience peace of mind.

I was also a big complainer. I complained about everything, at least that's what I was told. I had never realized this before, but that's what my friends and family told me. I complain a little now but not like before. If my Beau made me a cup of coffee, I complained because it was not sweet enough or it was too sweet. I complained about the cream, either it had too much cream or not enough cream. I did not realize this, but this is what I was told. If something was not pleasing to my satisfaction, I had to learn to smile and say thank you. The treatment was working. Thank God, it was working. I was beginning to feel normal.

The Bright Light

I began to realize and to see all of my blessings. There is light at the end of the road, even when you have no idea where the road is going to lead you. I would not have had the time to write and share my story with you had I been working the long hours I worked before today. It was not as difficult as I thought it would be, getting over the job at the credit background company. The job was just another job.

It did not take as long as I thought it would to move on with my life. It was just a wake-up call to let me know who is. I know who is. I know because the Bible tells me so. I don't have a job, but I have shelter and a roof over my head. I don't have a job, but I have food, plenty of food. I don't have a job, but I have clothes on my back, nice beautiful clothes, and shoes on my feet. I don't have a job, but all of my bills are paid. I don't have a job, but I have all I need. I have a testimony. Because whatever God has done and is doing for me, he will do the same for you. Yes, it is true that:

My God shall supply all of my needs according
to his riches in heaven.

Philippians 4:19.

At first, even I did not understand. I was unable to answer the questions people were always asking me: "How is it that you can be without work and still look happy? How is it that you manage to meet all your financial obligations without working?" When I mentioned this to my friend, Leon (beau) he said, "Yeah, baby, I am beginning to wonder if you are rich or something myself. Here I am working everyday and wondering how am I going to pay my rent, and you on the other hand don't seem worried about a *thang*. I wished I could be like my baby," he said.

I told him. "You can; trust God." God knows our willing hearts. When you have done all that you can, just stand and let God do for you.

Now I understand why God always made it possible for me to pay my bills while I was without work. I understand why I was able to loan money without a job to people who proclaimed to be struggling more than I. I understand why my family expected me to continue to give my share of whatever I was supposed to make a contribution towards. It didn't matter that I was out of work. God supplies all of my needs, and he gives me the desires of my heart. I can not give more than I receive, because God constantly gives to me.

It is my God who supplies all my needs. This is the only thing that rings true for my being able to survive each and every time I lost my job. No one, not even my church or my friends expected me to stop giving whether I worked or whether I was not working. I gave. I gave my time, I gave what energy I had, I gave my advice, counseling—which is what I went to school to be, a social worker, a counselor—and I gave my advice the best I knew how. My sister and I never stopped cooking Sunday dinners and inviting our friends and family members over for dinner. I gave what I had left over after paying all my bills to whoever needed it.

One Sunday following the weekend I had lost my job, I saw one of my choir members who had been faithful in calling to check up on me. She called periodically just to say hello and to see how I was doing. She never talked long, never more than three minutes. Sometimes she would give me leads on jobs. She saw me as I was leaving church one Sunday. She had recently congratulated me on my new job. She had expressed four months earlier how happy she was that I had found a job. She had no idea that I had lost it already. I guess it really didn't matter. I was about to cross the street going to the parking lot. She waved me down. "Kenzie, Kenzie she called out. Do you have some change? I need to get home. I need some gas for my car." I did not ask her any questions. I didn't explain to her that I had just lost the job that she had recently given praise for; I just went into my bag, pulled out a five-dollar bill, and gave it to her. I told her I did not have much, but I hoped this would help out. She was so grateful, but I was more grateful because I knew what God was going to give back to me would be much greater than what I had just given to her. I do not know where it comes from. It comes from God.

Let us not be weary in well doing; for in due season we shall reap,
if we faint not.

Galatians 6:9

I Have Overcome

Nay, in all these things we are more than conquerors
through him that loved us.

Romans 8:37

God is truly my source of strength. He is the source of my life. He is the source of my livelihood. I did not know that life could be so wonderful. I did not know life could be lived free from constant worries. Worrying may come now and may always come, but I do not let the worries get me down. I pray my prayer of serenity. If there is something in my life that I cannot change, then Lord, don't let me worry. I ask God to give me the wisdom and the strength to turn it all over to him. I pray for wisdom to know when and how to release my worries, my problems, and my concerns to him. But before I could do any of these things, I had to know who I was. I had to acknowledge I am who I am. Through self-examinations I discovered the problem, and I accepted it. I sought help, and through God's guidance and chosen one, I found help. I opened up my mind and my heart and discovered freedom, freedom of the mind. I am free at last! Free, Free, Free. I have love, peace, joy and happiness. I love and I am loved.

Liberation of the mind has allowed me to wake up each day and enjoy seeing the sun peek through my windows. I love the morning air that goes into my nostrils down into my lungs. I love and appreciate the freshness of the air that God has made. I love tress, I love plants, and I love grass. I love it all. I love you. It is all so beautiful.

Liberation of the negative thinking of the mind changed my life. I can look at the world and all the millions and many different people which God created, and smile. I can smile at the beauty: the beauty of just being able to smile, the beauty of knowing that all men are created equal in God's sight, the beauty of colors. I can look at all races, all nationalities, and all people and see beauty. One of the hardest things for me was to love me for me, and love God for making me who I am. I have the joy and peace of mind that God promises. Because my life was already planned.

For I know the plans I have for you, declares the Lord, plans to prosper you and not to harm you, plans to give you hope and a future.

Jeremiah 29:11.

Oh Lord, thy hast searched me and known me, Thou knowest my downsitting and mine uprising, thou understandest my thought afar off. Thou compassest my path and my lying down, and art acquainted with all my ways. For there is not a word in my tongue, but, lo, O Lord, thou knowest it altogether. Thou has beset me behind and before, and laid thine hand upon me, Such knowledge is too wonderful for me; it is high, I cannot attain unto it. Whither shall I go from thy spirit? Or whither shall I flee from thy presence? If I ascend up into heaven, thou art there; if I make my bed in hell, behold, thou art there. If I take the wings of the morning, and dwell in the uttermost parts of the sea: Even there shall thy hand lead me, and thy right hand shall hold me. If I say, Surely the darkness shall cover me; even the night shall be light about me. Yea, the darkness hideth not from thee; but the night shineth as the day; the darkness and the light are both alike to thee. For thou hast possessed my reins: thou hast covered me in my mother's womb. I will praise thee; for I am fearfully and wonderfully made: marvelous are thy works; and that my soul knoweth right well.

Psalms 139:1-14

Printed in the United States
109758LV00001B/1-24/A

Doris Dee Walker
Contact: 770-490-0518
Thank You!

9 781434 335128